KEY TO SYMBOLS

KT-403-785

CATEGORIES

 Hostels in popular cities and towns. These are often very busy and are used particularly by groups and young travellers, both from home and abroad.

 Busy Hostels with a wide range of facilities which are especially useful for groups and popular with families.

Medium sized Hostels in country and coastal locations ideal for a variety of hostellers - whether individuals, families or parties.

Small Hostels of a simple style, often in remote areas, which are of particular attraction to walkers and cyclists.

OTHER SYMBOLS

Open (at the top of each Hostel entry) Indicates the time the Hostel opens. Hostels are also open 07.00 - 10.00 hrs.

 Telephone number

 Table licence available

 Camping

 Games room

 Laundry facilities

 Secure lockers available

 Suitable for wheelchairs

 No Smoking Hostel

 Parking

 Available on the Book-a-Bed-Ahead scheme

 Hostel can be booked via International Booking Network (see page 23)

 Number of rooms with **2 - 4 beds**

 Number of rooms with **5 - 8 beds**

 Number of rooms with **9 or more beds**

 Bus information

 Train information

 Ferry Information

 Tourist Information Centre

 Ordnance Survey 1:50000 map

 Grid reference

Opening Dates All dates inclusive.
Open .... open every night between given dates.
X........ except.
eg........ Open X:Sun = Closed from 10.00 hrs Sunday to 17.00 hrs Monday.

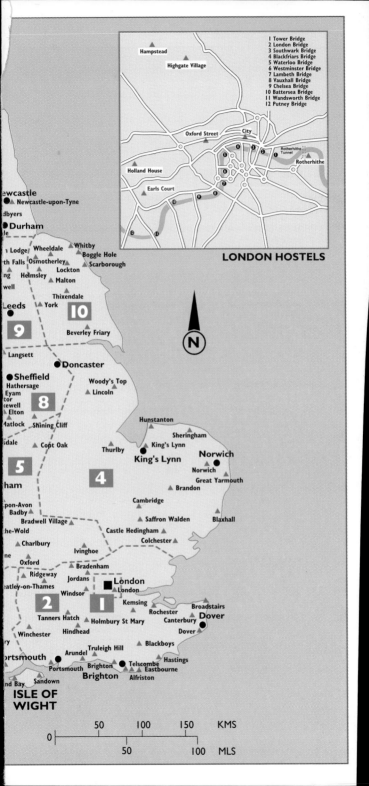

LONDON HOSTELS

1 Tower Bridge
2 London Bridge
3 Southwark Bridge
4 Blackfriars Bridge
5 Waterloo Bridge
6 Westminster Bridge
7 Lambeth Bridge
8 Vauxhall Bridge
9 Chelsea Bridge
10 Battersea Bridge
11 Wandsworth Bridge
12 Putney Bridge

Hampstead
Highgate Village
Oxford Street
City
Rotherhithe Tunnel
Rotherhithe
Holland House
Earls Court

N

ewcastle
Newcastle-upon-Tyne
dbyers
Durham
le

Lodge
Wheeldale
Whitby
th Falls
Osmotherley
Boggle Hole
ng
Helmsley
Lockton
Scarborough
well
Malton
Thixendale
Leeds
York

10

9

Beverley Friary

Langsett

Doncaster

Sheffield
Woody's Top
Hathersage
Eyam
Lincoln
tor
cewell
Elton
Matlock
Hunstanton
Shining Cliff
Sheringham
sdale
King's Lynn

5
Copt Oak
Thurlby
Norwich

4
King's Lynn
Norwich
Great Yarmouth
ham
Brandon
pon-Avon
Badby
Cambridge
Bradwell Village
Saffron Walden
Blaxhall
he-Wold
Castle Hedingham
Charlbury
Colchester
Ivinghoe
ne
Bradenham
Oxford
Jordans
Ridgeway
London
eatley-on-Thames
Windsor
London

2
Kemsing
Broadstairs

1
Rochester
Dover
Tanners Hatch
Canterbury
Holmbury St Mary
Winchester
Hindhead
Dover
Blackboys
Truleigh Hill
Arundel
Hastings
rtsmouth
Telscombe
Portsmouth
Brighton
Eastbourne
nd Bay
Sandown
Brighton
Alfriston

**ISLE OF
WIGHT**

50   100   150   KMS
0
50   100   MLS

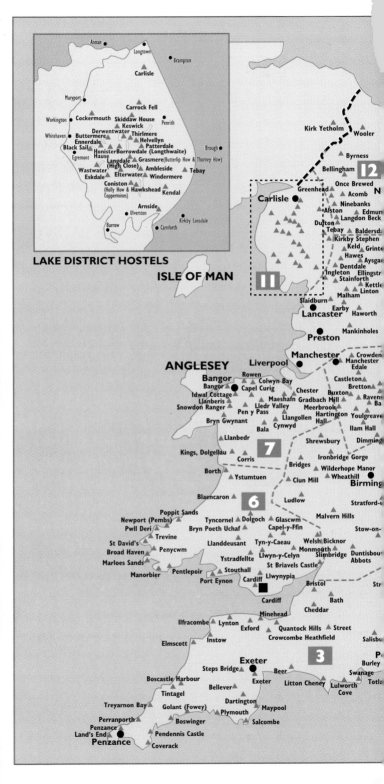

LAKE DISTRICT HOSTELS

ISLE OF MAN

ANGLESEY

Annan
Longtown
Brampton
Carlisle
Maryport
Carrock Fell
Workington ▲ Cockermouth ▲ Skiddaw House
Keswick Penrith
Whitehaven ▲ Derwentwater ▲ Thirlmere
Buttermere ▲ Helvellyn
Ennerdale Patterdale Brough
Black Sail Honister Borrowdale (Longthwaite)
Egremont Hause Langdale Grasmere (Butterlip How & Thorney How)
Wastwater (High Close) Ambleside Tebay
Eskdale Elterwater Windermere
Coniston Kendal
(Holly How & Hawkshead
Coppermines)
Arnside
Ulverston
Barrow Kirkby Lonsdale
Carnforth

Kirk Yetholm ▲ Wooler
Byrness ▲
Bellingham ▲ **12**
Greenhead Once Brewed ▲ N
Carlisle Acomb ▲
Ninebanks ▲ Edmun
Alston Langdon Beck
Dufton ▲
Tebay ▲ Baldersd
Kirkby Stephen
Keld Grinte
Hawes Aysga
Dentdale
Ingleton Ellingstr
Stainforth Kettle
Linton
Malham
Slaidburn
Earby Haworth
Lancaster
Mankinholes
Preston
Crowden
Liverpool Manchester Edale
Castleton
Rowen Bretton
Bangor Colwyn Bay Buxton
Bangor Capel Curig Chester Gradbach Mill Ravens
Idwal Cottage Maeshafn Meerbrook Ba
Llanberis Lledr Valley Hartington Youlgreave
Snowdon Ranger Pen y Pass Llangollen Hall
Bryn Gwynant Llangollen Ilam Hall
Bala Cynwyd Shrewsbury Dimming
Llanbedr
7
Kings, Dolgellau Ironbridge Gorge
Corris Wilderhope Manor
Borth ▲ Ystumtuen Bridges Wheathill ▲ Birming
Clun Mill
Blaencaron **6**
Ludlow Stratford-
Poppit Sands Malvern Hills
Newport (Pembs) Tyncornel Dolgoch Glascwm Stow-on-
Pwll Deri Bryn Poeth Uchaf Capel-y-Ffin
Trevine Welsh Bicknor
St David's Llanddeusant Tyn-y-Caeau Monmouth Duntisbou
Broad Haven Penycwm Llwyn-y-Celyn Slimbridge Abbots
Marloes Sands Ystradfellte St Briavels Castle
Pentlepoir Stouthall
Manorbier Port Eynon Cardiff Llwynypia
Bristol Str
Cardiff
Bath
Minehead Cheddar
Ilfracombe Lynton
Instow Exford Quantock Hills Street
Crowcombe Heathfield Salisbu
Elmscott
Exeter **3** P
Steps Bridge Beer Burley
Boscastle Harbour Exeter Swanage
Bellever Litton Cheney Lulworth Totla
Tintagel Dartington Cove
Treyarnon Bay Golant (Fowey) Maypool
Plymouth
Perranporth Boswinger Salcombe
Penzance
Land's End Pendennis Castle
Penzance Coverack

11

Points mean _sur_prizes!

Fancy a _free_ Hertz car for the weekend?

That's just one of the surprises in store with our Hertz Leisure Points scheme. And they're so easy to collect!

Every Hertz leisure rental means low, low rates _and_ 10

Highest Quality. Low, Low Prices.

Leisure Points towards the prize of your choice - including free AIR MILES, free car use or free use of a mobile phone.

The more you collect, the bigger the prizes, so why not call us now?

Worldwide Reservations
0345 555 888

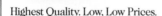

Contents

YHA NATIONAL OFFICE, 8 ST STEPHEN'S HILL,
ST ALBANS, HERTS AL1 2DY
TEL: 01727 855215   FAX: 01727 844126

Membership Prices (from 1 January 1996)

UNDER 18	£3.20	
ADULT	£9.30	
FAMILY	£18.60	(for both parents with children aged under 18 enrolled free)
	£9.30	(for one parent with children aged under 18 enrolled free)
LIFE	£125.00	(or 5 annual covenanted Direct Debit payments of £30)

Overnight and Meal Prices
(from 1 March 1996)
Overnight prices appear under each Hostel entry

Adult overnight prices start at £5.50 for Hostels like Hindhead (page 39) which offer very simple facilities in a rural setting, with the top prices being charged at city locations with all mod cons such as Rotherhithe (page 31) where a bed in an en suite room costs £19.75 inclusive of breakfast. Some Hostel overnight prices are inclusive of breakfast and these are indicated in the relevant Hostel entries.

Overnight prices for under 18's start at only £3.75 at the cheapest locations such as Skiddaw House (page 175) and rise to £8.20 for a night in the heart of the city at Manchester (page 138).

Youth Hostels offer flexibility. You can take full or half-board, self cater or mix the two to suit your needs and your budget.

YHA meals offer value for money. Get the day off to a good start with either an English or Continental breakfast for **£2.80.**

YHA packed lunch is ideal for your day's travels at **£2.35.**

Selected Hostels also offer a bigger lunch pack at **£3.10.**

Your evening meal could be a three course dinner with choices including a vegetarian option at only **£4.15** or you could make a selection from the cafeterias at many Hostels.

The Youth Hostels Association, a registered charity founded in 1930, aims: *"to help all, especially young people of limited means, to a greater knowledge, love and care of the countryside, particularly by providing Hostels or other simple accommodation for them in their travels, and thus to promote their health, rest and education."*

The Youth Hostels Association (YHA) has 240 places to stay in England and Wales, many in glorious town, coastal and countryside locations. The Youth Hostels are as individual as their visitors and vary from converted historic houses in our towns and cities to simple accommodation in remote, next-to-nature settings. Wherever you stay, you'll be free to discover the spectacular landscapes of England and Wales. Come by yourself, with friends or family — everyone's welcome!

When you stay at a Youth Hostel you can always be sure of friendly and helpful service from our staff. Accommodation is in comfortable bunk bedded rooms. Prices start from just £3.75 to stay the night and include bed linen and the use of all facilities — lounge, self-catering kitchen, plus drying room and cycle shed. Many Youth Hostels have on-site parking and grounds available for recreation, as well as extras like a self-service laundry — look for the relevant symbols under the individual Hostel entries (you'll find a key to symbols on the inside map flap).

Most Youth Hostels also offer a full catering service, with prices starting from just £4.15 for a delicious three course evening meal (with a vegetarian option). Some Youth Hostels even have a table licence so adults can enjoy a drink of wine or beer with their meal!

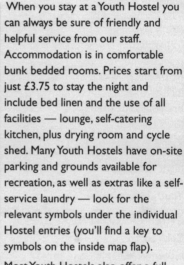

How To Join YHA

You need to be a YHA member to stay at a Youth Hostel. Residents of England and Wales should just complete and send the membership form in this Guide (p.203). One year's YHA membership costs £9.30 for adults and £3.20 for under 18s.

If you're applying for family membership — £18.60 for one year or £9.30 if only one parent wishes to join — please make sure you list the names of all adults and children in your family. Anyone aged under 18 is entitled to free membership when their parent(s) join and will receive their own card.

Formal groups can get hold of a Group/Organisation Card for just £10 which entitles all members of a group to use a Youth Hostel (see page 8). Overseas visitors can buy membership from the Youth Hostel Association of their home country. Alternatively, you can take out International Membership when you arrive at most Youth Hostels.

(You need 6 stamps for membership costing £1.55 each.)

What You Get

Having a YHA membership card gives you access to hundreds of places to stay in England and Wales as well as over 5000 Youth Hostels worldwide. **It also means you can join a YHA Local Group and take part in Hostel-based activities while meeting new friends.**

In addition, YHA members will receive:

▲ regular copies of YHA's **Triangle** magazine (full of special offers and competitions as well as travel articles on the UK and abroad);

▲ the annual **YHA (England & Wales) Accommodation Guide**

▲ a **Members Discount Book,** packed with discounts on travel, places of interest and outdoor gear.

You are also entitled to a ten per cent discount on most goods at YHA Adventure Shops (more details on p.197).

Other membership concessions include:

▲ **Bring a Friend.** If you know someone who'd like to try Youth Hostelling before becoming a member, you can bring them along next time you hostel. There is no need for them to take out membership while they are hostelling with you in England and Wales but of course they have to pay normal overnight and other charges and are not entitled to any membership benefits until they join. Ask at Reception for a "Bring a Friend" voucher. The scheme is limited to one member, one friend!

▲ Students aged 18 to 25 who are not travelling as part of a group will receive a £1.00 reduction on the Youth Hostel's overnight charge on production of a valid student card at the Hostel Reception.

Available at all Youth Hostels at all times.

▲ Adults who are YHA (England & Wales) members who are not travelling as part of a group and who can provide proof that they receive means tested benefits related to low income will be charged the Under 18 rate for their overnight stay.

Available at all Youth Hostels at all times except in London. This concession is not applicable for Family Room or Family Annexe accommodation.

Rest Assured – You'll Get a Warm Welcome

New standards of welcome, comfort, cleanliness, security, privacy and care for the environment have been devised for Youth Hostels around the world and YHA (England & Wales) is among the first to adopt them. Any Hostels in this country carrying the Hostelling International logo will provide the consistent level of service and facilities described below.

WELCOME

All enquiries will be dealt with promptly and you can reserve a bed in advance.

Reception will be open from 08.00 to 10.00 and 17.00 to 22.00 at least, and there will be shelter available even when the Hostel is closed.

Above all, the Hostel staff will be totally committed to welcoming and helping you. From the staff at our smallest Hostels to YHA's Chief Executive, everyone has participated in the Wales and Englist Tourist Board's Welcome Host training scheme to help us improve our customer care.

COMFORT

You will get a comfortable bed, with linen provided, sufficient hot showers, wash basins and toilets. The Hostel will be well lit with inside and outside noise kept to acceptable levels.

CLEANLINESS

Standards of hygiene and cleanliness are high throughout every Hostel.

SECURITY

We will do all we can to ensure your personal safety and the security of your possessions while you are with us. Many Hostels offer secure lockers – look for the ☒ symbol under individual entries.

PRIVACY

Generally you will share a room with others of the same sex unless you have reserved a private or family room. Shower and washing facilities will provide proper levels of privacy.

ENVIRONMENTAL STANDARDS

Hostels are committed to stated criteria for improving our conservation of resources.

You will find many differences between small, remote Hostels and large, busy ones but the basic standards apply regardless of size and style. Wherever you stay, let us know if you are dissatisfied with any aspect by writing to:–

The Chief Executive,
YHA (England & Wales)
8 St Stephen's Hill,
St Albans AL1 2DY

YHA membership opens up a wide range of holiday options.

Whether you're after a short break in the city or a tough walk along a long distance footpath – there's probably a Youth Hostel where you're heading. Use a Youth Hostel as a base for visiting an event, exploring an area, or tour around staying at a different Youth Hostel each night. Whether you're travelling by foot, bike, public transport or car you'll find the facilities you need at the end of the day – plus other hostellers to share your experiences with.

To make it easier for you to plan ahead, YHA operates booking bureaux on established routes such as the Pennine Way and the Pembrokeshire Coast Path. Or if you want to join a led walk with luggage carried we can arrange that too! Just ring YHA Customer Services section on 01727 855215.

Another way of making the most of your membership is to try one of the many 'What's On' breaks which feature in Triangle – what a way to meet people. Then there are YHA Local Groups – see page 15 for how you can make life more interesting by joining one.

RENT-A-HOSTEL

YHA's Rent-a-Hostel scheme — which runs from September to March each year — offers families, friends and groups the chance to take over an entire Youth Hostel, coming and going as they please. The minimum stay is two nights and the more people in your group the cheaper the price per person.

There are 55 Hostels on the scheme, ranging from cottages to farmhouses in some of the prettiest parts of England and Wales. Prices start from £147 for a two night break (no matter how many in your group) and can work out from as little as £3.25 per person.

To make it easier to rent a Hostel YHA runs a booking service. All you need to do is ring the office which covers the area which you are interested in visiting:

South East, South West, East of England, and Heart of England

Tel: 01722 337494

South Wales and North Wales
Tel: 01222 396766/222122

Peak District, Yorkshire Dales, North York Moors, Lake District and Northumbria
Tel: 01629 825850

HOSTELLING WITH A GROUP

Youth Hostels are also available for group residentials, with many offering facilities for educational trips, such as leader rooms and class/meeting rooms (there may be a small extra charge). All-inclusive packages are also on offer which can include transport, itineraries, activities and excursions.

The YHA can give a helping hand to group holiday organisers by providing free planning visits. Group leaders are also entitled to free leader places on a one for ten ratio if their organisation has booked full board accommodation and paid in advance (subject to the booking conditions on our group booking form).

Some Hostels may be available for advance group bookings when otherwise closed – contact the Hostel for more information.

Several Hostels are suitable as conference and meeting venues — just look in the Additional Info section under individual Hostel entries.

If you would like to receive our free Groups Away colour brochure, and for assistance in finding the most appropriate venue for your group's residential visit, or a free copy of our Rent-a-Hostel brochure, contact YHA Customer Services on 01727 855215.

Youth hostelling is ideal for families — it offers good value accommodation and wholesome meals or self-catering facilities in locations which provide access to outdoor activities and attractions for all the family to enjoy.

Families are welcome at all Youth Hostels and you'll find a variety of accommodation to give you freedom and flexibility. You can make your own selections from the following:

FAMILY ANNEXES

A few Hostels have self-contained annexes which are fully equipped, offer self-catering facilities and all day access with a key. Annexes are usually booked for seven days at a weekly rate — turn to page 13 for details.

Family Annexes are available for families with children of all ages.

FAMILY ROOMS

More and more Youth Hostels have family rooms which offer a comfortable standard of accommodation, plus the freedom to come and go as you please during the day. Families are provided with their own key and the facilities will vary between Youth Hostels: some have en suite facilities and all are equipped with wash-basins, together with adequate storage space. Prices are charged per room per night — turn the page for details.

Family Rooms are available for families with children aged three and over (though younger children may be accommodated at the Warden's discretion).

FAMILY DORMITORIES

At most Hostels families may be accommodated in small dormitories. Please check room sizes under the individual Hostel entries before contacting the Hostel direct. You'll be charged per person per night.

Family Dormitories are available for families with children aged five and over.

All our family accommodation is very popular so please book well in advance.

If you are unable to book a room for your family you can stay in traditional single sex rooms with other customers. There are, however, a few restrictions: Children need to be at least five years old. Children aged 5 - 8 must share the same dormitory as their parent or guardian of the same sex. Children aged 9 - 13 do not have to share the same room but they must be accompanied on their stay by a parent or responsible adult. Young people aged 14 or over can go hostelling on their own or with friends.

▲ **Family membership scheme:** when parent(s) join YHA, children under 18 are enrolled FREE and will receive their own membership cards.

▲ **Family membership discount on overnights:** All children hostelling with their parent(s) or guardian as part of the family membership scheme will receive a discount of £1.00 off the Under 18 overnight charge. We regret that this discount is not available for Family Rooms or Family Annexes.

HOSTEL	SEASON	Number of beds 2	3	4	5	6
LONDON						
City of London (p.28)	All Year	£40.50	£56.00	£72.50	£89.00	£105.50
Breakfast is included in the price at this Hostel						
Hampstead Heath (p.29)	All Year	£35.40	£45.00	£60.50	£75.00	£88.00
Breakfast is included in the price at this Hostel						
Rotherhithe (p.31)	All Year	£40.50		£72.00		£105.50
Breakfast is included in the price at this Hostel						
SOUTH EAST						
Arundel (p.34)	All Year			£25.50		
Broadstairs (p.36)	All Year		£23.50	£28.50	£33.50	£38.50
Canterbury (p.37)	All Year					£43.00
Dover (p.38)	All Year	£20.50		£31.50		£43.00
Hastings (p.39)	High		£23.50	£28.50		£38.50
	Rest of Year		£21.50	£25.50		£34.50
Holmbury St Mary (p.40)	All Year	£19.00		£28.50		
Kemsing (p.41)	All Year			£28.50		£40.00
Portsmouth (p.42)	All Year					£38.50
Sandown (p.43)	High	£20.50		£31.50		£43.00
	Rest of Year	£19.00		£28.50		£37.50
Streatley-on-Thames (p.44)	All Year			£31.50	£37.50	£43.00
The Ridgeway (p.42)	All Year			£31.50		
Totland Bay (p.46)	High			£31.50	£37.50	£43.00
	Rest of Year			£28.50	£33.50	£40.00
Truleigh Hill (p.46)	All Year			£28.50		£38.50
SOUTH WEST						
Beer (p.50)	High			£28.50		£40.00
	Rest of Year			£26.00		£37.50
Bellever (p.51)	All Year			£28.50		£38.50
Boswinger (p.52)	High			£28.50		£38.50
	Rest of Year			£25.50		£34.50
Bristol (p.53)	All Year	£28.40	£34.00	£47.50	£58.00	£68.00
Breakfast is included in the price at this Hostel						
Burley (p.53)	High			£33.00		£45.00
	Rest of Year			£30.00		£42.00
Cheddar (p.54)	All Year	£16.00		£26.00		£37.50
Coverack (p.54)	High			£28.50		
	Rest of Year			£25.50		
Dartington (p.56)	High			£28.50		£38.50
	Rest of Year			£25.50		£34.50
Exeter (p.57)	High	£20.50		£31.50		£43.00
	Rest of Year	£19.00		£28.50		£38.50
Exford (p.57)	All Year	£19.00		£28.50	£33.50	£40.00

KEY: High Season = 1 July - 31 August

SOUTH WEST CONT'D

HOSTEL	SEASON	2	3	4	5	6
Golant (p.58)	All Year	£20.50	£26.50	£32.00		£44.00
Ilfracombe (p.59)	All Year	£19.00	£23.50	£28.50	£33.50	£40.00
Instow (p.59)	All Year			£27.50		
Lulworth (p.61)	High			£28.50	£33.50	
	Rest of Year			£26.00	£30.00	
Minehead (p.63)	All Year			£26.00		£37.50
Pendennis (p.63)	High	£20.50		£31.50		£43.00
	Rest of Year	£19.00		£28.50		£38.50
Plymouth (p.65)	High	£20.50	£26.00	£31.50	£37.50	£43.00
	Rest of Year	£19.00	£23.50	£28.50	£33.50	£38.50
Salcombe (p.66)	High			£28.50		
	Rest of Year			£25.50		
Salisbury (p.67)	All Year			£31.50		
Street (p.68)	All Year		£21.50	£26.00	£30.00	

EAST OF ENGLAND

HOSTEL	SEASON	2	3	4	5	6
Brandon (p.72)	All Year			£28.50		£38.50
Colchester (p.74)	All Year		£21.50	£25.50		
Cambridge (p.73)	All Year	£26.60	£35.00	£44.50	£54.00	£64.00
Breakfast is included in the price at this Hostel						
Great Yarmouth (p.76)	All Year			£28.50		£38.50
Hunstanton (p.77)	High		£26.00	£31.50		£43.00
	Rest of Year		£23.50	£28.50		£38.50
Lincoln (p.78)	All Year	£19.00	£23.50	£28.50		£38.50
Norwich (p.78)	All Year	£18.00	£23.50	£28.50	£33.50	£38.50
Sheringham (p.79)	High	£20.50	£26.00	£31.50	£37.00	£43.00
	Rest of Year	£19.00	£23.50	£28.50	£33.50	£38.50
Thurlby (p.80)	All Year			£25.50		
Woody's Top (p.80)	All Year			£21.50		£30.00

HEART OF ENGLAND

HOSTEL	SEASON	2	3	4	5	6
Charlbury (p.86)	All Year	£16.00	£21.00	£25.00	£30.00	£34.00
Duntisbourne (p.89)	All Year		£21.50		£30.00	£34.00
Ludlow (p.91)	All Year			£23.50		£33.00
Slimbridge (p.93)	All Year	£20.00		£31.50	£37.50	£43.00

SOUTH AND WEST WALES PLUS THE WYE VALLEY

HOSTEL	SEASON	2	3	4	5	6
*Borth (p.98)	All Year		£24.00	£29.00	£34.00	£39.00
Broad Haven (p.99)	High		£27.50	£32.50	£38.00	£44.00
	Rest of Year		£23.00	£28.00	£33.00	£38.50
Llanddeusant (p.103)	High			£22.50		£30.00
	Rest of Year			£20.50		£27.50

*Stay for seven nights for the price of six

KEY: High Season = 1 July - 31 August

HOSTEL	SEASON	2	3	4	5	6

SOUTH AND WEST WALES PLUS THE WYE VALLEY (CONTD)

HOSTEL	SEASON	2	3	4	5	6
*Llwynypia (p.104)	All Year			£29.00	£34.00	
*Manorbier (p.105)	High				£38.00	£44.00
	Rest of Year				£33.00	£38.50
Newport (Pembs) (p.107)	High			£26.00	£30.50	£35.50
	Rest of Year			£22.50	£26.50	£30.00
*Penycwm (Solva) (p.108)	All Year	£20.00		£30.00	£33.00	£38.00
Poppit Sands (p.108)	High			£26.00		
	Rest of Year			£22.50		
Trevine (Trefin) (p.112)	High	£18.00		£26.00	£30.50	£35.50
	Rest of Year	£16.00		£22.50	£26.50	£30.00
*Welsh Bicknor (p.113)	All Year		£24.00	£29.00	£34.00	£39.00

NORTH WALES & CHESTER

HOSTEL	SEASON	2	3	4	5	6
*Bryn Gwynant (p.119)	All Year		£24.00	£29.00	£34.00	£39.00
Capel Curig (p.119)	All Year			£29.00	£34.00	£39.00
Corris (p.121)	High	£17.00	£23.00	£28.00	£32.00	£36.00
	Rest of Year	£16.00	£22.00	£26.00	£30.00	£34.00
Kings (p.123)	All Year				£28.00	£32.00
Llanbedr (p.123)	All Year		£22.50	£26.00	£31.00	£36.00
Pen-y-Pass (p.126)	All Year		£27.00	£32.00	£39.00	£46.00

THE PEAK DISTRICT AND MANCHESTER

HOSTEL	SEASON	2	3	4	5	6
Castleton (p.131)	All Year	£18.50		£29.50		£39.50
Castleton (Vicarage)	All Year	£22.00		£37.00		£51.00
Gradbach Mill (p.135)	All Year	£18.50	£23.50	£30.00	£35.00	£40.50
Hartington Hall(p.135)	All Year			£37.00		£51.00
Ilam Hall (p.137)	All Year			£37.00		£51.00
Manchester (p.138)	All Year			£50.00		£72.00
Breakfast is included in the price at this Hostel.						
Matlock (p.139)	All Year	£20.00	£27.00	£33.00		£43.50

THE YORKSHIRE DALES AND SOUTH PENNINES

HOSTEL	SEASON	2	3	4	5	6
Aysgarth Falls (p.144)	All Year	£18.50	£23.00	£28.00	£32.00	£37.00
Ingleton (p.147)	All Year		£22.00	£27.00	£31.00	£36.00
Kettlewell (p.148)	All Year	£18.50	£23.00	£28.00		
Kirkby Stephen (p.149)	All Year	£19.00		£28.00		
Malham (p.150)	All Year	£20.00	£27.00	£33.00	£38.00	£43.50

THE YORKSHIRE MOORS, WOLDS AND COAST

HOSTEL	SEASON	2	3	4	5	6
Boggle Hole (p.154)	All Year	£19.00		£30.00		
Osmotherley (p.156)	All Year	£18.50	£23.00	£28.00	£32.00	£37.00
York (p.159)	All Year			£44.00		£67.00
Breakfast is included in the price at this Hostel						

*Stay for seven nights for the price of six

KEY: High Season = 1 July - 31 August

HOSTEL	SEASON	2	3	4	5	6

THE LAKE DISTRICT

HOSTEL	SEASON	2	3	4	5	6
Ambleside (p.162)	All Year	£20.00	£27.00	£33.00	£38.00	£43.50
Borrowdale (p.163)	All Year			£28.00		
Buttermere (p.164)	All Year			£30.00	£35.00	£40.50
Eskdale (p.169)	All Year	£18.50		£30.00		
Grasmere Butterlip How (p.170)	All Year	£18.50	£23.50	£30.00		
Hawkshead (p.171)	All Year		£27.50	£37.00	£41.00	
Wastwater (p.176)	All Year			£30.00		
Windermere (p.177)	All Year		£23.00	£28.00		£37.00

NORTHUMBERLAND AND THE NORTH PENNINES

Once Brewed (p.186)	All Year		£23.50	£30.00		

FAMILY ANNEXE PRICES

THE SOUTH WEST

Boswinger (p.52)	High	£181.00 per week	Sleeps 4
	Rest of Year	£155.00 per week	

SOUTH WALES

Bryn Poeth Uchaf (p.100)	Price varies according to season – please enquire Tel: 01222 396766	From £72-£90 week (Sleeps four plus baby)
Manorbier (p.105)	Price varies according to season – please enquire Tel: 01222 396766	From £150-£270 week (Sleeps four plus baby)
St David's (p.111)	Price varies according to season – please enquire Tel: 01222 396766	From £99-£160 week (Sleeps four plus baby)

NORTH WALES

Cynwyd (p.121)	Price varies according to season – please enquire Tel: 01222 396766	From £88-£105 week (Sleeps four plus baby)

Activity Centres

YHA has two Activity Centres – Edale in Derbyshire and Llangollen on the Welsh Border – where many different activities can be enjoyed under the supervision of YHA's own qualified instructors.

The specialist courses, which last a weekend, three, five or seven days, are pitched at several different levels to suit all abilities – ideal for children, adults, families and groups. The Centres also run multi-activity breaks where you can sample several activities in a weekend or longer.

Prices start from as little as £71 per person for a weekend break inclusive of all meals, accommodation, instruction, specialist equipment and one year's YHA membership (or renewal of existing membership).

SAFETY

The YHA Activity Centres are respected providers of outdoor and adventure holidays. The Centres work within the stringent guidelines laid down by the governing bodies of each sport (such as the British Canoe Union and the Royal Yachting Association) and the recently issued Outdoor Adventure Activity Providers Code of Practice. The staff have a wide range of qualifications and experience and ensure that strict safety precautions are taken at all times. The Wales Tourist Board, which has set up a national scheme for the regulation and registration of Activity Centres, has accredited our Centre at Llangollen. The YHA is an active participant in the establishment of a UK accreditation scheme.

MORE DETAILS

To find out what's on offer at our Activity Centres, either contact them direct, or ring YHA Customer Services on 01727 855215.

Llangollen Youth Hostel and Activity Centre.

Llangollen YHA Activity Centre,
Tyndwr Hall,
Tyndwr Road, Llangollen,
Clwyd LL20 8AR

Tel: 01978 860330
Fax: 01978 861709

Edale Youth Hostel and Activity Centre.

Edale YHA Activity Centre,
Rowland Cote,
Nether Booth,
Edale, Sheffield S30 2ZH

Tel: 01433 670302
Fax: 01433 670243

Andover
West Anglia
Aylesbury
Barnet
Barrow & S Lakeland
Bedford
North Birmingham
West Birmingham
Blackburn
Bolton
Bournemouth
Brighton & Hove
Bristol
Bromley
Bucks & Berks
Cambridge
Canterbury & Thanet
Cardiff
Carlisle
Chelmsford
Cheltenham &
Gloucester
East Cheshire
Chester
Chippenham
Colchester
Coventry
Crawley
Croydon
Cumbria (West)
Dartford
Derby
Doncaster
Dunstable
Durham North
Ealing
Eltham & Sidcup
Essex
Exeter
Fylde
Harrogate
Mid Glamorgan
Grantham
Guildford
Halifax
Harlow
Harrow & Wembley
Hounslow (S Middx)
Hull
Ipswich
Kendal

Kingston
Lancaster &
Morecambe

Leicester
Leeds
South Leicestershire

Lincoln
London (Central)
London (S Bank)
Luton
Manchester
Mid Kent
Mid Wales
Milton Keynes
Newcastle
Newport
Northampton
Norwich
Nottingham
Oxford
Potteries
Preston
Reading
Redhill & Reigate
St Albans
Sale
Salisbury
Sheffield
Southampton
Stafford
Stockport
Sunderland
Sutton
Swansea
Swindon
Taunton
Telford & Shropshire
Walthamstow &
Chingford
Wakefield
Watford
Wolverhampton
Worcester
York

YHA LOCAL GROUPS

offer social activities from slideshows to skating, badminton to barbecues, and we'd like individuals of all ages, and families too, to join the fun.

Groups organise walking, cycling, sight-seeing, water sports and many other activities, sometimes for a weekend or longer. Local Groups also give you the chance to help YHA, organising publicity events and working parties at Hostels. With 100 Local Groups around the country you should find one not too far away – or why not start one yourself? 'YHA News' – the Association's own newspaper will keep you in touch with the Local Group scene. For more information contact the Local Groups Officer, YHA, Trevelyan House, 8 St Stephen's Hill, St Albans, Herts AL1 2DY.

HOSTELLING INTERNATIONAL

Universities
Durham
Loughborough
London Imperial
College
Special Interest
Postellers (Youth
in London/Birm)
Over 50s
Single Parent
Travel Club
YHA Adventure Gp

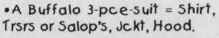

Here are some handy hints and advice to help make your stay as enjoyable as possible.

How to Book

The best way to be sure of your bed is to book in advance. Simply contact the Hostel direct by 'phone (Access and Visa credit cards accepted at most Hostels) or by letter with correct payment. It's usually a good idea to call before 10.00hrs or after 17.00hrs when Hostel staff can also take your meal orders. Reservations which have been taken without pre-payment will only be held until 18.00hrs unless an alternative time has been agreed.

Once on the hostelling trail you'll find that many Hostels will be able to book your next night for you at no extra cost — just look for the BABA sign under individual Hostel entries. You can also turn up at the Youth Hostel on the day (bring your membership card or join at the Hostel) but remember we cannot guarantee you a bed as at busy times we're often full!

What you need to know...

Most Hostels are open between 07.00hrs -10.00hrs and 17.00hrs - 23.00hrs. Several now open earlier (at 13.00hrs) or can offer some access during the afternoon. Details of access available when the Hostel is closed appears under the 'Additional Info' section under each Hostel entry. **If there is no statement, and the Hostel is closed, there is no access to any shelter.** Most London Hostels offer 24hr access.

In the evenings you can check in until 22.30hrs. Youth Hostels are open until 23.00hrs and 'lights out' is usually at 23.30hrs. Some Youth Hostels are more flexible on these hours, especially those in towns and cities. Please check with the Hostel staff as you may not be able to get in if you arrive or return late.

For security reasons and to avoid disturbing other guests the Youth Hostel is closed until 07.00hrs, so even if it is a lovely morning please don't get up too soon! (If for any reason you need an early start, please discuss this with the Hostel staff. Packed breakfasts can be arranged at many Hostels). Please also bear in mind that most Hostel staff have their time off during the day, so try not to disturb them.

How To Find The Hostel

Under each Hostel entry there are clear instructions and/or a map giving the best routes to the Youth Hostel, as well as Ordnance Survey map references and public transport details. As you get nearer to the Youth Hostel, you may see the following signs:

Brown and white pointer signs at road junctions

At the Hostel entrance

On Arrival

When you arrive, check in at the Hostel Reception where you will be given your room number. As well as our friendly staff who are always happy to help, Youth Hostels contain lots of useful information about the Hostel and what to do in the area.

You will stay in comfortable bunk bedded rooms sharing with people of the same sex unless you have made special arrangements in advance — for instance, families or groups of friends may be able to have their own private room (see p.9). More and more Youth Hostels now offer smaller rooms, often with their own washing facilities — check under individual entries. Otherwise you will find showers, toilets and washing facilities close to your room. Freshly laundered bed linen will be given to you. It is very important that this is used. Pillows, duvets and/or blankets are also provided.

Youth Hostels have self-catering kitchens (fully equipped with cooking facilities, pots, pans, crockery, cutlery and food storage) as well as small shops which sell non-perishable foodstuffs such as tinned foods (soup, meat, vegetables, fruit) tea, instant coffee, biscuits, chocolate, sweets and canned drinks. Bread and milk will usually be available as well. Most Youth Hostels also provide a full meals service. Several Youth Hostels have table licences which means they are able to sell beer, wine and cider with meals. Otherwise alcohol should not be brought into the Hostel unless special arrangements have first been made with the Warden. The use of illegal drugs and other substances is also not permitted on Hostel premises. The Hostel staff will refuse admission to anyone under the influence of alcohol or drugs.

While many Hostels have areas specially set aside for smoking, there are also around 50 'No-Smoking' Hostels highlighted by the ⊠ symbol under individual entries.

To keep prices as low as possible, Wardens may ask for help with simple household tasks, like washing up, and you are asked to clear up after yourself.

Pets are not allowed in Youth Hostels, although special arrangements can be made for Guide Dogs for the Blind. Overnight grazing for horses can be arranged near 30 Hostels in northern England (leaflet available).

Facilities for People with Disabilities

Many Youth Hostels are in traditional buildings which may make access difficult for people in wheelchairs. Some Youth Hostels — like Broad Haven, Manorbier and Newport in Pembrokeshire, West Wales, Manchester, Sheringham in Norfolk, Wooler in Northumberland, Ilam Hall in the Peak District and Rotherhithe in London — have special facilities for people with disabilities (look for the 🦽 symbol under individual entries). Always contact the Hostel staff before booking to check that the facilities are suitable for your needs.

Camping (at permitted Hostels only)

YHA members who bring their own tents and bedding may camp in the grounds at Youth Hostels which display the ⛺ symbol in the Guide.

The charge for camping is half the adult overnight fee for the Hostel per person regardless of the age of the camper(s). No price concessions are available.

Campers are strongly recommended to book ahead as Wardens may have to restrict numbers when Hostels are busy to avoid overloading facilities. Campers must register at the Hostel reception and present their YHA membership card before pitching their tent.

The charge for camping normally covers the use of Hostel washing, toilet, laundry/drying, self-catering and recreational facilities.

Campers must observe restrictions which may have to be imposed by Wardens in the interest of people staying in the Hostel.

No Hostel equipment may be taken out to the camping area. Campers may prefer to use their own cooking equipment especially when this would relieve crowding in the self-catering kitchens.

Watch Out

Although thefts at Youth Hostels are rare we advise you not to leave valuables and cash in dormitories or unattended during your stay. Some Youth Hostels now provide secure lockers for your belongings (see 🔒 symbol under individual entries).

YHA And The Environment

David Bellamy, the internationally famous environmentalist, is now in his 13th year as our President and takes an active interest in the work of the YHA.

YHA (England & Wales) has been an enthusiastic partner in the International Youth Hostelling movements' development of an Environmental Charter which commits Youth Hostels around the world to a responsible approach to the environment. Practical work is undertaken in Hostel grounds and neighbourhood to create conservation areas and we try to reduce our effect on the environment by minimising waste and controlling its disposal.

To find out how members can help in this important work, contact:

John Kingsbury, the YHA's Countryside Officer, at YHA, 8 St Stephen's Hill, St Albans, Herts AL1 2DY.

You can travel the world with a YHA membership which entitles you to stay at over 5000 Youth Hostels in 64 countries. Always look for the Hostelling International logo which assures you of safe, clean and comfortable accommodation all over the world.

HOSTELLING INTERNATIONAL

You can also book a bed ahead at key Hostels worldwide (see list below for the countries and main locations covered) by using the International Booking Network available from the following England and Wales Youth Hostels: all London YHs, Ambleside, Bath, Bristol, Cambridge, Canterbury, Cardiff, Chester, Dover, Oxford, Salisbury, Stratford-upon-Avon, Windsor and York — as well as from our Central Booking Offices (at 14 Southampton Street, Covent Garden, London. Tel: 0171 836 1036, Fax: 0171 836 6372 and 52 Grosvenor Gardens, Victoria, London. Tel: 0171 730 5769, Fax: 0171 730 5779).

ARGENTINA
Buenos Aires

AUSTRALIA
Adelaide
Brisbane
Melbourne
Perth
Sydney

AUSTRIA
Innsbruck
Salzburg
Vienna

BELGIUM
Antwerp
Bruges
Brussels
Gent

BRAZIL
Rio de Janeiro
Sao Paulo

CANADA
Calgary
Montréal
Ottawa
Quebec
Toronto
Vancouver

CHILE
Santiago

COSTA RICA
San José

CZECH REPUBLIC
Prague

DENMARK
Copenhagen

FINLAND
Helsinki

FRANCE
Boulogne
Lyons
Marseille
Montpellier
Nice
Paris

GERMANY
Berlin
Cologne
Düsseldorf
Hamburg
Munich

GREECE
Athens

HONG KONG
Hong Kong

INDONESIA
Bali

NORTHERN IRELAND
Belfast

REP. OF IRELAND
Dublin

ITALY
Florence
Rome
Venice

JAPAN
Kyoto
Nagasaki
Tokyo

KENYA
Nairobi

LITHUANIA
Vilnius

LUXEMBOURG
Luxembourg City

MALAYSIA
Kuala Lumpur
Melaka

NETHERLANDS
Amsterdam
Rotterdam

NEW ZEALAND
Auckland
Christchurch
Wellington.

NORWAY
Oslo

PERU
Lima

PORTUGAL
Lisbon
Oporto

RUSSIA
St Petersburg

SCOTLAND
Aviemore
Edinburgh
Glasgow
Oban

SOUTH AFRICA
Cape Town
Durban
Johannesburg

SPAIN
Barcelona

SWEDEN
Stockholm

SWITZERLAND
Basle
Klosters
Lausanne
Montreaux
St Moritz
Zürich

TAIWAN
Taipei

THAILAND
Bangkok

USA
Boston
Chicago
Fort Lauderdale
Honolulu
Los Angeles
Miami Beach
New York
Orlando
San Francisco
Seattle
Washington

URUGUAY
Montevideo

Other YHAs In Britain & Ireland

YHA (England and Wales) is separate from the other YHA's in Britain and Ireland but your membership is valid at all of them.

Youth Hostel Association of Northern Ireland (YHANI)
22 Donegall Road
Belfast BT12 5JN
Tel: (01232) 324733
Fax: (01232) 439699

Irish Youth Hostel Association (An Oige)
61 Mountjoy Street
Dublin 7
Tel: (0103531) 8304555
Fax: (0103531) 8305808

Scottish Youth Hostels Association (SYHA)
7 Glebe Crescent
Stirling FK8 2JA
Tel: (01786) 451181
Fax: (01786) 450198

Details about Youth Hostels worldwide and National Association addresses can be found in the two Hostelling International Guides — one detailing Europe and the Mediterranean and the second covering Africa, America, Asia and the Pacific. These essential reference guides cost £7.00 each (incl. p&p) and are available from YHA (address on p.1).

Full Hostel details for YHANI, An Oige and SYHA are given in their National Handbooks, which are available direct from the Association concerned or from YHA.

Youth Hostel Directory

Different types of Youth Hostel

The following general descriptions are designed to help you to find the Youth Hostels which are most likely to meet your particular needs.

 Hostels in popular cities and towns. These are often very busy and are used particularly by groups and young travellers, both from home and abroad.

 Busy Hostels with a wide range of facilities which are especially useful for groups and popular with families.

 Medium sized Hostels in country and coastal locations ideal for a variety of hostellers – whether individuals, families or parties.

Small Hostels of a simple style, often in remote areas, which are of particular attraction to walkers and cyclists.

Just look for the symbol at the top of each Hostel entry to identify Hostels to suit you.

The map below indicates the areas used in this Guide. As well as the Youth Hostels in England and Wales, we've included a section on Camping Barns (pages 188-193).

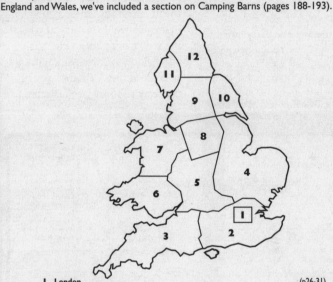

1	London	(p26-31)
2	South East England	(p32-47)
3	South West England	(p48-69)
4	East of England	(p70-81)
5	Heart of England	(p82-95)
6	South and West Wales plus the Wye Valley	(p96-115)
7	North Wales & Chester	(p116-127)
8	The Peak District and Manchester	(p128-141)
9	The Yorkshire Dales and South Pennines	(p142-151)
10	The Yorkshire Moors, Wolds and Coast	(p152-159)
11	The Lake District	(p160-177)
12	Northumberland and the North Pennines	(p178-187)
13	Camping Barns	(p188-193)

Please note that although we do our best to make sure that the Youth Hostel details in this Guide are accurate at the time of going to press, we reserve the right to change opening times and other Hostel details and prices if circumstances warrant. It's also a good idea to check details with the Youth Hostel before you arrive. **Triangle** magazine (mailed regularly to members) carries a special Guide Update to keep you informed.

YOUTH HOSTEL DIRECTORY

London

There's no chance of running out of things to do in London. Sightsee on foot or from the top of a bus, browse around museums and galleries, window shop in world class stores and ancient street markets. See a West End Show or try a new production in a pub or fringe theatre. London doesn't have to be expensive if you stay at one of the well placed Youth Hostels. You'll find you have the capital on your doorstep. Whether you're in the leafy suburbs of Hampstead

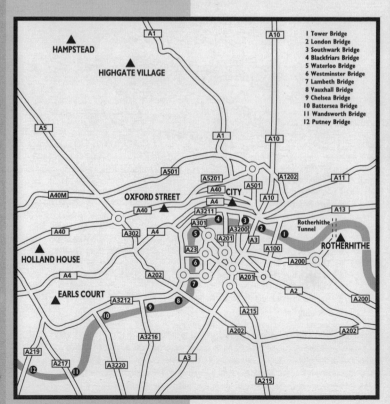

1 Tower Bridge
2 London Bridge
3 Southwark Bridge
4 Blackfriars Bridge
5 Waterloo Bridge
6 Westminster Bridge
7 Lambeth Bridge
8 Vauxhall Bridge
9 Chelsea Bridge
10 Battersea Bridge
11 Wandsworth Bridge
12 Putney Bridge

or the central parkland area around Holland House, you'll be a short tube ride from all the main attractions.

With your YHA membership card and Discount Booklet you'll get discounts at attractions such as London Zoo, Tower Bridge, the London Dungeon, Wembley Stadium and London Pride Sightseeing Tours. All London Hostels sell tickets for theatres, attractions, National Express and London Underground travelcards.

Useful Publications

Individual Hostel leaflets are available – just send a SAE to the Central Bookings Office listed below.

Helping You to Book Ahead

To make a booking in London, or for further information about London Hostels contact:

Central Bookings Office, Rotherhithe Youth Hostel Salter Road, Rotherhithe, London SE16 1PP

Tel: 0171 248 6547
Fax: 0171 236 7681

City Of London

191 BEDS Open: 24hrs

☎ 0171 236 4965 Fax: 0171 236 7681

Youth Hostel, 36 Carter Lane, London EC4V 5AD

Overnight Charges: Under 18 £16.55 Adult £19.75

Bed & Breakfast included.

Family accommodation prices on p.10-13

🛏 🔲 🚿 🅿 NCP Queen Victoria Street. Coaches park at St Pauls 150 metres. BABA IBN

Open every day of the year.

ACCOMMODATION 🛏²⁻⁴ 21 🛏⁵⁻⁸ 12 🛏⁹⁺ 2

Wake up to the sound of the bells ringing from St Paul's Cathedral — it's opposite! Formerly the Choir School for the cathedral, the Hostel has retained many of its original features including the oak panelled chapel — now used as a meeting room, and the playground — which is actually on the roof and hosts regular BBQ's in the summer! Recently refurbished, accommodation is provided in modern small rooms, some singles and twins with a TV and tea and coffee making facilities (extra charge). The Hostel is very popular with individual travellers and families and so it is advisable to book in advance as the Hostel is extremely busy!

TRAVEL INFO
🚇 Frequent LT services (☎ 0171 222 1234). Underground: St Pauls ¼m. 🚆 Blackfriars ¼m; City Thameslink ¼m; Liverpool Street 1m
🛈 ☎ 0171 730 3488

NEXT HOSTELS
Rotherhithe 3m, Oxford Street 2m, Earl's Court 5m

ADDITIONAL INFO
No self-catering kitchen. The chapel and roof-top are available for hire. Ask for more details.

HOW TO GET THERE
From Blackfriars underground turn right onto Queen Victoria St and take 2nd left into St Andrews Hill. Carter Lane is at the top with the entrance on the left.
OS 176 GR 319811

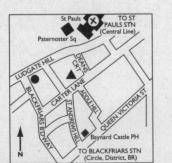

Earl's Court

130 BEDS Open: 24hrs

☎ 0171 373 7083 Fax: 0171 835 2034

Youth Hostel, 38 Bolton Gardens, London SW5 0AQ

Overnight Charges: Under 18 £15.55 Adult £17.70

Bed & Breakfast included.

🔲 🚿 🅿 None. Warwick Road ¾m. BABA IBN

Open every day of the year.

ACCOMMODATION 🛏²⁻⁴ 8 🛏⁵⁻⁸ 5 🛏⁹⁺ 8

The most accessible Hostel from Heathrow Airport and Victoria Coach, Rail and Bus stations, Earl's Court Youth Hostel is a lively international Hostel particularly popular with individual travellers. In the heart of a cosmopolitan area full of shops, cafes, restaurants and bars as well as being just a five minute walk from Earl's Court and Olympia Exhibition Centres. The Hostel offers dormitory accommodation in rooms of various sizes as well as a lounge with Cable TV and a small courtyard garden which is host to BBQ's in the summer. The Hostel also sells coach tickets around Britain and to Europe, has a bureau de change facility and a good value meals service.

TRAVEL INFO
🚇 Frequent LT services (☎ 0171 222 1234). Underground Earl's Court ¼m. Gloucester Rd ½m 🚆 Kensington Olympia 1m.
🛈 ☎ 0171 730 3488

NEXT HOSTELS
Holland House 1m, City of London 5m, Oxford Street 5m

ADDITIONAL INFO
National Express ticket sales. Bureau de change.

HOW TO GET THERE
Leave Earl's Court underground station by Earl's Court Road exit. Turn right outside station and take fifth street on left (Bolton Gardens).
OS 152 GR 258783

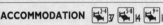

200 BEDS   Open: 24hrs

Hampstead Heath

☎ 0181 458 9054/7196 Fax: 0181 209 0546

Youth Hostel, 4 Wellgarth Road, London NW11 7HR

Overnight Charges: Under 18 £12.30 Adult £14.40

Family accommodation prices on p.10-13

🛏 🔍 📋 🛁 🅿 Small car park for 8 cars and on street parking. BABA (IBN)

Open every day of the year.

ACCOMMODATION 🛏2-4 7 🛏5-8 4 🛏9+ 1

Stay here and you will be staying amongst pop stars and actors! The homes of the rich and famous are scattered all around the Heath which boasts impressive views of London and is just minutes from the Hostel. Accommodation is in small rooms all with wash basins and overlooking the Hostel garden. The cafeteria offers a tempting choice of meals and is licensed so you may enjoy an alcoholic drink with your meal. Wembley Stadium, Camden Market and Kenwood House are within easy reach of the Hostel and central London is just 20 minutes by tube. The Hostel sells tickets to attractions/theatres, has a bureau de change facility and sells National Express/ Eurolines coach tickets in Britain and Europe. A perfect location for groups with easy access from the North and for individual travellers wishing to visit London but looking for a quiet retreat at the end of the day.

TRAVEL INFO
🚌 Frequent LT services (☎ 0171 222 1234). Underground: Golders Green ¼m. National Express depot, Golders Green. 🚉 Hampstead Heath 1 ½m.
🚆 ☎ 0171 730 3488

NEXT HOSTELS
Highgate 2m, Holland House 5m, Oxford Street 7m

HOW TO GET THERE
From bus station - turn left onto North End Road. Take the 1st left which is Wellgarth Road. Reception entrance past car park on the right or Bus 268/210 1st stop. Night Bus N13. From the city - Bus No's 13/139/82.
OS 176 GR 258973

---

72 BEDS   Open: All Day

Highgate Village

☎ 0181 340 1831 Fax: 0181 341 0376

Youth Hostel, 84 Highgate West Hill, London N6 6LU

Overnight Charges: Under 18 £8.50 Adult £12.25

🅿 Roadside parking for cars. Coach parking difficult. BABA (IBN)

Feb 1 - Dec 17   Open

Reception may not be staffed until 5pm during winter.

ACCOMMODATION 🛏2-4 3 🛏5-8 2 🛏9+ 4

For some of the best hot chocolate in town, come to Highgate Village. Without 24 hours staffing (so be in by midnight!) but with comfy dorms and mostly self catering, it's London's cheapest Hostel — and nearby Archway station is only 15 minutes ride from Leicester Square. George Michael, Sting and Annie Lennox live in Highgate Village, Karl Marx doesn't but he is in our cemetery. Eight great pubs have music, food and decent prices. Relax in the Hostel garden or take a stroll on the heath with views of London.

TRAVEL INFO
🚌 Frequent LT services (☎ 0171 222 1234). Underground: Archway 1m. 214 from Kings Cross, 271 from Liverpool St Station, 210 from Golders Green National Express depot, 210 from Finsbury Park BR station.
🚆 ☎ 0171 730 3488

NEXT HOSTELS
Hampstead Heath 2m, City of London 5m, Holland House 6m

ADDITIONAL INFO
Bureau de change.

HOW TO GET THERE
From Archway station walk or take bus (271, 210, 143) up to the Angel Pub. Turn left at South Grove, walk five minutes.
OS 176 GR 281871

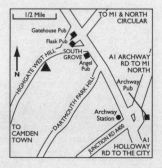

201 BEDS — Open: 24hrs

Holland House

☎ 0171 937 0748 Fax: 0171 376 0667

Youth Hostel, Holland House, Holland Walk, Kensington, London W8 7QU

Overnight Charges: Under 18 £15.55 Adult £17.70

Bed & Breakfast included.

🖥 🛁 P Cars/coaches NCP 15 mins walk. Drop off/pick up corner of Duchess of Bedford Walk & Phillimore Gdns. No parking at Hostel. BABA IBN

Open every day of the year.

ACCOMMODATION 🛏²⁻⁴4 🛏⁵⁻⁸2 🛏⁹⁺12

You can't beat this location! A former Jacobean mansion built in 1607 in the attractive surroundings of Holland Park with it's woodlands, lawns, squash and tennis courts, the Hostel offers comfortable dormitory accommodation with the added value of great views! You would not believe you are in central London! Due to it's location in Kensington, the Hostel is particularly popular with groups and individual travellers. All London's major attractions are easily accessible including the Science and Natural History Museums, the Royal Albert Hall and Kensington Palace — right on the Hostels doorstep! Don't miss the Open Air Theatre in Holland Park in July and August which is adjacent to the Hostel.

TRAVEL INFO
🚌 Frequent LT services (☎ 0171 222 1234). Underground: Holland Park ¼m; High Street Kensington ¼m; 🚇 Kensington Olympia ½m. 🚲 ☎0171 730 3488

NEXT HOSTELS
Earl's Court 1m, City of London 5m, Oxford Street 5m

ADDITIONAL INFO
Theatre and attraction booking service. National Express ticket sales and Bureau de change.

HOW TO GET THERE
Turn left out of High Street Kensington Station and walk down the High Street to the entrance of Holland Park. The Hostel is at the top of the walkway inside the park.
OS 176

---

89 BEDS — Open: 24hrs

Oxford Street

☎ 0171 734 1618 Fax: 0171 734 1657

Youth Hostel, 14 Noel Street, London W1V 3PD

Overnight Charges: Under 18 £14.10 Adult £17.30

🛁 P NCP parking ¼m BABA IBN

Open every day of the year.

ACCOMMODATION 🛏²⁻⁴33

If you want to be where the action is, this is the place for you. In the heart of Soho and Oxford Street and just a short stroll from some of London's most famous landmarks, this self-catering Hostel is perfect for individuals travelling on a budget. Sleeping accommodation is in small bedrooms with modern bunks and security lockers and there is a comfortable TV lounge as well as a recently improved kitchen. The Hostel sells theatre and attraction tickets, London Transport travelcards, has a bureau de change facility. Just minutes from the Hostel are Oxford Street and Regent Street as well as Selfridges and Libertys, two of Londons' most famous department stores and Carnaby Street, where London's eccentric fashion victims congregate. It is advisable to book your bed at Oxford Street Youth Hostel in advance as it is extremely busy all year round.

TRAVEL INFO
🚌 Frequent LT services (☎ 0171 222 1234). Underground: Oxford Circus, Tottenham Ct Rd, both ¼m. 🚇 Charing Cross ¾m; Euston 1m. 🚲 ☎0171 730 3488

NEXT HOSTELS
City of London 2m, Holland House 5m, Earl's Court 5m

ADDITIONAL INFO
Theatre and attraction booking service. Bureau de change.

HOW TO GET THERE
From Tottenham Ct Rd Station walk along Oxford Street for 5 mins until you reach Poland Street which is on the left hand side towards Oxford Circus. Walk down Poland St and take 1st left. The Hostel is opposite.

320 BEDS Open: 24hrs

Rotherhithe

☎ 0171 232 2114 Fax: 0171 237 2919

Youth Hostel, Salter Road, London SE16 1PP

Overnight Charges: Under 18 £16.55 Adult £19.75

Bed & Breakfast included.

Family accommodation prices on p.10-13

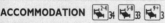

Open every day of the year.

ACCOMMODATION

For those who like a little extra comfort, Rotherhithe Youth Hostel is the choice for you. In London's Docklands with views of Canary Wharf, the river within easy reach of Tower Bridge and many other London attractions. The Hostel provides modern ensuite accommodation in mostly 2, 4 and 6 bedded rooms, is fully accessible to people with disabilities including six specially adapted bedrooms. Premium rooms (2 bedded) are also available for an extra charge and include a TV. The Hostel is open 24 hours, provides good value meals and is licensed so you may enjoy an alcoholic drink with your meal. Very popular Hostel with international groups during Spring and Autumn and a perfect base for families and individual travellers in the Summer!

TRAVEL INFO

🚌 LT 225, P11, N47, N70 (☎ 0171 222 1234). Underground: Rotherhithe 300 metres. 🚉 London Bridge 2m

ℹ ☎ 0171 730 3488

NEXT HOSTELS

City of London 3m, Holland House 8m, Hampstead Heath 10m

ADDITIONAL INFO

Well equipped meeting rooms for hire. Theatre and attraction bookings service, National Express ticket sales and Bureau de change.

HOW TO GET THERE

Exit Rotherhithe underground station, turn left and the Hostel is 300 metres on the same side of the road. Channel Tunnel service stops approx. 1m from Hostel (P11 bus runs door to door).

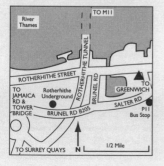

2 South East England

Famous for its rolling hills and
chalk downs, the south east
corner of England is also steeped
in history. At Canterbury, the
country's spiritual capital, you'll
find the first Christian Cathedral
in England while Winchester, seat
of the monarch during King
Alfred's reign is equally impressive. Continue the royal theme
with a visit to historic Windsor
on the River Thames.

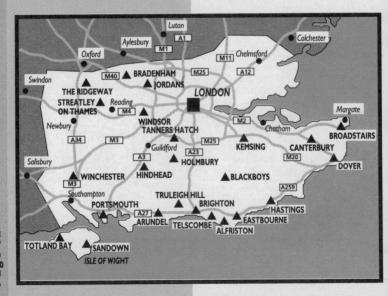

Head for the Coast and visit Portsmouth to explore its maritime history or the sunny Isle of Wight just a short ferry ride away. Also worth a visit is the bustling regency resort of Brighton and lively Dover with its many attractions – don't miss the exciting Eurotunnel exhibition.

With the delightful countryside of the North and South Downs plus the old Wessex Ridgeway, it's easy to see why this area makes an ideal choice for holidays.

Present your YHA membership card to obtain discounts on your entrance to the White Cliffs Experience, the Crown Jewels of the World Exhibition, and the Sealife Centres at Brighton, Portsmouth and Hastings.

Useful Publications

Individual Hostel leaflets are available at no charge – just specify which Hostel you're interested in and send a SAE to YHA South England Regional Office at the address below. Alternatively, leave a request on our YHA 24 hour literature line on 01426 951683 (local call charge).

For more information about hostelling in this area contact:

YHA South England Regional Office, 11b York Road, Salisbury, Wilts SP2 7AP

Tel: 01722 337494
Fax: 01722 414027

Alfriston

68 BEDS | **Open: 17.00hrs**

☎ 01323 870423 Fax: 01323 870615

Youth Hostel, Frog Firle, Alfriston, Polegate, East Sussex BN26 5TT

Overnight Charges: Under 18 £5.55 Adult £8.25

🅿 Ample space for cars and minibuses - coaches by arrangement. BABA

Feb 1 - Jun 30	Open X:Sun*
Jul 1 - Sep 1	Open
Sep 2 - Oct 31	Open X:Sun
Nov 1 - Dec 14	Open Fr/Sat
Dec 27 - Dec 31	Open for New Year

* Open Bank Hol Sun. The Hostel may be available for groups when otherwise closed - please contact Warden.

ACCOMMODATION 🛏2-4 4 🛏5-8 4 🛏9+ 3

This beautiful Sussex flint house — set in the Cuckmere valley with views over the river and close to the picturesque village of Alfriston — offers comfortable accommodation with two lounges, including a cosy Tudor beamed room. Popular with groups from April to June. There are many local attractions ranging from the South Downs Way with superb walks and some of the most spectacular downland views in England, to Drusillas Zoo with its own railway, craft centre and gardens.

TRAVEL INFO
🚌 Stagecoach South Coast 713
Eastbourne-Brighton (passes close BR Seaford & Polegate) (☎ 0345 581457); Autopoint 125 from Lewes to within 1 mile (☎ 01273 474747).
🚉 Seaford 3m; Berwick 3m. ⚓ Newhaven-Dieppe. Newhaven 6m, 4hrs to Dieppe, 3 or 4 services daily.
ℹ ☎ 01323 442667

NEXT HOSTELS
Eastbourne 8m, Telscombe 11m, Blackboys 17m

ADDITIONAL INFO
Daytime access to basic room and w.c.

HOW TO GET THERE
On foot, follow river bank to Litlington footbridge, take bridle path west for 400yds. By road, ¾m south of Alfriston on east side where road narrows.
OS 199 GR 518019

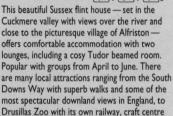

Arundel

60 BEDS | **Open: 17.00hrs**

☎ 01903 882204 Fax: 01903 882776

Youth Hostel, Warningcamp, Arundel, West Sussex BN18 9QY

Out of season contact: Regional Booking Service, 11B York Road, Salisbury, Wilts SP2 7AP
☎ 01722 337494 Fax: 01722 414027

Overnight Charges: Under 18 £5.00 Adult £7.45

Family accommodation prices on p.10-13

🅰 🔍 🅿 For cars and minibuses only. BABA

Apr 1 - Jun 30	Open X:Sun*
Jul 1 - Aug 31	Open
Sep 3 - Nov 2	Open X:Sun/Mon

* Open Bank Hol Sun.

ACCOMMODATION 🛏2-4 4 🛏5-8 4 🛏9+ 2

This large Georgian house — in its own peaceful grounds near the South Downs Way — makes an ideal base, especially for touring holidays. A mixture of small rooms and larger dormitories make it suitable for families and individuals wanting budget accommodation. You'll find a magnificent castle, cathedral, antiquities, heritage centre and safe sandy beaches (good for watersports) close by. The area, known as the Pride of West Sussex, offers a wealth of things to do — for instance, if you've always wondered what goes on behind the scenes at The Body Shop, join their tour in Littlehampton and all will be revealed.

TRAVEL INFO
🚌 Stagecoach Coastline 11 Worthing - Bognor Regis, alight Arundel Station, then 1m (☎ 01243 783251). 🚉 Arundel 1m.
ℹ ☎ 01903 882268

NEXT HOSTELS
Truleigh Hill 16m, Brighton 20m, Portsmouth 26m.

ADDITIONAL INFO
Daytime access to covered veranda and w.c. outside. Family rooms give all day access to w.c., shower and bedroom.

HOW TO GET THERE
OS 197 GR 032076

	29 BEDS	**Open: 17.00hrs**

Blackboys

☎ 01825 890607 Fax: 01825 890104

Youth Hostel, Blackboys, Uckfield, East Sussex TN22 5HU

Out of season contact: Regional Booking Service, 11B York Road, Salisbury, Wiltshire SP2 7AP
☎ 01722 337494 Fax: 01722 414027

Overnight Charges: Under 18 £4.60 Adult £6.75

Ⓐ 🏠 🅿 Cars and mini-buses BABA

Jan 1 - Apr 1	Rent-a-Hostel
Apr 2 - Aug 31	Open X:Sun/Mon*
Sep 1 - Dec 31	Rent-a-Hostel

* Open Bank Hol.

ACCOMMODATION 5 5

This rustic wooden cabin in a forest setting offers good basic self catering accommodation with a cosy open fire, spacious lounge/dining room and well fitted kitchen. Walk the Wealden Way long distance path or take a scenic drive to Batemans at Burwash (once the home of Rudyard Kipling).

TRAVEL INFO

🚌 Stagecoach South Coast/RDH 218, 728 Eastbourne-Uckfield (pass close BR Uckfield and close BR Eastbourne), alight Blackboys ½m (☎ 01273 478007) 🚆 Buxted 2 ½m; Lewes 11m. 🚢 Newhaven to Dieppe, 22m from Hostel
🛈 ☎ 01273 483448

NEXT HOSTELS

Alfriston 17m, Telscombe 17m, Brighton 17m

HOW TO GET THERE

From Cross-in-Hand take right fork at Crown Inn, then second right. From Uckfield take Heathfield Road, 4m, then turn left into Gunn Road. Hostel on right after ½m.
OS 199 GR 521215

---

	18 BEDS	**Open: 17.00hrs**

Bradenham

☎ 01494 56 2929 Fax: 01494 564743

Youth Hostel, The Village Hall, Bradenham, High Wycombe, Buckinghamshire HP14 4HF

Bookings to G. Lee, 54a Brixham Crescent, Ruislip Manor, Middlesex HA4 8TX ☎ 01895 673188

Overnight Charges: Under 18 £4.15 Adult £6.10

🅿 On roadside layby. BABA

Jan 5 - Mar 30	Open Fr/Sat*
Mar 31 - Apr 20	Open
Apr 26 - May 18	Open Fr/Sat* (also open Sun May 5)
May 24 - Jun 1	Open
Jun 7 - Jul 6	Open Fr/Sat*
Jul 7 - Sep 1	Open
Sep 6 - Dec 21	Open Fr/Sat*

* Opens at 19.30hrs on Fr. Available on all other nights for pre-booked groups/families/schools.

ACCOMMODATION 1 2

Known as the 'friendly Hostel with the simple appeal', this self catering Hostel was formerly a village school and it is in a beautifully kept National Trust village tucked away in the folds of the Chiltern Hills. This is a spectacular area for walking and cycling, with some 3,300 way marked footpaths, as well as many local attractions.

TRAVEL INFO

🚌 Wycombe Bus/Aylesbury Bus X14/15, 321/5, 332, Yellow Bus M15 High Wycombe - Princes Risborough, alight Bradenham ¼m or Walter's Ash 1m (☎ 01296 382000). 🚆 Saunderton (not Sun) 1 ¼m; High Wycombe 4 ½m.
🛈 ☎ 01494 421892

NEXT HOSTELS

Jordans 12m, Ivinghoe 17m, Windsor 18m

ADDITIONAL INFO

Daytime access to outside w.c. and simple shelter.

HOW TO GET THERE

At E end of village opposite church. Turn off West Wycombe - Princes Risborough Road (A4010) at Red Lion.
OS 165 GR 828972

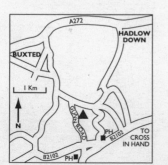

84 BEDS	Open: 13.00hrs

Brighton

☎ 01273 556196 Fax: 01273 509366

Youth Hostel, Patcham Place, London Road, Brighton BN1 8YD

Overnight Charges: Under 18 £6.15 Adult £9.10

🔲 🖿 🔏 **P** BABA

Feb 1 - Dec 27	Open

The Hostel will open at 17.00 hrs during the winter period. The Hostel may be available for groups when otherwise closed - please contact Warden.

ACCOMMODATION 🛏5-8 4 🛏9+ 4

This magnificent mansion — originally built in the 16th century (but with 18th century additions) and ideally located on the outskirts of this famous seaside resort — offers traditional bunk-room accommodation. Brighton offers all the attractions of a traditional and stylish seaside resort: the beach and watersports; the pier and amusements; theatres and restaurants; even history too — with museums, galleries, and the famous Brighton Pavillion. The South Down Way passes close by.

TRAVEL INFO

🚌 Brighton & Hove 5/A from Brighton (pass close BR Brighton & BR Preston Park; Stagecoach Coastline 107, 137 Brighton-Horsham; 770 Brighton-Haywards Heath (pass close BR Preston Park & BR Haywards Heath) (☎ 01273 886200).
🚉 Preston Park 2m; Brighton 3 ½m.
⛴ Newhaven - Dieppe Ferry (14m) - 4 sailings per day.
☎ 01233 647047
🛈 ☎ 01273 323755

NEXT HOSTELS

Truleigh Hill 6m, Telscombe 10m, Alfriston 14m

ADDITIONAL INFO

Reception is open from 1.00 pm except during the winter.

HOW TO GET THERE

On W. side of main London Road (A23), opp. Black Lion Hotel 3m N. of Brighton close to junction with A27.

OS 198 GR 300088

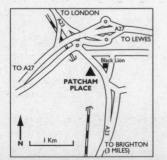

---

36 BEDS	Open: 16.00hrs

Broadstairs (Ramsgate)

☎ 01843 604121 Fax: 01843 604121

Youth Hostel, Thistle Lodge, 3 Osborne Road, Broadstairs, Isle-of-Thanet, Kent CT10 2AE

Overnight Charges: Under 18 £5.55 Adult £8.25

Family accommodation prices on p.10-13

🖿 🏊 BABA

Jan 1 - Mar 17	Rent-a-Hostel
Mar 18 - Nov 16	Open
Nov 17 - Dec 31	Rent-a-Hostel

The Hostel may be available for groups when otherwise closed - please contact Warden.

ACCOMMODATION 🛏2-4 4 🛏5-8 4

A Victorian villa imaginatively converted to offer comfortable bunkrooms, a family atmosphere and pleasant garden with a barbecue for summer evenings. Easy access from London makes it ideal for short breaks or longer seaside holidays. Folk festival (August) and Dickens Festival (June). Famous for its connections with Charles Dickens, our traditional seaside resort offers museums, coastal walks and a sheltered sandy beach. You're also close to Ramsgate for ferries to Dunkerque and Ostend.

TRAVEL INFO

🚌 From surrounding areas (☎ 0800 696996)
🚉 Broadstairs 100metres. ⛴ 2 ½m to Ramsgate for ferry to Dunkerque and ferry or jetfoil to Ostende.
🛈 ☎ 01843 862242

NEXT HOSTELS

Canterbury 18m, Dover 20m, Ostende 3m (via ferry)

ADDITIONAL INFO

Hostel opens at 4.00 pm. Family rooms have full access. Lunchpacks and breakfasts available. Discounts on ferry tickets purchased via the Hostel. Foreign exchange. This is a privately owned Hostel operated under an agreement with YHA.

HOW TO GET THERE

From railway station go under bridge and turn left at traffic lights.

OS 179 GR 390679

Calshot Activities Centre

Youth Hostel,

ACCOMMODATION
We regret that this Youth Hostel is now closed. The nearest Youth Hostels are Winchester (27m), Burley (32m) and Portsmouth (34m).

Canterbury

 01227 462911 Fax: 01227 470752

Youth Hostel, 'Ellerslie', 54 New Dover Road, Canterbury, Kent CT1 3DT

Overnight Charges: Under 18 £6.15 Adult £9.10

Family accommodation prices on p.10-13

  P BABA IBN

Feb 1 - Dec 30	Open

The Hostel may be available for groups when otherwise closed - please contact Warden. The Hostel is open from 13.00 hrs each day.

ACCOMMODATION 🛏️²⁻⁴1 🛏️⁵⁻⁸7 🛏️⁹⁺3
This splendid Victoria villa is ideally placed close to the centre of the historic city. All the facilities required by the city tourist are available along with a friendly atmosphere. Popular with groups from April to June. Close to the Kent Downs, the Hostel is within easy reach of the North Downs Way and Pilgrims Way footpaths — while the city itself has the cathedral, St Augustines Abbey, various museums, guided tours and theatres. Further afield you'll find zoos, gardens and castles to explore.

TRAVEL INFO
🚌 Frequent from surrounding areas (01800 696996). 🚉 Canterbury East ³/₄m; Canterbury West 1 ¹/₄m. ⛴️ Dover/Calais (15m), Ramsgate/Dunkirk, Ramsgate/Ostend (18m). 🛈 01227 766567

NEXT HOSTELS
Dover 14m, Broadstairs 18m, Kemsing 42m

ADDITIONAL INFO
Reception open from 1.00 pm.

HOW TO GET THERE
OS 179 GR 157570

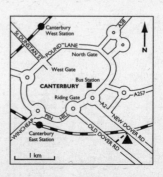

Dover

110 BEDS **Open: 13.00hrs**

☎ 01304 201314 Fax: 01304 202236

Youth Hostel, 306 London Road, Dover, Kent CT17 0SY

Overnight Charges: Under 18 £6.15 Adult £9.10

Family accommodation prices on p.10-13

🔍 ⑧ Ⓟ Nearby. BABA IBN

| Jan 1 - Dec 31 | Open |

The Hostel is open from 1pm each day - however, during the winter the reception may not be manned until 5pm.

ACCOMMODATION 🛏7 🛏9 🛏5

This Georgian town house is one of two Hostel buildings in Dover. It has a mix of small and larger bedrooms suitable for families and individuals. Meet international travellers out on the patio, enjoy a game of pool or just relax in front of the TV. The Ferry Port is within easy reach for a quick hop over to France. There are spectacular cliff walks amid superb birdwatching country. Historic Dover has many attractions on offer, including Dover Castle and Hellfire Corner, the White Cliffs Experience and even Dover Goal.

TRAVEL INFO
🚌 Frequent from surrounding areas (☎ 01304 240024). 🚉 Dover Priory 1m (☎ 01732 770111). 🚢 Stena Sealink ☎ 01233 647047, P&O ☎ 01304 203388, Hover Speed & Sea Cat ☎ 01304 240241, Le Shuttle (channel tunnel) ☎ 01303 271100.
🛈 ☎ 01304 205108

NEXT HOSTELS
Canterbury 14m, Broadstairs 20m, Kemsing 50m

ADDITIONAL INFO
Reception open 1.00 pm. Family rooms give all day access to w.c., kitchen and bedroom.

HOW TO GET THERE
From BR Dover Priory turn left to roundabout, 1st exit, ½m on left. M20/A20 3rd roundabout 1st exit, roundabout 3rd exit ½m on left (directions to London Road only).
OS 179 GR 311421

Eastbourne

32 BEDS **Open: 17.00hrs**

☎ 01323 721081 Fax: 01323 721081

Youth Hostel, East Dean Road, Eastbourne, East Sussex BN20 8ES

Out of season contact: Regional Booking Service, 11B York Road, Salisbury, Wiltshire SP2 7AP
☎ 01722 337494 Fax: 01722 414027

Overnight Charges: Under 18 £5.00 Adult £7.45

Ⓐ Ⓟ Limited. BABA

Jan 1 - Mar 31	Rent-a-Hostel
Apr 4 - Jun 30	Open X:Tu/Wed
Jul 1 - Aug 31	Open
Sep 1 - Dec 31	Rent-a-Hostel

ACCOMMODATION 🛏3

This simple self catering Hostel is a former golf clubhouse with large dormitories and well equipped kitchen. The area offers a plethora of recreational opportunities. In the neighbouring Seven Sisters Country Park there is open downland, forested areas and a dramatic coastline which is dominated by the towering cliffs of Beachy Head. On the doorstep is the start of the South Downs Way and the Weald Way. Local attractions range from castles to a butterfly centre. Eastbourne is a distinguished seaside resort which hosts an extensive programme of sporting and culturally based events.

TRAVEL INFO
🚌 Brighton & Hove/Stagecoach South Coast 712 Eastbourne-Brighton (passes close BR Eastbourne & Newhaven Town) (☎ 0345 581457)
🚉 Eastbourne 1 ½m. 🚢 Newhaven/Dieppe 10m
🛈 ☎ 01323 411400

NEXT HOSTELS
Alfriston 8m, Blackboys 19m, Hastings 25m

ADDITIONAL INFO
Daytime access to verandah with access to the drying room.

HOW TO GET THERE
OS 199 GR 588990

Hastings

57 BEDS Open: 17.00hrs

📞 01424 812373 Fax: 01424 814273

Youth Hostel, Guestling Hall, Rye Road, Guestling, Hastings, East Sussex TN35 4LP

Overnight Charges: Under 18 £5.00 Adult £7.45

Seasonal Prices Jul 1 - Aug 31: Under 18 £5.55 Adult £8.25

Family accommodation prices on p.10-13

🅰 🖻 🅿 Limited. BABA

Feb 16 - Apr 1	Open X:Sun/Mon
Apr 2 - Jun 30	Open X:Sun*
Jul 1 - Sep 1	Open
Sep 2 - Nov 2	Open X:Sun/Mon
Nov 8 - Dec 21	Open Fr/Sat

* Open Bank Hol Sun. The Hostel may be available for groups when otherwise closed.

ACCOMMODATION 🛏2 🛏3 🛏3

This large Victorian manor house, set in four acres of beautiful grounds with its own small lake and leafy woodland, is in an isolated setting only 4m from Hastings town centre. Trails lead from the Hostel to nearby beauty spots. The Hostel has a spacious lounge well stocked with games to while away an hour or two! Steeped in history, the area has much to offer — including the Smugglers Adventure and 1066 Story.

TRAVEL INFO
Stagecoach South Coast 11, 711 Hastings-Rye (pass BR Hastings & Rye); Bexhill Bus 346 BR Hastings-Pett (📞 01273 474747). Three Oaks; Ore 2 ½m; Hastings 6m.
📞 01424 718888

NEXT HOSTELS
Eastbourne 25m, Blackboys 25m, Alfriston 33m

ADDITIONAL INFO
Daytime access to outside w.c. Family rooms have access to all facilities.

HOW TO GET THERE
From Hastings follow A259 Folkstone/Rye, 4m from Hastings Centre. The Hostel is 200yds past the White Hart Beefeater on left. From Rye approaching the Hostel on right 500yds after Guestling School.
OS 199 GR 848133

Hindhead

16 BEDS Open: 17.00hrs

📞 01428 604285

Youth Hostel, Devils Punchbowl, off Portsmouth Rd, Thursley, Near Godalming, Surrey GU8 6NS

Out of season contact: Regional Booking Service, 11B York Road, Salisbury, Wilts. SP2 7AP
📞 01722 337494 Fax: 01722 414027

Overnight Charges: Under 18 £3.75 Adult £5.50

🅿 NT car park ¾m.

Jan 1 - Mar 31	Rent-a-Hostel
Apr 3 - Aug 31	Open X:Mon/Tu
Sep 1 - Dec 31	Rent-a-Hostel

ACCOMMODATION 🛏2 🛏1

This self catering simple Hostel is set in the peaceful haven of the Devils Punchbowl and has been converted from three National Trust Cottages. It has been sympathetically refurbished to a good standard, with a large open fire in the lounge adding to the cosy atmosphere. Sorry, we have not been able to fit a shower. This Area of Outstanding Natural Beauty can be easily reached with good road links from London and the South West. An abundance of flora and fauna can be found here, with the Pilgrims Way and an old fashioned steam fairground close by. Access for cars to within 300 metres of the Hostel is possible for unloading only. Cars cannot be parked in this much loved beauty spot. The nearest carpark is ¾ mile from the Hostel.

TRAVEL INFO
Stagecoach Hants & Surrey 18/9, 518/9 Aldershot-Haslemere (pass close BR Haslemere); 271, 292, 571 from Guildford (pass close BR Godalming & Farnham). Alight in Hindhead area; ½m to 1m according to stops (📞 01737 223000) Haslemere 2 ½m by path, 4 ½m by road. Portsmouth/Le Havre, Caen, Cherbourg, St Malo (30m)
📞 01483 444007

NEXT HOSTELS
Holmbury St Mary 20m, Portsmouth 29m, Winchester 30m

HOW TO GET THERE
OS 186 GR 892368

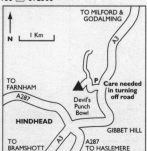

Holmbury St Mary

52 BEDS   Open: 17.00hrs

☎ 01306 730777 Fax: 01306 730933

Youth Hostel, Radnor Lane, Holmbury St Mary, Dorking, Surrey RH5 6NW

Overnight Charges: Under 18 £5.55 Adult £8.25

Family accommodation prices on p.10-13

A ⌂ P BABA

Feb 17 - Mar 31	Open X:Sun/Mon
Apr 1 - Jun 30	Open X:Sun*
Jul 1 - Sep 1	Open
Sep 3 - Nov 2	Open X:Sun/Mon
Nov 8 - Dec 14	Open Fr/Sat

* Open Bank Hol Sun. The Hostel may be available for groups when otherwise closed.

ACCOMMODATION 14

Get away from it all at this comfortable Hostel set in its own grounds in the Surrey hills. Surrounded by 4000 acres of woodland in an Area of Outstanding Natural Beauty, you're still only 30m from London. Small rooms offer ideal accommodation for individuals and families. Particularly popular with groups from April to June. The Hostel offers excellent board games, an orienteering course and treasure hunt. Mountain bike hire and guided weekend breaks can be arranged locally. Local attractions include National Trust properties and Downs Link path.

TRAVEL INFO
🚌 Tillingbourne 22 Guildford - Dorking (Ask for Woodhouse Farm) (☎ 01737 223000).
🚉 Gomshall 3m; Dorking 6m.
ℹ ☎ 01483 444007

NEXT HOSTELS
Tanners Hatch 6m, Hindhead 20m, Windsor 27m

ADDITIONAL INFO
Daytime access to simple shelter only. The family rooms with keys, wash hand basins and storage have access to all facilities during the day.

HOW TO GET THERE
2m south of Abinger Hammer on A25 (between Guildford and Dorking). Follow signs to Holmbury St Mary on B2126, Hostel 1m north of village.
OS 187 GR 104450

Jordans

👣 👣 👣   **24 BEDS**   **Open: 17.00hrs**

📞 **01494 873135 Fax: 01494 875907**

Youth Hostel, Welders Lane, Jordans, Beaconsfield, Buckinghamshire HP9 2SN

Overnight Charges: Under 18 £4.60 Adult £6.75

Family accommodation prices on p.10-13

Ⓐ 🚵 Ⓟ Cars and mini-buses (coaches by arrangement). BABA

Jan 1 - Feb 29	Rent-a-Hostel
Mar 1 - Mar 31	Open X:Wed/Th
Apr 1 - Sep 1	Open X:Th
Sep 20 - Oct 29	Open X:Wed/Th
Nov 1 - Dec 31	Rent-a-Hostel

ACCOMMODATION 🛏️5-8 4

Set in two acres of woodland, this small self catering Hostel is full of character — with comfortable bedrooms and cheerful open fire. The village of Jordans is closely associated with early Quakerism. View the 17th century meeting house, the Mayflower barn and William Penn's grave. There are also many way marked paths and country lanes providing varied routes for walkers and cyclists. Further afield are the attractions of Bekonscot Model Village and Milton's cottage.

TRAVEL INFO

🚌 Chiltern Bus 305 High Wycombe - Uxbridge underground station, alight Seer Green ¾m; 353 Slough - Berkhamsted, alight Chalfont Leisure Centre 1m (📞 01494 464647). Also bus No. 74 Heathrow - Beaconsfield and 290 Oxford - Beaconsfield. 🚇 Seer Green ¾m. Taxis available. 🚲 📞 01494 421892

NEXT HOSTELS

Bradenham 12m, Windsor 13m, Ivinghoe 19m

ADDITIONAL INFO

Daytime access to outside wc's and verandah.

HOW TO GET THERE

ⓄⓈ 175 ⒼⓇ 975910

Kemsing

👥 ☀️   **56 BEDS**   **Open: 17.00hrs**

📞 **01732 761341 Fax: 01732 763044**

Youth Hostel, Church Lane, Kemsing, Sevenoaks, Kent TN15 6LU

Overnight Charges: Under 18 £5.55 Adult £8.25

Family accommodation prices on p.10-13

Ⓐ Ⓟ 10 cars max. Coaches in public car park by 'Wheatsheaf' Pub. No access to Hostel for coaches. BABA

Feb 2 - Mar 30	Open X:Sun/Mon
Apr 1 - Jun 30	Open X:Sun*
Jul 1 - Sep 1	Open
Sep 3 - Nov 9	Open X:Sun/Mon
Nov 15 - Dec 14	Open Fr/Sat
Dec 27 - Dec 31	Open for New Year

* Open Bank Hol Sun. The Hostel may be available for groups when otherwise closed - please contact Warden.

ACCOMMODATION 🛏️2-4 2 🛏️5-8 4 🛏️9+ 2

At the foot of the North Downs in a conservation area, this imposing former vicarage has comfortable accommodation. Its own mature grounds command fine views over the valley towards Knole Park in Sevenoaks, London is just 25m away. From Romans at Lullingstone to Tudors and Stuarts at Knole and Ightham Mote, this is an area steeped in history. Enjoy rural studies at Whitbread Hop Farm, Paddock Wood and the Museum of Kent Life, Maidstone. Enjoy a walk on the Pilgrims Way which passes the Hostel.

TRAVEL INFO

🚌 Kentish Bus 425, 436 from Sevenoaks (pass close BR Sevenoaks), alight Kemsing PO, 250yds (📞 01800 696996). East Surrey 321 from Sevenoaks alight Kemsing (Sun only). 🚇 Kemsing (not Sun) 1½m; Otford 1¾m. ⛴️ Dover 60m 🚲 📞 01732 450305

NEXT HOSTELS

Canterbury 42m, London 26m, Dover 50m

ADDITIONAL INFO

Daytime access to w.c. in entrance hall.

HOW TO GET THERE

ⓄⓈ 188 ⒼⓇ 555588

66 BEDS Open: 17.00hrs

Portsmouth

☎ 01705 375661 Fax: 01705 214177

Youth Hostel, Wymering Manor, Old Wymering Lane, Cosham, Portsmouth, Hampshire PO6 3NL

Overnight Charges: Under 18 £5.55 Adult £8.25

Family accommodation prices on p.10-13

P Cars and mini-buses (coaches contact Warden) BABA

Feb 1 - Jun 30	Open X:Sun
Jul 1 - Sep 1	Open
Sep 2 - Nov 2	Open X:Sun
Nov 8 - Dec 21	Open Fr/Sat
Dec 27 - Dec 31	Open for New Year

The Hostel may be available for groups when otherwise closed - please contact Warden.

ACCOMMODATION 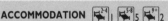 1 5-8 5 9+ 2

This beautiful Tudor manor house with a magnificent entrance hall and two 350 year old Jacobean staircases is one of the oldest known houses in Hampshire — and the ultimate place to stay to experience England's historic maritime heritage. Home of the Mary Rose and Lord Nelson's HMS Victory, Portsmouth has much to offer — whether you want to explore historic flagships, discover the underwater world or visit a military museum.

TRAVEL INFO
Frequent from surrounding areas (☎ 01962 868944). Cosham ½m.

Portsmouth/Caen-Cherbourg-St Malo-Le Havre-Santander-Bilbao, Isle of Wight
☎ 01705 826722

NEXT HOSTELS
Sandown 10m via ferry, Winchester 25m, Arundel 26m

ADDITIONAL INFO
Family rooms have daytime access to bedroom, w.c. and self catering kitchen.

HOW TO GET THERE
From Cosham police station, take Medina Road; seventh turning on right, Old Wymering Lane. Hostel opposite church entrance.
OS 196 GR 640955

---

59 BEDS Open: 17.00hrs

The Ridgeway

☎ 012357 60253 Fax: 012357 68865

Youth Hostel, The Court Hill Ridgeway Centre, Court Hill, Wantage, Oxfordshire OX12 9NE

Overnight Charges: Under 18 £5.00 Adult £7.45

Beds in small cabins with washing facilities may also be booked: Under 18 £6.15 Adult £9.10

Family accommodation prices on p.10-13

A ⬚ ⬚ ⬚ P BABA

Feb 16 - Jun 29	Open X:Sun*
Jul 1 - Sep 1	Open
Sep 2 - Dec 21	Open X:Sun

* Open Bank Hol Sun. The Hostel may be available for groups when otherwise closed.

ACCOMMODATION 2-4 7 9+ 2

This modern purpose built Hostel on the Ridgeway has been beautifully reconstructed from five former barns around a traditional courtyard with stabling for horses, a Beech Wood, conservation area, campsite, barbecue and picnic area. Close to many famous walks and mountain bike routes.

TRAVEL INFO
Thames Transit 32/A, 35/A, 36/A from BR Didcot Parkway, alight Wantage, 2m (☎ 01865 772250). Didcot Parkway 10m.
☎ 01235 760176

NEXT HOSTELS
Streatley 14m, Oxford 17m, Charlbury 32m

ADDITIONAL INFO
Daytime access to w.c. and day room. Family rooms have access to all facilities. Ideal venue for conferences and meetings.

HOW TO GET THERE
Turn at junction 14 on M4, follow signs to Wantage. From Oxford A420 turn on to A338. Well sign posted from A338 and market square. No direct route from Ridgeway. Access only from A338.
OS 174 GR 393851

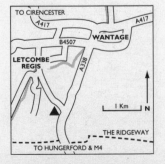

Rochester

 46 BEDS   Open: 17.00hrs

☎ 01722 337494 Fax: 01722 414027

**Youth Hostel, For bookings and info contact:
YHA South England Regional Office, 11B
York Road, Salisbury, Wiltshire SP2 7AP**

ACCOMMODATION

Due to open in 1996. This brand new Hostel is a
restored oast house and farm buildings with
excellent facilities for families and individual
travellers. Next to the Hostel is the Capstone
Farm Country Park with dry ski slopes, open
areas, walks, fishing lake, interpretation centre
and horse riding. Rochester's own Dickens
Museum, castle and cathedral, the historic
dockyard of Chatham, combined with the North
Downs, provide plenty of attractions for all
tastes.

TRAVEL INFO

🚌 Grey-Green 11¾ from BR Gillingham;
otherwise Grey-Green 123/7 from BR Chatham to
within ¾m (☎ 0800 696996). 🚉 Gillingham
(Kent) 2m.

Sandown

🌲☀ 75 BEDS   Open: 17.00hrs

☎ 01983 402651 Fax: 01983 403565

**Youth Hostel, The Firs, Fitzroy Street,
Sandown, Isle of Wight PO36 8JH**

Out of season contact: Regional Booking Service,
11B York Road, Salisbury, Wilts SP2 7AP
☎ 01722 337494 Fax: 01722 414027

Overnight Charges: Under 18 £5.00 Adult £7.45

Seasonal Prices Jul 1 - Aug 31: Under 18 £6.15
Adult £9.10

Family accommodation prices on p.10-13

🅿 Small car park. BABA

Feb 16 - Jun 30	Open X:Mon*
Jul 1 - Aug 31	Open
Sep 1 - Nov 2	Open X:Tu/Wed

* Open Bank Hol Mon.

ACCOMMODATION 🛏2-4 3 🛏5-8 2 🛏9+ 2

The Firs — originally a 19th century house —
offers pleasant accommodation within minutes of
the thriving town centre and beach. Although
popular with young individuals this Hostel also
offers comfortable family accommodation. Ideal
for traditional seaside holidays and for those
interested in watersports, walking or cycling, the
island also offers many sites of historical and
geographical interest. The scenic Bembridge
Downs and Harbour are within easy reach.

TRAVEL INFO

🚌 Frequent from surrounding areas (☎ 01983
862224). 🚉 Sandown ½m (No cycles permitted on
island trains). Ferry Terminal: Ryde Pierhead
(Wightlink) 8m (☎ 01705 827744); East Cowes
(Red Funnel) 12m (☎ 01983 292101).
🛈 ☎ 01983 403886

NEXT HOSTELS

Portsmouth 10m (via ferry), Totland Bay 24m

ADDITIONAL INFO

Family rooms have daytime access to room, w.c.,
shower and self catering facilities. As an alternative
to evening meals, barbecues can be provided for
groups.

HOW TO GET THERE

OS 196 GR 597843

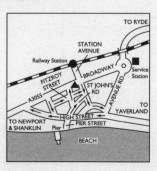

53 BEDS Open: 17.00hrs

Streatley On Thames

☎ 01491 872278 Fax: 01491 873056

Youth Hostel, Hill House, Reading Road, Streatley, Reading, Berkshire RG8 9JJ

Overnight Charges: Under 18 £6.15 Adult £9.10

Family accommodation prices on p.10-13

P Limited. Coaches by arrangement nearby. BABA

Jan 5 - Feb 20	Open Fr/Sat/Sun
Feb 21 - Mar 31	Open X:Mon/Tu
Apr 1 - Jun 30	Open X:Mon
Jul 1 - Sep 1	Open
Sep 4 - Nov 2	Open X:Mon/Tu
Nov 8 - Dec 15	Open Fr/Sat/Sun
Dec 23 - Dec 28	Open for Christmas

The Hostel may be available for groups when otherwise closed - please contact Warden.

ACCOMMODATION 🏠²⁻⁴2 🏠⁵⁻⁸6 🏠⁹⁺1

This homely Victorian family house in the beautiful village of Streatley-on-Thames has been completely refurbished to offer a high standard of accommodation suitable for the individual traveller or family group. Streatley village lies in a conservation area nestling in the gap between the Chiltern Hills and Berkshire Downs on an extremely pretty stretch of the Thames. Watch the canal boats at Goring, tackle the Ridgeway path or visit the surrounding houses of historial interest.

TRAVEL INFO

🚌 Reading Buses 105 Reading-Wallingford (☎ 01734 509509). 🚉 Goring & Streatley 1m.
🛈 ☎ 01734 566226

NEXT HOSTELS

Ridgeway 14m, Oxford 19m, Windsor 25m

ADDITIONAL INFO

Daytime access to w.c. and shelter. Family rooms have access to all facilities. Excellent facilities for meetings and (small) conferences - contact Warden for details.

HOW TO GET THERE

OS 174 GR 591806

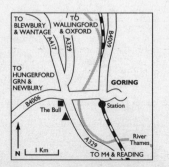

---

28 BEDS Open: 17.00hrs

Tanners Hatch

☎ 01372 452528

Youth Hostel, Polesden Lacey, Dorking, Surrey RH5 6BE

Overnight Charges: Under 18 £4.15 Adult £6.10

A P National Trust car park ¾m (small charge).

Jan 1 - Jan 6	Open
Jan 12 - Mar 31	Open X:Tu/Wed
Apr 1 - Sep 30	Open X:Tu
Oct 1 - Dec 21	Open X:Tu/Wed
Dec 27 - Dec 31	Open for New Year

The Hostel may be available for groups when otherwise closed - please contact Warden.

ACCOMMODATION 🏠⁹⁺2

This National Trust cottage offers very simple self catering accommodation in a truly next-to-nature setting in the Surrey Hills Area of Outstanding Natural Beauty. Boots, compass and torch essential. Shops are some distance away but the Hostel does have its own with a limited selection of goods. Sorry no showers. Discover the abundance of flora and fauna while walking through the acres of Surrey Hills — with the scenic route of the North Downs Way proving popular with walkers, cyclists and horse riders. Please note there is no parking or road access near the Youth Hostel. Nearest parking is ¾ miles from the Hostel in the National Trust carpark (a small charge is made).

TRAVEL INFO

🚌 London & Country 465 Kingston - Horsham, alight West Humble, 2 ¼m (☎ 01737 223000).
🚉 Box Hill & Westhumble 1 ¾m; Dorking Town 2 ½m (by paths); Bookham 3 ½m.
🛈 ☎ 01483 444007

NEXT HOSTELS

Holmbury St Mary 6m, Hindhead 25m, London 23m

ADDITIONAL INFO

Daytime access to w.c. only.

HOW TO GET THERE

OS 187 GR 140515

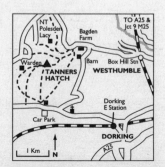

Telscombe

☎ 01273 301357

Youth Hostel, Bank Cottages, Telscombe, Lewes, East Sussex BN7 3HZ

When Hostel is open, bookings & enquiries to: Blackboys Youth Hostel, Blackboys, Uckfield, East Sussex TN22 5HU. ☎ 01825 890607 Fax: 01825 890104.

Out of season contact: Regional Booking Service, 11B York Road, Salisbury, Wilts. SP2 7AP ☎ 01722 337494 Fax: 01722 414027

Overnight Charges: Under 18 £5.00 Adult £7.45

🅿 By arrangement with Warden.

Jan 1 - Mar 31	Rent-a-Hostel
Apr 4 - Aug 31	Open X:Tu/Wed
Sep 1 - Dec 31	Rent-a-Hostel

ACCOMMODATION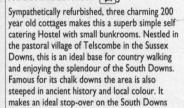

Sympathetically refurbished, three charming 200 year old cottages makes this a superb simple self catering Hostel with small bunkrooms. Nestled in the pastoral village of Telscombe in the Sussex Downs, this is an ideal base for country walking and enjoying the splendour of the South Downs. Famous for its chalk downs the area is also steeped in ancient history and local colour. It makes an ideal stop-over on the South Downs Way.

TRAVEL INFO

🚌 Stagecoach South Coast Buses 123 BR Lewes-Newhaven (goes to Hostel on request) (☎ 01273 474747); otherwise Brighton & Hove 14/B from Brighton (passes close BR Brighton), alight Heathy Brow, ¾m (☎ 01273 886200).

🚉 Southease 2½m; Lewes 6½m; Brighton 7m.
⛴ Newhaven/Dieppe 5m
ℹ ☎ 01273 23755

NEXT HOSTELS

Brighton 10m, Alfriston 11m, Blackboys 17m

ADDITIONAL INFO

Daytime access to outside w.c. and simple shelter. Credit cards are not accepted.

HOW TO GET THERE

OS 198 GR 405033

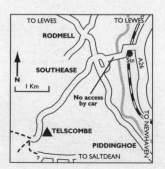

THE ISLE OF WIGHT...

FOR ALL YOUR FANCIES

Quiet and relaxing, or sporting and energetic - the Isle of Wight has all the ingredients for an unforgettable stay. Getting there is quick and easy with the choice of ferry routes.

Don't forget that YHA members are entitled to discounted entrance to a wide range of attractions, including English Heritage sites at Carisbrooke Castle, Osbourne House and Yarmouth Castle.

With 2 Youth Hostels on the West and East coast of the Isle of Wight, it is the ideal choice for a two centre break, on foot, by bike or car.

Making your booking couldn't be simpler, just contact either Hostel to make your reservation.

YHA: Sandown
Tel (01983) 402651
YHA Totland Bay
Tel : (01983) 752165

Totland Bay (West Wight)

76 BEDS **Open: 17.00hrs**

☎ 01983 752165 Fax: 01983 756443

Youth Hostel, Hurst Hill, Totland Bay, Isle of Wight PO39 0HD

Overnight Charges: Under 18 £5.55 Adult £8.25

Seasonal Prices Jul 1 - Aug 31: Under 18 £6.15 Adult £9.10

Family accommodation prices on p.10-13

[A] [P] In grounds, coaches in road. [BABA]

Apr 1 - Jun 30	Open X:Sun*
Jul 1 - Sep 1	Open
Sep 2 - Nov 2	Open X:Sun

* Open Bank Hol Sun. The Hostel may be available for groups when otherwise closed - please contact Warden.

ACCOMMODATION 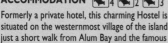 4 2 3

Formerly a private hotel, this charming Hostel is situated on the westernmost village of the island just a short walk from Alum Bay and the famous 'Wight' Needles. Accommodation is comfortable and will suit families and individual travellers alike. Near National Trust land, this Area of Outstanding Natural Beauty boasts downland, cliffs, beaches and beautiful, quiet country walks. Good ferry and public transport access makes this an ideal base for exploring the island.

TRAVEL INFO

🚌 Southern Vectis 7/A, 17, 42 from Yarmouth; 1B/C from Ryde, alight Totland War Memorial, ¼m (☎ 01983 523831). 🚢 Ferry Terminal: Yarmouth (Wightlink) 3m ☎ 01705 827744; West Cowes (Red Funnel) 15m ☎ 01983 292101.
🛈 ☎ 01983 867979

NEXT HOSTELS

Sandown 24m, Burley 17m

ADDITIONAL INFO

Daytime access to w.c. and day room. Family rooms have access to all facilities.

HOW TO GET THERE

From roundabout in centre of Totland, take left fork past garage up Weston Road. Take second left up Hurst Hill - Hostel at top of short hill on left.
[OS] 196 [GR] 324865

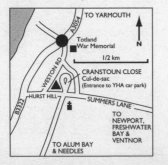

Truleigh Hill

64 BEDS **Open: 17.00hrs**

☎ 01903 813419 Fax: 01903 812016

Tottington Barn, Truleigh Hill, Shoreham-by-Sea, West Sussex BN43 5FB

Overnight Charges: Under 18 £5.55 Adult £8.25

Family accommodation prices on p.10-13

[🏠] [P] [BABA]

Jan 1 - Feb 15	Rent-a-Hostel
Feb 16 - Mar 31	Open X:Sun/Mon
Apr 2 - Jun 30	Open X:Sun*
Jul 1 - Sep 1	Open
Sep 3 - Nov 2	Open X:Sun/Mon
Nov 3 - Dec 31	Rent-a-Hostel

* Open Bank Hol Sun. The Hostel may be available for groups when otherwise closed.

ACCOMMODATION 7 6

This modern Hostel offers comfortable small bedrooms and is situated on top of the South Downs with panoramic views over the sea. There is a conservation area in the Hostel grounds with a Dew pond and climatological station. Iron Age Hillforts, Doomsday villages and town conservation areas are accessible on foot, plus circular walking routes. The area is ideal for mountain biking, walking and watersports, close to coastal resorts for entertainment and shopping, and is particularly popular with families.

TRAVEL INFO

🚌 Brighton & Hove/Access Cars 20 from BR Shoreham-by-Sea, alight ½m S of Upper Beeding, then 1 ¾m by bridlepath (☎ 01273 886200). 🚉 Shoreham-by-Sea 4m.
🛈 ☎ 01273 23755

NEXT HOSTELS

Brighton 6m, Arundel 16m, Holmbury 35m

ADDITIONAL INFO

Daytime access to day room and w.c. Family rooms have access to all facilities. Ideal for family groups, house parties, and conservation projects.

HOW TO GET THERE

From Upper Shoreham Road (signposted Southlands Hospital), north via Erringham Road and Mill Hill.
[OS] 198 [GR] 220105

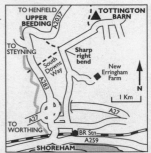

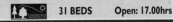

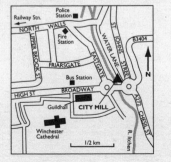

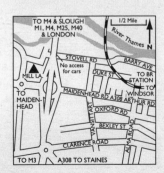

31 BEDS **Open: 17.00hrs**

Winchester

☎ 01962 853723 Fax: 01962 855524

Youth Hostel, The City Mill, 1 Water Lane, Winchester, Hampshire SO23 0ER

Overnight Charges: Under 18 £5.00 Adult £7.45

Seasonal Prices Jul 1 - Aug 31: Under 18 £5.55 Adult £8.25

P Chesil Street car park ¼m BABA

Feb 16 - Mar 30	Open X:Sun/Mon
Apr 1 - Jun 30	Open X:Sun*
Jul 1 - Aug 31	Open
Sep 3 - Nov 2	Open X:Sun/Mon
Nov 8 - Dec 21	Open Fr/Sat

* Open Bank Hol Sun.

ACCOMMODATION 🛏²⁻⁴ 1 🛏⁹⁺ 2

This simple Hostel, owned by the National Trust, is part of an attractive 18th century watermill which spans the River Itchen at the east end of King Alfred's capital. The interior is dominated by the magnificent beamed common room. A charming island garden lies within the mill-race. Facilities are limited in this historic building and you are advised to check your requirements with the staff when booking. Famous for its Cathedral, the city is rich in monuments and historic buildings — including the venerable College and the ancient almshouse of St Cross. Local attractions include Marwell Zoo (endangered species) and the Watercress Line Steam Railway.

TRAVEL INFO
Frequent from surrounding areas (☎ 01962 868944). Winchester 1m.
🛈 ☎01962 867871

NEXT HOSTELS
Burley 23m, Salisbury 24m, Portsmouth 25m

ADDITIONAL INFO
No daytime access. Close to town amenities. No luggage store. Very limited heating in winter months. Check requirements when booking.

HOW TO GET THERE
From Guildhall, walk over Eastgate Bridge and turn first left into Water Lane (no vehicle entry). The Hostel is the third door on the left.
OS 185 GR 486293

---

82 BEDS **Open: All Day**

Windsor

☎ 01753 861710 Fax: 01753 832100

Youth Hostel, Edgeworth House, Mill Lane, Windsor, Berkshire SL4 5JE

Overnight Charges: Under 18 £6.15 Adult £9.10

P Cars only - it is illegal for coaches to enter Mill lane (please use Windsor Coach Park) BABA IBN

Jan 2 - Dec 23	Open

ACCOMMODATION 🛏²⁻⁴ 1 🛏⁵⁻⁸ 7 🛏⁹⁺ 2

A 280 year old Queen Anne residence in a village suburb just 15 minutes walk from the town centre, this Hostel offers a warm welcome and great home cooked food in a relaxed and friendly atmosphere. It also has a large garden, with picnic tables, ideal for relaxing in. The Hostel is very popular with international travellers (Heathrow is only 10 miles away) and groups visit during term time. The historic towns of Windsor and Eton have plenty to offer visitors — from Windsor Castle and Eton College to annual events like the Royal Windsor Horse Show. Windsor Great Park, Hampton Court Palace and Saville Gardens are also nearby and Central London is only 18 miles away — perfect for a day trip by bus or train!

TRAVEL INFO
Frequent from surrounding areas (☎ 01753 524144) Windsor & Eton Central ¾m; Windsor & Eton Riverside 1m.
🛈 ☎01753 852010

NEXT HOSTELS
Jordans 13m, Bradenham 18m, London 23m

ADDITIONAL INFO
Reception closed between 10.00 and 13.00 hrs. Credit cards and eurocheques accepted. Foreign exchange.

HOW TO GET THERE
Jct 6 M4. At roundabout take turning towards Windsor. Take the 1st exit and at the roundabout take 3rd right (A308 to Maidenhead). At the mini roundabout turn into Mill Lane. The Hostel is on your right. There is no through access for cars on Stoveel Road.
OS 175 GR 955770

South West England

Spectacular scenery coupled with a wealth of attractions are all part of the south west of England's special appeal. From the safe, sandy beaches of Dorset to the rugged Cornish cliffs, the impressive coastline offers plenty of leisure opportunities. With two National Parks, Exmoor and Dartmoor – and the New Forest, there is plenty to do.

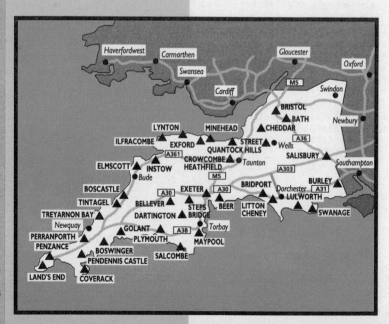

For a real contrast, try the caves at Wookey Hole or the famous Cheddar Gorge. Your YHA membership entitles you to discounted entrance fees for both of these attractions, as well as the Roman Baths and Dairyland Farmworld among others.

For culture, head straight for great cities like Bristol, Salisbury, Exeter, Plymouth and Bath – packed with historical monuments, heritage centres, cathedrals and museums.

There is a network of YHA Camping Barns offering simple accommodation to individuals and groups visiting Exmoor, Dartmoor and Tarka country – see pages 188-193.

Useful Publications

Individual Hostel leaflets are available at no charge – just specify which Hostel you're interested in. There are also inter-Hostel walking routes between Beer, Steps Bridge, Bellever, Dartington and Maypool – these cost just 25p each. For any of these publications just send a SAE to YHA South England Regional Office at the address below. Alternatively, leave a request on our YHA 24 hour literature line on 01426 951683 (local call charge).

The South West Way: a guide to the coast path – send £4.50 (inc p&p) to the South West Way Association, 1 Orchard Drive, Kingskerwell, Newton Abbot, Devon TQ12 5DG.

For more information about hostelling in this area contact:

**YHA South England
         Regional Office,
11b York Road,
Salisbury,
Wilts SP2 7AP**

**Tel: 01722 337494
Fax: 01722 414027**

🏙 121 BEDS   Open: All Day

Bath

☎ 01225 465674 Fax: 01225 482947

Youth Hostel, Bathwick Hill, Bath, Avon BA2 6JZ

Overnight Charges: Under 18 £5.55 Adult £8.25

Seasonal Prices Jul 1 - Aug 31: Under 18 £6.15 Adult £9.10

🖥 🅿 On Bathwick Hill. BABA IBN

Open every day of the year.

ACCOMMODATION 🛏2-4 10 🛏5-8 6 🛏9+ 3

A 19th century Italian-style mansion set in wooded grounds and with impressive views of the city, the Hostel is very popular with foreign individuals and has a relaxed, warm and friendly atmosphere. The Hostel has recently undergone improvements which include an impressive new cafeteria serving a tempting choice of meals, and plenty of hot showers. The Hostel is only a 20 minute walk from the town centre of this World Heritage City famous for its Hot Springs, Roman Baths and Georgian architecture. Attractions include Bath Abbey, the Royal Crescent and Theatre Royal. Don't miss the opportunity to go on the Mad Max Tour either. A fun and relaxed bus tour that takes you to the sights of Stonehenge, Avebury and Lacock National Trust Village.

TRAVEL INFO
🚌 Badgerline 18 from Bus Station adjacent BR Bath Spa (☎ 01225 464446). 🚉 Bath Spa 1 ¼m.
🛈 ☎ 01225 462831

NEXT HOSTELS
Bristol 14m, Cheddar 27m, Slimbridge 30m

ADDITIONAL INFO
Bureau de change. Madmax Tours booking service.

HOW TO GET THERE
From the city centre or A4 follow signs to University and American Museum.
OS 172 GR 766644

🏕 40 BEDS   Open: 17.00hrs

Beer

☎ 01297 20296 Fax: 01297 23690

Youth Hostel, Bovey Combe, Townsend, Beer, Seaton, Devon EX12 3LL

Out of season contact: Regional Booking Service, 11B York Road, Salisbury, Wilts. SP2 7AP
☎ 01722 337494 Fax: 01722 414027

Overnight Charges: Under 18 £5.00 Adult £7.45

Seasonal Prices Jul 1 - Aug 31: Under 18 £5.55 Adult £8.25

Family accommodation prices on p.10-13

🅿 Cars and minibuses in the grounds. Coaches in the village. BABA

Apr 1 - Jun 29	Open X:Sun*
Jul 1 - Sep 1	Open
Sep 3 - Nov 2	Open X:Sun/Mon

* Open Bank Hol Sun.

ACCOMMODATION 🛏2-4 5 🛏5-8 2 🛏9+ 1

An impressive stone-built country house with a mixture of small and larger bedrooms and large lawned gardens — ideal for games or just relaxing and making the most of the lovely views. Only 1/2m from Beer village with its good pubs, quaint shops and pebble beach, this is the perfect destination for a weekend break or main holiday. Why not stroll along a stretch of South West Coastal Footpath or try one of the many watersports on offer — like swimming, sailing and fishing. Steam train enthusiasts should enjoy the excitement of a trip tp Pecorama.

TRAVEL INFO
🚌 Axe Valley from Seaton with connections from BR Axminster (☎ 01392 382800). 🚉 Axminster 7m.
🛈 ☎ 01279 21689

NEXT HOSTELS
Exeter 24m, Litton Cheney 28m

ADDITIONAL INFO
Daytime access to all facilities.

HOW TO GET THERE
OS 192 GR 223896

Bellever (Dartmoor)

 36 BEDS Open: 17.00hrs

📞 01822 880227 Fax: 01822 880302

Youth Hostel, Bellever, Postbridge, Yelverton, Devon PL20 6TU

Out of season contact: Regional Booking Service, 11B York Road, Salisbury, Wilts. SP2 7AP
📞 01722 337494 Fax: 01722 414027

Overnight Charges: Under 18 £5.55 Adult £8.25

Family accommodation prices on p.10-13

🅿 Limited for cars. BABA

Jan 1 - Mar 16	Rent-a-Hostel
Mar 22 - Jun 29	Open X:Sun*
Jul 1 - Sep 2	Open
Sep 3 - Nov 2	Open X:Sun/Mon
Nov 8 - Dec 31	Rent-a-Hostel

* Open Bank Hol Sun.

ACCOMMODATION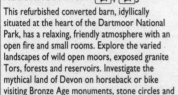

This refurbished converted barn, idyllically situated at the heart of the Dartmoor National Park, has a relaxing, friendly atmosphere with an open fire and small rooms. Explore the varied landscapes of wild open moors, exposed granite Tors, forests and reservoirs. Investigate the mythical land of Devon on horseback or bike visiting Bronze Age monuments, stone circles and medieval villages — a truly magical experience!

TRAVEL INFO
🚌 Western National 98 from Tavistock (Fr only); 82 Exeter-Plymouth, May-Sep only, alight Postbridge 1m; otherwise Western National 98/A Tavistock-Princetown 6m, or Red Bus 359 from BR Exeter Central, alight Chagford 9m (📞 01392 382800) 🚉 Newton Abbott 19m. ⛴ Plymouth to France and Spain
ℹ 📞 01822 880272

NEXT HOSTELS
Steps Bridge 18m, Dartington 19m, Plymouth 21m

ADDITIONAL INFO
Daytime access to lounge and outside w.c. Family rooms give all day access to w.c., kitchen and bedroom.

HOW TO GET THERE
OS 191 GR 654773

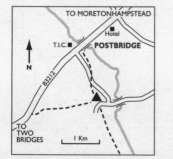

Boscastle Harbour

🚶 🚴 25 BEDS Open: 17.00hrs

📞 01840 250287

Youth Hostel, Palace Stables, Boscastle, Cornwall PL35 OHD

Out of season contact: Regional Booking Service: 11B York Road, Salisbury, Wiltshire SP2 7AP
📞 01722 337494 Fax: 01722 414027

Overnight Charges: Under 18 £5.00 Adult £7.45

Seasonal Prices Jul 1 - Aug 31: Under 18 £5.55 Adult £8.25

🅿 Public car park for cars and coaches 250yds.

Jan 1 - Mar 16	Rent-a-Hostel
Mar 20 - May 19	Open X:Mon/Tu
May 20 - Sep 30	Open
Oct 2 - Nov 2	Open X:Mon/Tu
Nov 8 - Dec 31	Rent-a-Hostel

ACCOMMODATION

This delightful stone Hostel overlooking the harbour was originally a stable for horses pulling boats ashore. The tastefully converted hayloft has single beds and retains the original beams. An open fire in the lounge/dining room gives a very cosy atmosphere. Set at the high water line where the River Valency meets the sea, the Hostel is on the South West Coastal Path surrounded by superb coastal scenery and walks. There are interesting Thomas Hardy connections too. The fishing harbour with its blow-hole is preserved by the National Trust.

TRAVEL INFO
🚌 Western National 52/B from BR Bodmin Parkway, X4 from Bude (📞 01209 719988); Fry's from Plymouth (passes close BR Plymouth) (infrequent) (📞 01840 770256) 🚉 Bodmin Parkway 24m.
ℹ 📞 01566 772321

NEXT HOSTELS
Tintagel 5m, Elmscott 28m, Golant 30m

ADDITIONAL INFO
Daytime access to self catering kitchen and unisex w.c. and common room.

HOW TO GET THERE
Walk from the bridge on the B3226 towards the harbour alongside the river. Last building on right.
OS 190 GR 096915

🏕️ ☀️ 38 BEDS Open: 17.00hrs

Boswinger

☎ 01726 843234

Youth Hostel, Boswinger, Gorran, St Austell, Cornwall PL26 6LL

Out of season contact: Regional Booking Service, 11B York Road, Salisbury, Wiltshire. SP2 7AP
☎ 01722 337494 Fax: 01722 414027

Overnight Charges: Under 18 £5.00 Adult £7.45

Seasonal Prices Jul 1 - Aug 31: Under 18 £5.55 Adult £8.25

Family accommodation prices on p.10-13

🅰 📷 🅿 (coaches at B&B in Gorran)

Jan 1 - Mar 23	Rent-a-Hostel
Mar 29 - Jun 30	Open X:Tu/Wed
Jul 1 - Aug 31	Open
Sep 1 - Nov 2	Open X:Tu/Wed
Nov 5 - Dec 31	Rent-a-Hostel

ACCOMMODATION

This former old farmhouse and stone barn, converted into a cosy Hostel, offers small bunk rooms and a snug atmosphere — ideal for families and individuals. Relax in the homely lounge, browse through the local information and decide where to go next. Friday night is BBQ night at Boswinger! Amid wonderful Cornish countryside and near the South Costal footpaths, this Hostel only 4m from the fishing village of Mevagissey and 10m from St Austell.

TRAVEL INFO
🚌 Western National 26/A from BR St Austell, alight Mevagissey, 4 ½m, with infrequent extension to Gorran Churchtown, 1m (☎ 01209 719988).
🚉 St Austell 10m. ⛴ Plymouth to France/Spain
ℹ ☎ 01872 74555

NEXT HOSTELS
Golant 17m, Pendennis 24m, Perranporth 25m

ADDITIONAL INFO
Daytime access to day room and outside w.c. Family rooms give all day access to w.c., kitchen and bedroom.

HOW TO GET THERE
Follow brown Boswinger YH signs.
OS 204 GR 991411

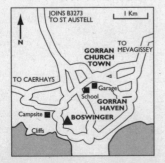

🏠 68 BEDS Open: 17.00hrs

Bridport

☎ 01308 422655 Fax: 01308 425319

Youth Hostel, West Rivers House, West Allington, Bridport, Dorset DT6 5BW

Out of season contact: Regional Booking Service, 11B York Road, Salisbury, Wilts. SP2 7AP
☎ 01722 337494 Fax: 01722 414027

Overnight Charges: Under 18 £5.00 Adult £7.45

🔍 🅿 Large car park suitable for coaches, cars and trailers. BABA

This Hostel may not open during 1996. Please check availability with YHA South England Regional Office, ☎ 01722 337494, Fax: 01722 414027

ACCOMMODATION

This spacious detached building, formerly a rope flaxmill, on the edge of a busy market town offers comfortable accommodation and good facilities with immediate access onto large playing fields. Founded on rope and net making — still a local trade — Bridport is set in the heart of Hardy's Wessex with rolling hills and breathtaking coastal scenery all around. Hunt for fossils at Charmouth, enjoy the shingle beach at West Bay or visit the interesting towns of Dorchester and Weymouth.

TRAVEL INFO
⛴ Weymouth 17m; Poole 40m; services to Cherbourg
ℹ ☎ 01308 424901

NEXT HOSTELS
Litton Cheney 7m, Lulworth Cove 30m, Beer 22m.

ADDITIONAL INFO
Public toilets nearby. Family rooms give all day access to all facilities.

HOW TO GET THERE
OS 193 GR 461930

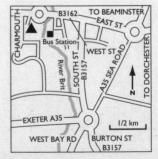

124 BEDS Open: All Day

Bristol

☎ 0117 9221659 Fax: 0117 9273789

International Youth Hostel, Hayman House, 14 Narrow Quay, Bristol, Avon BS1 4QA

Overnight Charges: Under 18 £7.45 Adult £10.90

Family accommodation prices on p.10-13

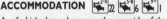 At NCP Prince St. Meter parking outside Hostel. Coach parking (10 mins walk). BABA IBN

Jan 2 - Dec 21	Open

ACCOMMODATION 🛏22 🛏6 🛏1

A refurbished warehouse on the quayside of the harbour, the Hostel boasts views of the waterways and is minutes from the centre of this young and vibrant city. The magnificent Avon Gorge, Brunel's suspension bridge, and the many theatres, museums and art galleries are some of the attractions in this fascinating city. Accommodation is in small rooms, several with ensuite facilities and the building is accessible to people with disabilities. Relax in the comfortable TV lounge, enjoy a round of pool in the games room or simply unwind over a cappuchino at the attractive cafeteria. There's an appetizing choice of dishes including hot and cold lunch time snacks. A very popular Hostel with groups in the Spring and Autumn and independent travellers and families enjoy the many attractions and events in the Summer and at weekends.

TRAVEL INFO
🚌 Frequent from surrounding areas (☎ 0117 9553231). Bus and coach station ¾m. 🚂 Bristol Temple Meads ¾m (☎ 0117 9294255).
🚉 ☎0117 9260767

NEXT HOSTELS
Bath 14m, Cheddar 20m, Slimbridge 25m

ADDITIONAL INFO
National Express Coach Ticket Sales. Bureau de change.

HOW TO GET THERE
From London or Southwolds: M4 to Junction 19 then M32. From Birmingham or South West: M5 to Junction 18 then A4.
OS 172 GR 586725

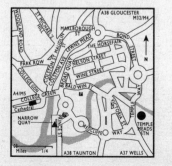

---

 36 BEDS Open: 17.00hrs

Burley

☎ 01425 403233 Fax: 01425 403233

Youth Hostel, Cottesmore House, Cott Lane, Burley, Ringwood, Hampshire BH24 4BB

Overnight Charges: Under 18 £5.55 Adult £8.25

Seasonal Prices Jul 1 - Aug 31: Under 18 £6.15 Adult £9.10

Family accommodation prices on p.10-13

A P Limited.

Jan 1 - Feb 15	Rent-a-Hostel
Feb 16 - Jun 29	Open X:Sun*
Jul 1 - Sep 1	Open
Sep 2 - Nov 2	Open X:Sun
Nov 3 - Dec 31	Rent-a-Hostel

* Open Bank Hol Sun.

ACCOMMODATION 🛏1 🛏3 🛏1

A former family home, the Hostel is set in grounds in the New Forest. Enjoy good food and a friendly atmosphere. A perfect setting to relax in the countryside, or make the most of the many tourist attractions such as Beaulieu Motor Museum, cycling, pony trekking and watersports.

TRAVEL INFO
🚌 Wilts & Dorset/Solent Blue Line X1 Bournemouth - Southampton (passes BR Lyndhurst Road & Southampton), alight Durmast Corner, ¼m; 105, 116 from Christchurch, alight Burley, ½m (☎ 01202 673555). 🚂 Sway 5 ½m; New Milton 6m, Brockenhurst 6m.
🚉 ☎01703 282269

NEXT HOSTELS
Totland Bay 17m, Salisbury 21m, Winchester 23m

ADDITIONAL INFO
Daytime access to simple shelter. Family rooms have access to room and self catering kitchen.

HOW TO GET THERE
From centre of Burley follow Lyndhurst Road past Burley School on left, carry on past golf course for ½m to crossroads. Follow sign post to White Buck Inn. At Inn turn left into Cott Lane and follow signs for Hostel.
OS 195 GR 220028

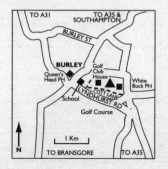

3

SOUTH WEST

Cheddar

56 BEDS | **Open: 17.00hrs**

☎ 01934 742494 Fax: 01934 744724

Youth Hostel, Hillfield, Cheddar, Somerset BS27 3HN

Overnight Charges: Under 18 £4.60 Adult £6.75

Family accommodation prices on p.10-13

🖥 P Cars & mini-buses only. Coaches nearby. BABA

Feb 16 - Jun 29	Open X:Sun*
Jul 1 - Sep 1	Open
Sep 3 - Nov 2	Open X:Sun/Mon
Nov 1 - Dec 21	Open X:Sun/Mon
Dec 27 - Dec 31	Open for New Year

* Open Bank Hol Sun. The Hostel may be available for groups when otherwise closed - please contact Warden.

ACCOMMODATION 4 5 1

At this Victorian stone-built house you'll find traditional accommodation and some wonderful home cooking — all set in the centre of this world famous village, only 5 mins walk from the Cheddar Gorge and extensive walks on the Mendip Hills (an Area of Outstanding Beauty). We can organise adventure courses for groups all year round. Local attractions include Wells (England's smallest Cathedral city), Glastonbury (with its famous Abbey) and the popular seaside resort of Weston-Super-Mare.

TRAVEL INFO
🚌 Badgerline 126, 826 Weston-super-mare - Wells (pass close BR Weston Milton & Weston-super-mare) (☎ 01934 621201).
🚆 Weston Milton 10m; Weston-super-mare 11m.
ℹ ☎ 01934 744071

NEXT HOSTELS
Street 17m, Bristol 20m, Bath 27m

ADDITIONAL INFO
Daytime access to simple shelter and wc's. Family rooms have access to all facilities.

HOW TO GET THERE
OS 182 GR 455534

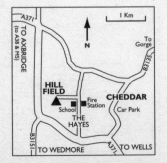

Coverack

40 BEDS | **Open: 17.00hrs**

☎ 01326 280687 Fax: 01326 280119

Youth Hostel, Park Behan, School Hill, Coverack, Helston, Cornwall TR12 6SA

Out of season contact: Regional Booking Service, 11B York Road, Salisbury, Wilts. SP2 7AP.
☎ 01722 337494 Fax: 01722 414027

Overnight Charges: Under 18 £5.00 Adult £7.45

Seasonal Prices Jul 1 - Aug 31: Under 18 £5.55 Adult £8.25

Family accommodation prices on p.10-13

▲ 🔍 🖥 P BABA

Mar 29 - Nov 2	Open

The Hostel may be available for groups when otherwise closed - please contact Warden.

ACCOMMODATION 1 4 1

This lovely country house is situated above an old fishing village, once a notorious smuggling haunt, with panoramic views of the coast. There is an ancient orchard for camping, extensive lawns and volleyball court. Good home cooking and barbecues are a speciality! There is easy access to the South West Coastal Footpaths, dramatic cliffs and deserted coves — ideal for sea bathing, fishing and boating trips. The RYA windsurfing school offers week or weekend courses, plus you can hire mountain bikes and surf-skis.

TRAVEL INFO
🚌 Truronian 326 from Helston with frequent connections from BR Penzance (☎ 01872 73453 or 01209 719988 for connections). 🚆 Penryn or Penmere (Not Sun, except Jun - Sep), both 18m.
🚢 Penzance to Scilly Isles.
ℹ ☎ 01326 312300

NEXT HOSTELS
Pendennis 20m, Penzance 25m, Lands End 31m

ADDITIONAL INFO
Daytime access to shelter and w.c. Family rooms give all day access to w.c., kitchen and bedroom.

HOW TO GET THERE
200yds W of village centre, take road opposite to harbour, drive entrance next to village school
OS 204 GR 782184

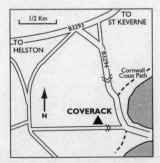

36 BEDS   Open: 17.00hrs

Crowcombe Heathfield

☎ 01984 667249 Fax: 01984 667249

Youth Hostel, Denzel House, Crowcombe Heathfield, Taunton, Somerset TA4 4BT

Out of season contact: Regional Booking Service, 11B York Road, Salisbury, Wiltshire SP2 7AP
☎ 01722 337494 Fax: 01722 414027

Overnight Charges: Under 18 £4.60 Adult £6.75

🅰 🅿 Plenty for cars and minibuses. Coaches 100yds.
BABA

Mar 1 - Mar 24	Rent-a-Hostel
Mar 29 - Apr 21	Open
Apr 26 - May 19	Open Fr/Sat/Sun*
May 24 - Jun 2	Open
Jun 7 - Jul 14	Open Fr/Sat/Sun*
Jul 19 - Sep 1	Open
Sep 6 - Nov 2	Rent-a-Hostel

* Mon - Th, open for families and groups booked in advance.

ACCOMMODATION 🛏5 🛏2 🛏1

This delightful country house in large attractive grounds offers self catering accommodation with several small rooms. Enjoy active days walking on the Quantock Hills, cycle on the many quiet lanes or catch the West Somerset Railway steam train from the nearby station for a 'journey back in time'. All within easy reach of the M5.

TRAVEL INFO

🚌 Southern National 28/C Taunton - Minehead (passes BR Taunton), alight Triscombe Cross, ¾m (☎ 01823 272033). 🚉 Taunton 10m; Crowcombe (West Somerset Rly) ½m.
🛈 ☎ 01823 274785

NEXT HOSTELS
Quantock Hills 10m by road (7m by foot), Minehead 16m, Exford 22m

ADDITIONAL INFO
Daytime access to wc's in classroom when classroom is not otherwise booked.

HOW TO GET THERE
A385 from Taunton 10m. Turn left at Triscombe Cross signposted Crowcombe Station. Hostel ¾m on right after railway bridge.
OS 181 GR 138339

Dartington

🏃 🏃 🏃 **30 BEDS** **Open: 17.00hrs**

📞 **01803 862303 Fax: 01803 862303**

Youth Hostel, Lownard, Dartington, Totnes, Devon TQ9 6JJ

Out of season contact: Regional Booking Service, 11B York Road, Salisbury, Wiltshire SP2 7AP
📞 01722 337494 Fax: 01722 414027

Overnight Charges: Under 18 £5.00 Adult £7.45

Seasonal Prices Jul 1 - Aug 31: Under 18 £5.55 Adult £8.25

Family accommodation prices on p.10-13

🖥 ✉ 🅿 Cars and mini-buses only. Coaches - use public car park in Shinners Bridge ¼m. BABA

Jan 1 - Mar 31	Rent-a-Hostel
Apr 2 - Jun 30	Open X:Mon
Jul 1 - Sep 1	Open
Sep 4 - Nov 2	Open X:Mon/Tu
Nov 3 - Dec 31	Rent-a-Hostel

ACCOMMODATION 🛏²⁻⁴2 🛏⁵⁻⁸3

Beside a babbling brook this simple self catering Hostel is set in the beautiful Dart Valley village of Dartington — a peaceful haven enjoyed by country lovers and urban escapees alike! An ideal base for exploring the River Dart and South Hams with its Norman Castle, medieval Guildhall and many interesting shops, is only 2m away.

TRAVEL INFO

🚌 Western National X80 Torquay - Plymouth (passes BR Paignton & Totnes), alight Shinner's Bridge, ¼m (📞 01752 664011). 🚂 Totnes 2m.
ℹ️ 📞 01803 863168

NEXT HOSTELS

Maypool 11m, Bellever 19m, Plymouth 22m

ADDITIONAL INFO

Daytime access to simple shelter, w.c. and brew point. Family rooms give all day access to w.c., kitchen and bedroom. We can cater for groups of 10 or more booked in advance.

HOW TO GET THERE

Take the A385 from the Shinners bridge roundabout in the centre of Dartington. Turn right after ¼m into narrow lane. Hostel 200yds on right.
OS 202 GR 782622

Elmscott (Hartland)

🏃 🏃 🏃 **36 BEDS** **Open: 17.00hrs**

📞 **01237 441367 Fax: 01237 441367**

Youth Hostel, Elmscott, Hartland, Bideford, Devon EX39 6ES

Out of season contact, Regional Booking Service, 11B York Road, Salisbury, Wiltshire SP2 7AP
📞 01722 337494 Fax: 01722 414027

Overnight Charges: Under 18 £3.75 Adult £5.50

Seasonal Prices Jul 1 - Aug 31: Under 18 £4.15 Adult £6.10

🅿 For cars and minibuses. Coaches - ask Warden. BABA

Mar 29 - Jun 30	Open X:Th
Jul 1 - Sep 21	Open
Sep 26 - Nov 2	Rent-a-Hostel

ACCOMMODATION 🛏²⁻⁴1 🛏⁵⁻⁸5

This converted Victorian school offers comfortable self catering accommodation in a remote, next-to-nature setting with views out to sea towards Lundy Island. Spectacular sunsets viewed from the pretty walled garden make for a memorable stay! Do bring food supplies, the Hostel shop has basics but nearest shops are some distance away. Get away from it all in this glorious location — with unspoilt coastline, amazing rock formations, a profusion of wild flowers and many quiet lanes to explore. The surfing beaches of north Cornwall are within easy reach.

TRAVEL INFO

🚌 Filer's Travel from Barnstaple (passes close BR Barnstaple), alight Hartland, 3 ½m (📞 01392 382800). 🚂 Barnstaple 25m.
ℹ️ 📞 01237 477676

NEXT HOSTELS

Instow 19m, Boscastle 28m, Tintagel 32m

ADDITIONAL INFO

Daytime access to w.c. and simple shelter. Fresh bread and milk available if ordered in advance.

HOW TO GET THERE

Hostel is signposted from A39 just N of West Country Inn. Ignore signs for Hartland.
OS 190 GR 231217

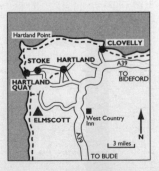

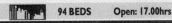

	94 BEDS	Open: 17.00hrs

Exeter

☎ 01392 873329 Fax: 01392 876939

Youth Hostel, 47 Countess Wear Road,
Exeter, Devon EX2 6LR

Overnight Charges: Under 18 £5.55 Adult £8.25

Seasonal Prices Jul 1 - Aug 31: Under 18 £6.15
Adult £9.10

Family accommodation prices on p.10-13

▲ 🔲 🔲 🅿 For cars and minibuses. BABA

Jan 1 - Dec 7	Open
Dec 27 - Dec 31	Open for New Year

The Hostel may be available for groups when
otherwise closed - please contact Warden.

ACCOMMODATION 🛏️²⁻⁴4 🛏️⁵⁻⁸3 🛏️⁹⁺3

The Hostel, which provides a high standard of
accommodation, is set in its own grounds near
the River Exe. You can walk to the city along the
river or the historic Exeter Ship Canal to visit the
beautiful Cathedral and Exeter Quay. Exeter's
historic past is best explored by strolling through
its intriguing lanes and alleyways. Take time to
visit the Royal Albert Museum and the world
renowned Maritime Museum.

TRAVEL INFO
🚌 Exeter Bus K, T, Devon General 57 (pass close
BR Exeter Central), alight Countess Wear PO, ¼m
(☎ 01392 56231) 🚉 Topsham 2m; Exeter Central
3m; Exeter St David's 4m.
🛈 ☎ 01392 265297

NEXT HOSTELS
Steps Bridge 10m, Beer 24m, Dartington 27m

ADDITIONAL INFO
Daytime access to w.c., self-catering kitchen and
dining area.

HOW TO GET THERE
From A30 or M5 jct 30 follow signs for Topsham:
turn right at Countess Wear Roundabout, then left
in to School Lane. From A379 follow signs for
Topsham; turn left at Countess Wear Roundabout,
then left into School Lane. From Exeter city centre
follow signs to Exmouth and Topsham; turn right
into School Lane at Countess Wear Post Office.
OS 192 GR 941897

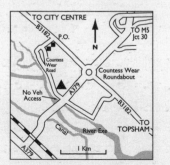

---

	51 BEDS	Open: 17.00hrs

Exford (Exmoor)

☎ 01643 831288 Fax: 01643 831650

Youth Hostel, Exe Mead, Exford, Minehead,
Somerset TA24 7PU

Out of season contact: Regional Booking Service,
11B York Road, Salisbury, Wilts SP2 7AP
☎ 01722 337494 Fax: 01722 414027

Overnight Charges: Under 18 £5.55 Adult £8.25

Family accommodation prices on p.10-13

🔲 🅿 Cars, mini-buses and coach. BABA

Jan 1 - Feb 15	Rent-a-Hostel
Feb 16 - Mar 30	Open X:Sun/Mon
Apr 1 - Jun 30	Open X:Sun*
Jul 1 - Sep 1	Open
Sep 3 - Nov 2	Open X:Sun/Mon
Nov 3 - Dec 31	Rent-a-Hostel

* Open Bank Hol Sun. The Hostel may be
available for groups when otherwise closed -
please contact Warden.

ACCOMMODATION 🛏️²⁻⁴8 🛏️⁵⁻⁸4

This attractive Victorian house is perfectly
situated for exploring atmospheric Exmoor. The
Hostel — which is fitted out to a high standard —
is surrounded by lovely grounds with the river
Exe flowing through the garden. Enjoy Exmoor
National Park with its heather covered heights
and byways offering excellent walking and cycling.
Glimpse red deer, Exmoor ponies and buzzards
in the land of Lorna Doone.

TRAVEL INFO
🚌 Lyn Valley L4/5 Taunton-Lynton (Mon, Fri, Sat
only) (calls BR Taunton if booked by phone: 01598
52470); otherwise Scarlet Coaches from Minehead,
alight Porlock, 7m (☎ 0823 255696). 🚉 Taunton
28m; Minehead (West Somerset Rly) 13m.
🛈 ☎ 01398 23665 / 01643 702624

NEXT HOSTELS
Minehead 13m, Lynton 15m, Crowcombe 22m

ADDITIONAL INFO
Daytime access to dining room and self-catering
kitchen, w.c.'s. Family rooms have access to all
facilities.

HOW TO GET THERE
OS 181 GR 853383

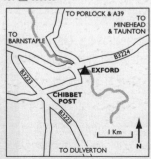

 94 BEDS   **Open: 17.00hrs**

Golant

 01726 833507 Fax: 01726 832947

Youth Hostel, Penquite House, Golant, Fowey, Cornwall PL23 1LA

Overnight Charges: Under 18 £6.15 Adult £9.10

Family accommodation prices on p.10-13

Feb 1 - Aug 31	Open
Sep 1 - Nov 2	Open X:Fr

The Hostel may be available for groups when otherwise closed - please contact Warden.

ACCOMMODATION �️2-4 6 �️5-8 7 ⏫9+ 2

This imposing Georgian house — Grade II listed with superb decorative plasterwork — has been refurbished to a high standard. As well as three acres of grounds and 14 acres of woodland to explore, there is no passing traffic which means the Hostel is ideal for families with young children. Surrounded by farmland yet only four miles from the sea, the Hostel is an excellent base for discovering the rugged Cornish coastline and moorland. As well as many watersports on offer, there's a wide choice of local walks and cycle rides. Unspoilt Fowey and South West Coastal Footpath are 4m.

TRAVEL INFO

🚌 Western National 24 St Austell-Fowey (passes BR Par), alight Castle Dore Crossroads, 1½m (☎ 01209 719988) 🚂 Par (not Sun, except Jun - Sep) 3m; St Austell 7½m.

🚢 Plymouth/Roskoff-Santander 40m

ℹ ☎ 01726 833616

NEXT HOSTELS

Boswinger 17m, Tintagel 28m, Plymouth 38m

ADDITIONAL INFO

Daytime access to wc's, good sitting area and self catering kitchen. Family rooms have access to all facilities. Conference facilities available.

HOW TO GET THERE

Take B3269 (Fowey) from A390 1½m west of Lostwithiel. Hostel is signposted from Castle Dore crossroads after 2m.

OS 200 GR 118556

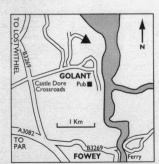

50 BEDS **Open: 17.00hrs**

Ilfracombe

 01271 865337 Fax: 01271 862652

Youth Hostel, Ashmour House, 1 Hillsborough Terrace, Ilfracombe, Devon EX34 9NR

Overnight Charges: Under 18 £5.55 Adult £8.25

Family accommodation prices on p.10-13

🔍 **P** Limited. BABA

Apr 1 - Jun 29	Open X:Sun*
Jul 1 - Aug 31	Open
Sep 2 - Sep 28	Open X:Sun

* Open Bank Hol Sun. The Hostel may be available for groups when otherwise closed.

ACCOMMODATION 🛏️2-4 10 🛏️5-8 3

This well preserved Georgian building is perfectly placed to observe activity in the picturesque harbour below — with magnificent views across the Bristol Channel from the splendid lounge. The many small rooms provide comfort and privacy for families and individuals. 'Moor to Sea' at the Centre of Attraction! You'll find Blue Flag sandy beaches and access to Exmoor National Park close by, as well as farm parks, theme parks, coastal and country walks, historic houses ..... and that's not all! Send for our brochure.

TRAVEL INFO

🚌 Red Bus 30, 62 & 300, B, Filer's 301 / 304 from Barnstaple (passing close BR Barnstaple) (01271 45444). 🚉 Barnstaple 13m. ⛴️ Lundy Island service on doorstep

ℹ️ 01271 863001

NEXT HOSTELS

Lynton 18m, Instow 18m, Exford 25m

ADDITIONAL INFO

Family rooms give daytime access to bedrooms and lounge. This a privately owned Hostel operated under an agreement with YHA.

HOW TO GET THERE

On main 'A' road. Follow Combe Martin road signs out of Ilfracombe High St. Opposite Cliffe Hydro Hotel.

OS 180 GR 524476

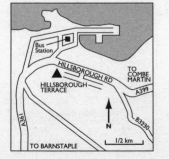

---

 58 BEDS **Open: 17.00hrs**

Instow

 01271 860394 Fax: 01271 860055

Youth Hostel, Worlington House, New Road, Instow, Bideford, Devon EX39 4LW

Overnight Charges: Under 18 £5.55 Adult £8.25

Family accommodation prices on p.10-13

🅿️ Cars and mini-buses only.

Feb 16 - Apr 30	Open X:Sun/Mon*
May 1 - Sep 2	Open
Sep 3 - Nov 2	Open X:Sun/Mon
Dec 20 - Dec 31	Rent-a-Hostel

* Open Bank Hol Sun. The Hostel may be available for groups when otherwise closed.

ACCOMMODATION 🛏️2-4 4 🛏️5-8 2 🛏️9+ 2

This Victorian House, set in two acres of garden with excellent views, has gained an excellent reputation for its food, friendly welcome and comfortable accommodation. Open most of the year with good transport links, it's an ideal location if you want to get off the beaten track. Popular with groups April to June. Instow, a charming village with a fine beach and views, is in the heart of 'Tarka Country'. Explore the whole of northern Devon — spectacular coast and moorland, lush green valleys, pretty villages and many more attractions for families and individuals. Travel the Tarka Trail on foot or by bike.

TRAVEL INFO

🚌 Red Bus 1, 2, B, Filers 301 from Barnstaple (passing BR Barnstaple), alight Instow, ¾m (01392 382800) 🚉 Barnstaple 6m.
ℹ️ 01271 388583/388584

NEXT HOSTELS

Ilfracombe 18m, Elmscott 19m, Lynton 25m

ADDITIONAL INFO

Daytime access to w.c. and shelter, payphone and coin operated washing machine. Family rooms have access to tea/coffee making facilities, washbasins and wc's.

HOW TO GET THERE

Turn off B3233 Barnstaple - Bideford Road at signpost, Hostel ¾m at top of hill
OS 180 GR 842303

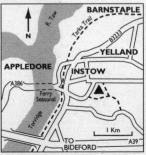

44 BEDS　　Open: 17.00hrs

Land's End (St Just)

☎ 01736 788437 Fax: 01736 787337

Youth Hostel, Letcha Vean, St Just, Penzance, Cornwall TR19 7NT

Overnight Charges: Under 18 £5.00 Adult £7.45

Seasonal Prices Jul 1 - Aug 31: Under 18 £5.55 Adult £8.25

A P Cars and mini-buses only, BABA

| Feb 16 - Nov 2 | Open |
| Dec 30 - Dec 31 | Open for New Year |

The Hostel may be available for groups when otherwise closed - please contact Warden.

ACCOMMODATION 🛏️³ 🛏️¹

A friendly Hostel with basic accommodation — set in three acres of grounds in the beautiful Cot Valley, there are open log fires, good food and fine sea views, as well as lots of local books, maps and guides on walking routes. This is an area with a spectacular coastline (seals and dolphins can often been seen), clean sandy beaches and wildflowers — as well as desolate moorland studded with stone circles, neolithic burial chambers and standing stones. Ideal for walking, cycling, surfing and birdwatching.

TRAVEL INFO

🚌 Western National 10/A/B, 11/A from Penzance (passes BR Penzance), alight St Just ¾m; 15 from St Ives (not Sat), Jun-Sep only, alight Kelynack, ½m (☎ 01209 719988) 🚉 Penzance 8m.
ℹ️ ☎ 01736 62207

NEXT HOSTELS

Penzance 8m, Pendennis 30m, Coverack 31m

ADDITIONAL INFO

Daytime access to self catering kitchen, w.c. and showers.

HOW TO GET THERE

By foot from St Just bus station walk past library, turn left, follow lane past chapel and farm to end, turn right down track to Hostel. By car from B3306 (only access for cars) turn right at Kelynack through farmyard and down lane marked 'dead end'.
OS 203 GR 364305

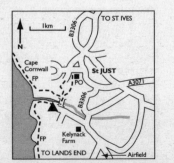

30 BEDS　　Open: 17.00hrs

Litton Cheney

☎ 01308 482340

Youth Hostel, Litton Cheney, Dorchester, Dorset DT2 9AT

Out of season contact: Regional Booking Service, 11B York Road, Salisbury, Wiltshire SP2 7AP
☎ 01722 337494 Fax: 01722 414027

Overnight Charges: Under 18 £3.75 Adult £5.50

✉️ P Limited.

| Apr 2 - Sep 7 | Open X:Mon |

ACCOMMODATION 🛏️²

This Dutch Barn, once a cheese and milk factory now offers self catering simple accommodation in an Area of Outstanding Natural Beauty in rural Dorset. Close to Chesil Beach (3m) and the inland coastal path (2 ½m) with connecting paths to the Hostel. There are many archaeological sites within easy walking distance and is ideal for an extended visit.

TRAVEL INFO

🚌 Southern National 31/X31 Weymouth - Dorchester - Taunton, alight Whiteway, 1 ½m. (☎ 01823 272033) 🚉 Dorchester South or West, both 10m. ⛴️ Weymouth/Channel Isles 14m, Poole/Cherbourg 35m
ℹ️ ☎ 01305 67992

NEXT HOSTELS

Lulworth Cove 25m, Beer 28m

ADDITIONAL INFO

Daytime access to outside w.c.

HOW TO GET THERE

From A35 into village follow International Youth Hostel signs. Next door to White Horse Pub.
OS 194 GR 548900

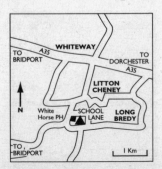

Lulworth Cove

☎ 01929 400564 Fax: 01929 400640

Youth Hostel, School Lane, West Lulworth, Wareham, Dorset BH20 5SA

Overnight Charges: Under 18 £5.00 Adult £7.45

Seasonal Prices Jul 1 - Aug 31: Under 18 £5.55 Adult £8.25

Family accommodation prices on p.10-13

⊠ P BABA

Jan 1 - Feb 15	Rent-a-Hostel
Feb 16 - Mar 30	Open X:Sun/Mon
Apr 1 - Jun 29	Open X:Sun*
Jul 1 - Sep 1	Open
Sep 3 - Nov 2	Open X:Sun/Mon
Nov 3 - Dec 31	Rent-a-Hostel

* Open Bank Hol Sun.

ACCOMMODATION 🛏²⁻⁴4 🛏⁵⁻⁸6

This purpose built single storey Hostel has small comfortable rooms, a bright sunny lounge and dining room with wonderful views of the Dorset countryside. You'll also find excellent home cooking! You'll be just off the South West Coastal Path in an Area of Outstanding Natural Beauty with some spectacular coastal walks. The unusual oyster shape of Lulworth Cove is of great geological interest and is popular with school groups between April and June. The stone arch of the Durdle Door and the rare fauna and flora are also nearby. Excellent centre for family holidays.

TRAVEL INFO
🚌 Garrison Cars 225 BR Wool - Lulworth Cove (☎ 01929 462467); Dorset Queen/Southern National 220 Dorchester - Lulworth (☎ 01305 224535). 🚆 Wool 5m.
🛈 ☎ 01929 422885

NEXT HOSTELS
Swanage 17m, Litton Cheney 25m

ADDITIONAL INFO
Daytime access to drying room only. Family rooms have access to all facilities.

HOW TO GET THERE
100yds east of B3070 turn opposite Castle Inn into School Lane.
OS 194 GR 832806

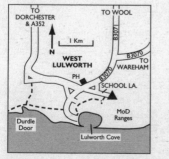

Lynton

☎ 01598 753237 Fax: 01598 753305

Youth Hostel, Lynbridge, Lynton, Devon EX35 6AZ

Out of season contact: Regional Booking Service, 11B York Road, Salisbury, Wilts. SP2 7AP
☎ 01722 337494 Fax: 01722 414027

Overnight Charges: Under 18 £5.00 Adult £7.45

Seasonal Prices Jul 1 - Aug 31: Under 18 £6.15 Adult £9.10

⊠ P Limited for cars and mini-buses. Coaches 1m in Lynton town centre. BABA

Feb 16 - Mar 31	Open X:Tu/Wed
Apr 1 - Jun 30	Open X:Sun
Jul 1 - Aug 31	Open
Sep 1 - Nov 3	Open X:Tu/Wed
Nov 8 - Dec 14	Open Fr/Sat
Dec 23 - Dec 27	Open for Christmas

The Hostel may be available for groups when otherwise closed - please contact Warden.

ACCOMMODATION 🛏²⁻⁴4 🛏⁵⁻⁸4

This homely Victorian house is set in the tranquil wooded gorge of the West Lyn river where Exmoor meets the sea at Lynmouth. Fine views and fresh air guaranteed. Lynton is an excellent country centre for families and individuals alike. This is a perfect base for moorland, riverside and coastal walks — with the Exmoor National Park and South West Coastal Path close by. Local attractions like the Cliff Railway, Valley of the Rocks and Watersmeet are within easy reach too.

TRAVEL INFO
🚌 Red Bus 310 from Barnstaple (passes close BR Barnstaple) (☎ 01271 45444). 🚆 Barnstaple 20m.
🛈 ☎ 01598 52225

NEXT HOSTELS
Exford 15m, Minehead 21m, Ilfracombe 18m

ADDITIONAL INFO
Daytime access to entrance hall, w.c. and shower.

HOW TO GET THERE
OS 180 GR 720487

Maypool

93 BEDS   **Open: 17.00hrs**

☎ 01803 842444 Fax: 01803 845939

Youth Hostel, Maypool House, Galmpton, Brixham, Devon TQ5 0ET

Overnight Charges: Under 18 £5.00 Adult £7.45

🔍 P BABA

Feb 16 - Mar 30	Open X:Sun
Apr 1 - Sep 1	Open
Sep 2 - Nov 2	Open X:Sun

The Hostel may be available for groups when otherwise closed - please contact Warden.

ACCOMMODATION 🛏2-4 3 🛏5-8 6 🛏9+ 4

A large Victorian country house with breathtaking views of the River Dart and Dartmouth, this Hostel was originally built for the local boat builder — with timbers in the beautiful minstrals gallery reputed to have come from old sailing ships. Accommodation is in the traditional dormitory style. Set in the heart of the English Riviera, there are many things to do and see. Hire boats or bring your own — we have moorings. Travel on the South Devon Steam Railway which runs across the bottom of the Hostel grounds or simply relax in this romantic idyll.

TRAVEL INFO
🚌 Bayline 100 Torquay BR Paignton-Brixham, alight Churston Pottery 1 ⅓m (☎ 01803 613226).
🚉 Paignton 5m; Churston (Dart Valley Rly) 1 ⅓m. Paignton and Dartmouth Steam Railway.
⛴ Plymouth/Roscoff 36m
🛈 ☎ 01803 558383

NEXT HOSTELS
Dartington 11m, Exeter 32m, Salcombe 26m

ADDITIONAL INFO
Daytime access to day room and w.c.

HOW TO GET THERE
A38 - A380 - A3022 intersection A379 second turning on right (Manor Vale Road). Follow signs to Youth Hostel.
OS 202 GR 877546

SOUTH WEST

36 BEDS **Open: 17.00hrs**

Minehead

☎ 01643 702595 Fax: 01643 703016

Youth Hostel, Alcombe Combe, Minehead, Somerset TA24 6EW

Overnight Charges: Under 18 £5.00 Adult £7.45

Family accommodation prices on p.10-13

🅿 Cars and mini-buses ONLY. Free coach park 2m - ask Warden. BABA

Jan 1 - Mar 31	Rent-a-Hostel
Apr 4 - Jun 30	Open X:Mon
Jul 1 - Sep 1	Open
Sep 4 - Nov 2	Open X:Mon/Tu
Nov 3 - Dec 31	Rent-a-Hostel

ACCOMMODATION 🛏2 🛏4

This attractive country house, surrounded by woodland in a beautiful secluded combe, is only 2m from the sea. As well as good facilities (including small well furnished bunkrooms) you'll find a friendly, homely atmosphere. Set in the Exmoor National Park, the Hostel has direct access to the footpath network — with some lovely walks close by. The medieval town of Dunster is a short walk away and the family holiday resort of Minehead is nearby. The South West Coastal Path starts by the harbour in Minehead.

TRAVEL INFO

🚌 Southern National 28, Taunton - Minehead (passes BR Taunton) alight Alcombe 1m.
🚆 Taunton 25m; Minehead or Dunster (West Somerset Rly) both 2m.
🛈 ☎01643 702624

NEXT HOSTELS

Exford 13m (10m on foot), Quantock Hills 14m, Crowcombe Heathfield 16m

ADDITIONAL INFO

Daytime access to self catering kitchen, wc's and shower. Family rooms have access to all facilities.

HOW TO GET THERE

Turn off A39 at Alcombe into Brook Street to Britannia Inn, then on to Manor Road which becomes a private road for ⅔m. Turn sharp left up to Hostel. NB: Difficult to find after dark.
OS 181 GR 973442

90 BEDS **Open: 17.00hrs**

Pendennis Castle

☎ 01326 311435 Fax: 01326 315473

Youth Hostel, Falmouth, Cornwall TR11 4LP

Overnight Charges: Under 18 £5.55 Adult £8.25

Seasonal Prices Jul 1 - Aug 31: Under 18 £6.15 Adult £9.10

Family accommodation prices on p.10-13

🖵 🅿 100yds overnight only - outside castle gates. BABA

Feb 16 - Sep 30	Open
Oct 1 - Nov 30	Open X:Sun/Mon
Dec 27 - Dec 31	Open for New Year

The Hostel may be available for groups when otherwise closed - please contact Warden.

ACCOMMODATION 🛏14 🛏4 🛏1

The Hostel — once a Victorian army barracks (and now much more comfortable!) — is perfectly sited inside a 16th century fortified castle. Floodlit at night, the castle faces out to sea on its own peninsula with breathtaking views across the rugged Cornish coastline. A truly magical setting for families with young children. You'll find safe sandy beaches and the South West Coastal footpath nearby, as well as a host of attractions including a Seal Sanctuary, Maritime museum and historical re-enactments with the Sealed Knot Society.

TRAVEL INFO

🚌 Frequent from surrounding areas (☎ 01209 719988). 🚆 Falmouth Docks (not Sun, except Jun-Sep) ¾m.
🛈 ☎01326 312300

NEXT HOSTELS

Boswinger 24m, Coverack 20m, Penzance 24m

ADDITIONAL INFO

Family rooms have passes through the English Heritage site for day access.

HOW TO GET THERE

From roundabout outside Falmouth Docks, follow English Heritage signs up hill and across to sea front. Youth Hostel is within castle grounds.
OS 204 GR 823319

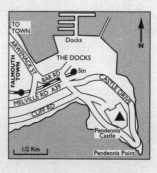

Page 63

| | 84 BEDS | Open: 17.00hrs |

Penzance

☎ 01736 62666 Fax: 01736 62663

Youth Hostel, Castle Horneck, Alverton, Penzance, Cornwall TR20 8TF

Overnight Charges: Under 18 £6.15 Adult £9.10

Ⓐ ☒ Ⓑ Ⓟ BABA

| Feb 2 - Dec 29 | Open |

The Hostel may be available for groups when otherwise closed - please contact Warden.

ACCOMMODATION 🛏²⁻⁴ 1, 🛏⁵⁻⁸ 5, 🛏⁹⁺ 4

This early 18th century Georgian mansion, built on the site of a 14th century medieval fort, is reputed to have a smugglers tunnel! There are superb views across Mounts Bay to the Lizard Peninsula and St Michael's Mount. Don't go home without trying the speciality ice cream. You'll find easy access to the South West Coastal footpath with miles of magnificent scenery and some of Britain's finest beaches. The area is steeped in Celtic culture with ancient burial chambers and stone circles. The subtropical climate fosters a varied selection of fauna and flora.

TRAVEL INFO
🚌 Western National 5B, 6B, 10B from BR Penzance to Pirate pub (☎ 01209 719988)
🚉 Penzance 2m.
🚶 ☎ 01736 62207

NEXT HOSTELS
Land's End 8m, Perranporth 29m, Pendennis Castle 24m

ADDITIONAL INFO
Daytime access to basement and w.c.

HOW TO GET THERE
All vehicles follow A30 and Penzance and turn at the 'Castle Horneck' signs. Do not go into Penzance Town Centre.
OS 203 GR 457302

| | 24 BEDS | Open: 17.00hrs |

Perranporth

☎ 01872 573812

Youth Hostel, Droskyn Point, Perranporth, Cornwall TR6 0DS

Out of season contact: Regional Booking Service, 11B York Road, Salisbury, Wilts. SP2 7AP
☎ 01722 337494 Fax: 01722 414027

Overnight Charges: Under 18 £4.60 Adult £6.75

Seasonal Prices Jul 1 - Aug 31: Under 18 £5.00 Adult £7.45

☒ Ⓟ Free parking 250yds.

Jan 1 - Mar 31	Rent-a-Hostel
Apr 4 - Aug 31	Open
Sep 1 - Sep 30	Open X:Sun
Oct 1 - Dec 31	Rent-a-Hostel

ACCOMMODATION 🛏²⁻⁴ 2, 🛏⁵⁻⁸ 1, 🛏⁹⁺ 1

Perched on the rugged west coast of Cornwall, this former coastguard station offers wonderful views over an exciting coastline with untamed seas and isolated bays. With three miles of excellent surf beach, it's also a surfer's paradise. This self catering Hostel stands on the South West Coastal Footpath with St Agnes, Holywell Bay and Newquay. Local attractions include the World in Miniature, St Agnes Leisure Park, Newquay Zoo and the historic city of Truro.

TRAVEL INFO
🚌 Western National 87/A/B/C, 88A Truro-Newquay (pass close BR Truro & Newquay) (☎ 01209 719988) 🚉 Truro 10m; Newquay (not Sun, except Jun - Sep) 10m.
🚶 ☎ 01872 573368

NEXT HOSTELS
Pendennis Castle 19m, Treyarnon Bay 22m, Bowsinger 25m

ADDITIONAL INFO
Daytime access to entrance area and w.c.

HOW TO GET THERE
Along cliff to W of village, Hostel beyond locked gate on coastal footpath. No vehicular access.
OS 204 GR 752544

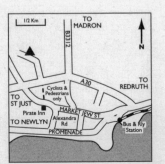

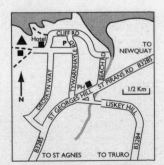

68 BEDS Open: 17.00hrs

Plymouth

☎ 01752 562189 Fax: 01752 605360

Youth Hostel, Belmont House, Belmont Place, Stoke, Plymouth, Devon PL3 4DW

Overnight Charges: Under 18 £5.55 Adult £8.25

Seasonal Prices Jul 1 - Aug 31: Under 18 £6.15 Adult £9.10

Family accommodation prices on p.10-13

🔍 **P** BABA

Jan 4 - Feb 28	Open X:Tu/Wed
Mar 1 - Nov 3	Open
Nov 6 - Dec 21	Open X:Mon/Tu
Dec 27 - Dec 31	Open for New Year

ACCOMMODATION 2-4 7 5-8 2 9+ 3

Inspired by Greek architecture, the building is one of the finest in Plymouth. Set in extensive grounds, the Hostel has many original features including an impressive entrance hall (with marble floor) and library. You can even dine in the old ballroom with its beautiful lantern ceiling. Soak up the historic atmosphere of the Barbican, remember Sir Francis Drake, Captain Cook, Darwin and the Pilgrim Fathers. Take a harbour cruise, stroll along the wide green promenade and spend the evening at the theatre or cinema. Dartmoor and safe sandy beaches are only ½ hour away.

TRAVEL INFO

🚌 Western National 14A, 15/A, 81, Plymouth Citybus 33/A, 34/A from City Centre (some pass BR Plymouth) (☎ 01752 222666 or 222221). 🚉 Devonport ¼m; Plymouth 1 ½m. ⛴ To Roscoff (France) and Santander (Spain)
🛈 ☎ 01752 264849

NEXT HOSTELS

Golant 38m, Bellever 21m, Salcombe 25m

ADDITIONAL INFO

Family rooms have daytime access to bedroom, self catering kitchen, lounge and w.c. Famous for sea and river fishing - trout, sea-trout and salmon.

HOW TO GET THERE

From A38 follow A386 to Torpoint. Past a small shopping centre the Hostel is signposted on the left.
OS 201 GR 461555

Bustling resorts, remote bays,
thatched cottages, cream teas, granite cliffs, picturesque
fishing harbours, sandy coves, moorland tors together with a mild climate are all to be found in Devon and Cornwall.

Saddles and Paddles and the YHA offer you the ideal cycling holiday on a 'go as you please' basis, to explore all of this and much, much more...

Why not contact us now to
receive suggestions and further information on our extensive bike hire service.

Saddles and Paddles
4 Kings Wharf, The Quay
Exeter, Devon EX2 4AP
Tel : (01392) 424241
Fax : (01392) 430370

🚶🏃⛷ 24 BEDS — Open: 17.00hrs

Quantock Hills (Holford)

📞 01278 741224

Youth Hostel, Sevenacres, Holford, Bridgwater, Somerset TA5 1SQ

Out of season contact: Regional Booking Service, 11B York Road, Salisbury, Wilts. SP2 7AP
📞 01722 337494 Fax: 01722 414027

Overnight Charges: Under 18 £4.60 Adult £6.75

Ⓐ Ⓟ No access for coaches. Limited for cars and mini-buses.

Jan 1 - Mar 31	Rent-a-Hostel
Apr 3 - Jun 29	Open X:Sun/Mon*
Jul 1 - Aug 31	Open
Sep 1 - Dec 31	Rent-a-Hostel

*Open Bank Hol Sun

ACCOMMODATION 🛏²⁻⁴2 🛏⁵⁻⁸3

Stay well off the beaten track at this characterful self catering country retreat where you can enjoy views from the terrace across the Bristol Channel to Wales. Leave the car behind and walk straight out onto open hills to appreciate the wildlife and beautiful scenery. Venture down to Kilve beach to hunt for fossils. Watchet Harbour, Hinkley Point, the West Somerset Steam Railway and Minehead are also within easy reach.

TRAVEL INFO
🚌 Southern National 15 Bridgwater-Mindhead (passing close BR Bridgwater) (📞 01823 272033) 🚉 Bridgwater 13m.
🛈 📞 01278 427652

NEXT HOSTELS
Crowcombe Heathfield 10m (7m by foot), Minehead 14m, Street 28m

ADDITIONAL INFO
Daytime access to self catering kitchen and outside wc's. Meals provided for groups booked in advance.

HOW TO GET THERE
WALKERS ONLY from Kilve, take Pardlestone Lane opposite Post Office (1m). Vehicular access from Holford, take road through the Alfoxton Park Hotel (1 ½m), cross 2nd cattle grid, uphill to sharp bend, take Hostel track on right.
OS 181 GR 145416

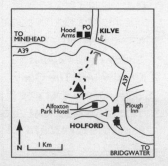

🏠☀ 54 BEDS — Open: 17.00hrs

Salcombe

📞 01548 842856 Fax: 01548 842856

Youth Hostel, 'Overbecks', Sharpitor, Salcombe, Devon TQ8 8LW

Out of season contact: Regional Booking Service, 11B York Road, Salisbury, Wiltshire SP2 7AP
📞 01722 337494 Fax: 01722 414027

Overnight Charges: Under 18 £5.00 Adult £7.45

Seasonal Prices Jul 1 - Aug 31: Under 18 £5.55 Adult £8.25

Ⓟ National Trust Car Park. Coaches 2m (Salcombe).
BABA

Apr 1 - Jun 30	Open X:Sun*
Jul 1 - Aug 31	Open
Sep 1 - Nov 2	Open X:Sun/Mon

*Open Bank Hol Sun.

ACCOMMODATION 🛏²⁻⁴4 🛏⁵⁻⁸1 🛏⁹⁺2

A truly stunning location overlooking the sea and estuary. The Hostel is part of the National Trust's 'Overbecks' museum and is set in the semi-tropical gardens on the cliffs just below Sharpitor rocks. Salcombe is renowned for its fine weather, sandy beaches, excellent sailing, watersports and superb walking. The Hostel has a reputation for its friendly atmosphere, good food and of course the beautiful views, making it popular with individuals and families.

TRAVEL INFO
🚌 Tally Ho! from Kingsbridge (connects from Plymouth, Dartmouth and, for BR connections, from Totnes), alight Salcombe, 2m (Devon C.C Enquiry Line 📞 01392-382800) 🚉 Totnes 20m. Plymouth 26m. ⛴ Ferry from Salcombe town centre to South Sands. Then 5 minute walk up hill to 'Overbecks'.
🛈 📞 01548 853195

NEXT HOSTELS
Dartington 21m, Plymouth 25m, Maypool 26m via Dart Ferry or Totnes

ADDITIONAL INFO
Daytime access to w.c. and room available. Afternoon tearoom.

HOW TO GET THERE
Follow signs for National Trust - Overbecks.
OS 202 GR 728374

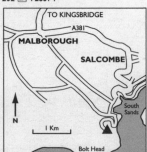

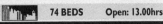
74 BEDS | **Open: 13.00hrs**

Salisbury

📞 **01722 327572 Fax: 01722 330446**

Youth Hostel, Milford Hill House, Milford Hill, Salisbury, Wiltshire SP1 2QW

Overnight Charges: Under 18 £6.15 Adult £9.10

Family accommodation prices on p.10-13

Cars and mini-buses. Space for one coach - arrange with Warden. BABA **IBN**

Jan 1 - Dec 31	Open

The Hostel is open from 13.00 hrs each day - however, during the winter the reception may not be manned until 17.00 hrs.

ACCOMMODATION 🛏️6 🛏️4 🛏️2

This 200 year old listed building is set in its own secluded grounds only a few minutes walk from the centre of the lovely cathedral city of Salisbury and has all the facilities needed by the international traveller. A fine old Cedar tree is the outstanding feature of the Hostel's well tended garden. The bustling market town is a pleasing mix of old and new. Traditional open markets are held on Tuesdays and Saturdays. The area offers good off road cycling and Stonehenge is only 9m away.

TRAVEL INFO

🚌 Frequent from surrounding areas (📞 01722 336855). 🚉 Salisbury 1m. ⛴ Portsmouth/France (Caen, Cherbourg, St Malo, Le Havre)-Spain (Santander) 40m

🛈 📞 01722 334956

NEXT HOSTELS

Burley 21m, Winchester 24m, Bath 39m

ADDITIONAL INFO

Open from 1.00 pm. Daytime access to outside w.c. Family rooms have access to all facilities. Foreign exchange. One single room. The Hostel reception may not open until 5pm in the winter.

HOW TO GET THERE

Motorists - avoid city centre. Hostel signposted from A36 (Southampton). Near Salisbury College.
OS 184 **GR** 149299

---

24 BEDS | **Open: 17.00hrs**

Steps Bridge

📞 **01647 252435 Fax: 01647 252435**

Youth Hostel, Steps Bridge, Dunsford, Exeter, Devon EX6 7EQ

Out of season contact: Regional Booking Service, 11B York Road, Salisbury, Wilts. SP2 7AP
📞 01722 337494 Fax: 01722 414027

Overnight Charges: Under 18 £4.15 Adult £6.10

Seasonal Prices Jul 1 - Aug 31: Under 18 £4.60 Adult £6.75

Public car park opposite end of Hostel drive. BABA

Jan 1 - Mar 31	Rent-a-Hostel
Apr 5 - Sep 30	Open
Oct 2 - Dec 31	Rent-a-Hostel

ACCOMMODATION 🛏️2 🛏️1

This self catering Hostel, ideally situated in secluded woodland overlooking the Teign Valley, has been a haven for generations of Hostellers seeking peace and tranquility. Steps Bridge is perfectly placed for walking on the rugged Dartmoor Tors and delightful lower slopes. Look out for rare and interesting wild flowers, butterflies and birds. Horse riding is available locally and with so much on offer, the Hostel makes an ideal base for all country lovers.

TRAVEL INFO

🚌 Red Bus 359 from Exeter departs Belgrave Road and passes BR Exeter Central (📞 01392 382800). Transmoor Express 82 Exeter - Plymouth, May-Sep only, alight Steps Bridge. 🚉 Exeter Central 9m; Exeter St David's 9m.

🛈 📞 01392 265297

NEXT HOSTELS

Exeter 10m, Bellever 18m, Dartington 25m

ADDITIONAL INFO

Daytime access to outwide w.c. and simple shelter. For safety reasons this Hostel is NOT suitable for children aged under 5 years old.

HOW TO GET THERE

OS 191 **GR** 802882

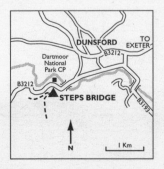

Street

🚶🏃🚲 **32 BEDS** **Open: 17.00hrs**

☎ 01458 442961 Fax: 01458 442738

Youth Hostel, The Chalet, Ivythorn Hill, Street, Somerset BA16 0TZ

Out of season contact: Regional Booking Service, 11B York Road, Salisbury Wilts. SP2 7AP
☎ 01722 337494 Fax: 01722 414027

Overnight Charges: Under 18 £5.00 Adult £7.45

Family accommodation prices on p.10-13

🅰 ⊠ 🅿 BABA

Jan 1 - Mar 31	Rent-a-Hostel
Apr 3 - Jun 30	Open X:Tu
Jul 1 - Aug 31	Open
Sep 1 - Nov 2	Open Tu/Wed
Nov 3 - Dec 31	Rent-a-Hostel

ACCOMMODATION 🛏4 🛏1 🛏1

This attractive Swiss-style chalet, built by the Clarks family (of shoemaking fame) as a holiday home for their employees and now a traditional cosy self catering Hostel, is set on a small hill overlooking Glastonbury Tor and the Mendip Hills in the heart of Somerset. Famous for Clarks shoes, the town of Street has many amenities while nearby Glastonbury is a centre for mysticism and Arthurian legends (plus host to the famous music festival) and the city of Wells boasts a magnificent cathedral. The hills and levels of Somerset offer easy walking and cycling.

TRAVEL INFO
🚌Badgerline 376, 676, Southern National 29A Bristol - Yeovil (passes BR Bristol Temple Meads), alight Marshalls Elm then 500m. (☎ 0117 955 3231). 🚉 Castle Cary 11m; Bridgwater 13m.
🛈 ☎01458 832954

NEXT HOSTELS
Cheddar 17m, Quantock Hills 28m, Bristol 33m

ADDITIONAL INFO
Daytime access to outside w.c. and verandah. Family rooms have access to all facilities.

HOW TO GET THERE
From Street, take the Somerton road (B3151) S for 2m. Turn right at crossroads at Marshalls Elm, Hostel 500yds on right.
OS 182 GR 480345

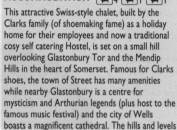

Swanage

🏰 **106 BEDS** **Open: 17.00hrs**

☎ 01929 422113 Fax: 01929 426327

Youth Hostel, Cluny, Cluny Crescent, Swanage, Dorset BH19 2BS

Overnight Charges: Under 18 £6.15 Adult £9.10

🔍 📷 🅿 BABA

Feb 16 - Nov 2	Open
Dec 27 - Dec 31	Open for New Year

The Hostel may be available for groups when otherwise closed - please contact Warden.

ACCOMMODATION 🛏6 🛏8 🛏4

This large Victorian house overlooking the town with fine views across the Bay to the Purbeck Hills has been refurbished to a high standard. There is a well equipped games room, a cosy lounge and comfortable dining room. The Hostel is popular with groups from April to June, and during school holidays families find this an excellent location. Swanage is a major unspoilt resort on the 'Isle of Purbeck'. Spectacular coastal scenery, safe sandy beaches and high sunshine ratings combine to make it an ever popular holidays destination.

TRAVEL INFO
🚌Wilts & Dorset 150 from Bournemouth (passes BR Branksome); 142-4 from Poole (pass BR Wareham). Alight Swanage Bus Station on all services, thence ¼m (☎ 01202 673555).
🚉Wareham 10m. ⚓Cherbourg/Poole 15m
🛈 ☎01929 422885

NEXT HOSTELS
Lulworth Cove 17m, Burley 29m

ADDITIONAL INFO
Daytime access to w.c. and shelter. Ideal venue for conferences.

HOW TO GET THERE
OS 195 GR 031785

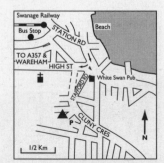

Tintagel

👣🚶 **26 BEDS**   **Open: 17.00hrs**

☎ 01840 770334

Youth Hostel, Dunderhole Point, Tintagel, Cornwall PL34 0DW

Out of season contact: Regional Booking Service, 11B York Road, Salisbury, Wilts. SP2 7AP
☎ 01722 337494 Fax: 01722 414027

Overnight Charges: Under 18 £5.00 Adult £7.45

Seasonal Prices Jul 1 - Aug 31: Under 18 £5.55 Adult £8.25

🅿 Limited. Alternative parking at Tintagel Church 300yds.

Jan 1 - Mar 23	Rent-a-Hostel
Mar 29 - May 19	Open X:Wed
May 20 - Sep 30	Open
Oct 1 - Dec 31	Rent-a-Hostel

ACCOMMODATION

This small self catering Hostel is a little 'gem', it offers comfortable accommodation in traditional dormitories and is perched on the Glebe Cliff with stunning views of the coastline, sea and wonderful sunsets. Enjoy the superb views along the South West Coastal footpath, visit Rocky Valley with its ancient rock carvings, or explore the 13th century remains of Tintagel Castle. Best known for its Arthurian legends, you can watch the waves break over the threshold of Merlin's Cave.

TRAVEL INFO

🚌 Western National 125 from BR Bodmin Parkway and Les Dawes Coaches No 245 from Bodmin, X4 from Bude (☎ 01209 719988); Fry's from Plymouth (passes close BR Plymouth) (infrequent) (☎ 01840 770256). On all, alight Tintagel, ¾m. 🚉 Bodmin Parkway 20m.
🛈 ☎ 01840 212954

NEXT HOSTELS

Boscastle Harbour 5m, Treyarnon Bay 23m (18m by ferry), Golant 28m

ADDITIONAL INFO

Daytime access to simple shelter.

HOW TO GET THERE

Vehicular access along rough track via Tregatta corner only.
🆗 200 🅶🆁 047881

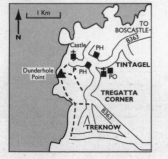

Treyarnon Bay

👪☀ **42 BEDS**   **Open: 17.00hrs**

☎ 01841 520322 Fax: 01841 520322

Youth Hostel, Tregonnan, Treyarnon, Padstow, Cornwall PL28 8JR

Out of season contact: Regional Booking Service, 11B York Road, Salisbury, Wilts. SP2 7AP
☎ 01722 337494 Fax: 01722 414027

Overnight Charges: Under 18 £5.00 Adult £7.45

Seasonal Prices Jul 1 - Aug 31: Under 18 £5.55 Adult £8.25

🅿 Cars and mini-buses BABA

Jan 1 - Mar 30	Rent-a-Hostel
Apr 1 - Jun 30	Open X:Fr
Jul 1 - Sep 1	Open
Sep 2 - Nov 2	Open X:Sun
Nov 3 - Dec 31	Rent-a-Hostel

ACCOMMODATION

This interesting seaside house has stunning views and is very close to the fine sandy beach. The picnic tables on the front terrace are a favourite spot in the evenings particularly when the barbeque is lit! The nearby lighthouse of Trevose Head watches over many fine surfing beaches, lifeguard patrolled from May to September. The resort of Padstow is 4m.

TRAVEL INFO

🚌 Western National 55 BR Bodmin Parkway-Padstow, alight Padstow, 4 ½m, on most, but some extended to Constantine, ½m; 56 Newquay-Constantine Jun-Sep only (☎ 01209 719988) 🚉 Newquay (not Sun, except Jun - Sep) 10m; Bodmin Parkway 21m.
🛈 ☎ 01841 533449

NEXT HOSTELS

Perranporth 22m, Tintagel 23m, Boscastle 24m

ADDITIONAL INFO

Daytime access to outside w.c. and lobby.

HOW TO GET THERE

From A39 take A389 or B3274 to Padstow then B3276 to St Merryn (Farmers Arms PH), then 3rd right turn signposted Treyarnon. From Newquay take B3276 towards Padstow then left turn after Porthcothan (11m).
🆗 200 🅶🆁 859741

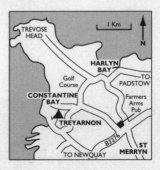

East of England

From the flat fenlands of rural Norfolk to the Suffolk coast and heaths, the east of England has something for everyone.

As well as inland Suffolk with its rolling countryside, sandy dunes and forests, there's also Norfolk with its famous Broads and historic buildings. Further south, you'll find the pastoral scenery and river estuaries of Essex, made famous by Constable and rich in wildlife and history.

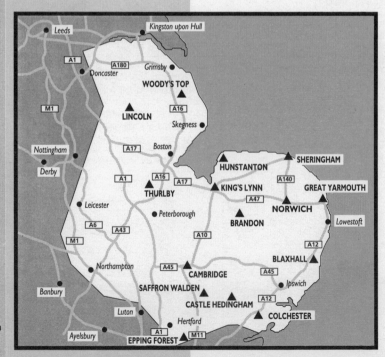

Discover the style and character of cathedral cities like Cambridge, Lincoln and Norwich where you'll find a wealth of historical buildings, museums, exhibitions, crafts and shops.

From the striped cliffs at Hunstanton to the ancient town of Colchester, the vast coastline has much to offer – with safe, unspoilt beaches (many Blue Flag) and historic seaside towns as well as many leisure facilities and attractions.

Your YHA membership entitles you to discounts at the Sealife Centre at Hunstanton, and the Welney Wildfowl and Wetlands Trust. You can also get 10% off the price of staying at Tunstall Camping Barn (on the Norfolk Broads), Manor Farm, Tunstall, Norwich NR13 3PS. Tel: 01493 700279.

Useful Publications

Individual Hostel leaflets are available at no charge – just specify which Hostel you're interested in and send a SAE to YHA South England Regional Office at the address below. Alternatively, leave a request on our YHA 24 hour literature line on 01426 951683 (local call charge).

Cycling in Norfolk + Suffolk - details of our routes, cycle hire and Hostels - available from Norwich Youth Hostel and Saffron Walden Youth Hostel.

For more information about hostelling in this area contact:

YHA South England Regional Office,
11b York Road,
Salisbury,
Wilts SP2 7AP

Tel: 01722 337494
Fax: 01722 414027

40 BEDS   Open: 17.00hrs

Blaxhall

☎ 01728 688206

Youth Hostel, Heath Walk, Blaxhall, Woodbridge, Suffolk IP12 2EA

Overnight Charges: Under 18 £4.60 Adult £6.75

🛗 🅿 For cars and coaches.

Jan 1 - Mar 31	Rent-a-Hostel
Apr 1 - Jun 30	Open X:Sun*
Jul 1 - Aug 31	Open
Sep 16 - Oct 31	Open X:Sun/Mon
Nov 1 - Dec 31	Rent-a-Hostel

* Open Bank Hol Sun.

ACCOMMODATION 🛏2 🛏5

This comfortable Hostel, once a village school, has mostly small bedrooms with showers and wc's across a courtyard. It is in a quite village in the midst of the Suffolk sandlings heathland. Home cooked food and a friendly atmosphere is not to be missed. As well as great cycling and walking country, you'll find estuaries, coastline, forest and reedbeds all close by. Visit the RSPB reserves of Minsmere and Havergate. Culture vultures should head for Snape Maltings concert hall only 2m away.

TRAVEL INFO
🚌Eastern Counties 80/1, 99 Ipswich - Aldeburgh (pass close BR Saxmundham), alight ½m SW of Stratford St Andrew, 2m (☎ 01473 265676).
🚉Wickham Market 3m; Saxmundham 5m.
⛴Harwich and Felixstowe to Rotterdam, Zeebruge, Hook of Holland, Hamburg and Oslo
🛈 ☎01394 282126

NEXT HOSTELS
Colchester 32m, Norwich 39m, Brandon 50m

ADDITIONAL INFO
Daytime access to w.c. and simple shelter.

HOW TO GET THERE
From A12 turn off at Wickham Market to Campsea Ashe, then follow signs to Tunstall and then to Hostel following signs.
OS 156 GR 369570

---

36 BEDS   Open: 17.00hrs

Brandon

☎ 01842 812075 Fax: 01842 812075

Youth Hostel, Heath House, Off Warren Close, Bury Road, Brandon, Suffolk IP27 0BU

Overnight Charges: Under 18 £5.55 Adult £8.25

Family accommodation prices on p.10-13

🅿 in grounds. BABA

Feb 16 - Mar 30	Open X:Sun/Mon
Apr 1 - Jun 30	Open X:Sun*
Jul 1 - Aug 31	Open
Sep 3 - Sep 14	Open X:Sun/Mon
Oct 1 - Oct 31	Open X:Sun/Mon
Nov 1 - Dec 21	Open Fr/Sat

* Open Bank Hol Sun. The Hostel may be available for groups when otherwise closed - please contact Warden.

ACCOMMODATION 🛏2 🛏1 🛏2

This charming Edwardian house with a homely atmosphere and two lounge rooms provides a comfortable stay at any time of the year. Well situated for exploring Thetford Chase, the largest forested area in England. Maps of the orienteering course in Brandon Country Park and the paths and cycle ways in the Thetford Forest are available from the Hostel. There are a wealth of other activities close by, hire a bike and explore further afield or go aircraft spotting at Mildenhall.

TRAVEL INFO
🚌National Express Eastern Counties. 🚉Brandon ¾m.
🛈 ☎01842 814955

NEXT HOSTELS
King's Lynn 25m, Cambridge 34m

ADDITIONAL INFO
Daytime access to w.c. in main entrance. Family rooms give all day access to w.c., kitchen and bedroom.

HOW TO GET THERE
OS 144 GR 786864

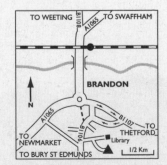

Cambridge

☎ 01223 354601 Fax: 01223 312780

Youth Hostel, 97 Tenison Road, Cambridge, Cambridgeshire CB1 2DN

Overnight Charges: Under 18 £6.80 Adult £10.00

Family accommodation prices on p.10-13

 Coach park 4m. Free parking for cars roadside from 1700 - 0900hrs (metered at other times).
BABA IBN

Open every day of the year.

ACCOMMODATION

A Victorian town house with modern facilities, the Hostel is just minutes from the station and only 15 minutes walk or a short bus ride from the centre. 1995 has seen many changes at the Hostel and visitors can enjoy the newly decorated lounge area with comfy sofas, a new games room, an attractive courtyard garden as well as improved facilities in all the bedrooms. The imaginative new menu has been well received. Cambridge is a typical English city with a lazy river, green fields and cows grazing alongside the ancient colleges, museums and art galleries. The best way to get around is Cambridge style — by bike or why not have a go at punting on the river! A very popular Hostel with groups during the Spring and Autumn with families and individuals flocking in the Summer.

TRAVEL INFO
🚌 Frequent from surrounding areas (☎ 01223 423554). 🚉 Cambridge ¼m.
🚲 ☎ 01223 322640

NEXT HOSTELS
Saffron Walden 15m, Ely 17m, Castle Hedingham 29m

ADDITIONAL INFO
All customers are provided with room keys. Bureau de change.

HOW TO GET THERE
Coming from the city centre follow signs to railway station. Take the last turning to the left (at Hostel sign) before you get to the railway station.
OS 154 GR 460575

Castle Hedingham

50 BEDS **Open: 17.00hrs**

☏ 01787 460799 Fax: 01787 461302

Youth Hostel, 7 Falcon Square, Castle Hedingham, Halstead, Essex CO9 3BU

Overnight Charges: Under 18 £5.55 Adult £8.25

⟨&⟩ P Nearby. BABA

Feb 16 - Mar 31	Open X:Sun/Mon
Apr 1 - Jun 30	Open X:Sun*
Jul 1 - Aug 31	Open
Sep 3 - Oct 31	Open X:Sun
Nov 4 - Dec 19	Open Mon/Tu/Wed/Th

* Open Bank Hol Sun. The Hostel may be available for groups when otherwise closed - please contact Warden.

ACCOMMODATION 🛏2-4 2 🛏5-8 3 🛏9+ 2

As well as a 16th century building with fine exposed oak timbers, there is also a modern annexe on the site of an old maltings which offers wheelchair access. There is a large lawned garden with mature fruit trees, picnic tables and a BBQ. Home-cooked food and vegetarian meals a speciality! Popular with groups mid week from May to mid July. One of the best kept secrets in East Anglia, the Hostel is set in a small attractive village square, overlooked by a well preserved Norman castle.

TRAVEL INFO

🚌Hedingham Omnibuses 6, 89/A from Braintree (pass close BR Braintree) (☏ 0345 000 333).
🚉Sudbury (Not Sun) 7m; Braintree 8m
⚓Harwich Ferry for Netherlands, Germany, Norway (25m)
🛈 ☏01376 550066

NEXT HOSTELS

Colchester 18m, Saffron Walden 20m, Cambridge 29m

ADDITIONAL INFO

Daytime access to simple shelter.

HOW TO GET THERE

Follow signs for Hedingham Castle. Opposite Castle entrance turn down Castle Lane. Hostel on left at bottom of hill. (This route is not suitable for coaches).
OS 155 GR 786355

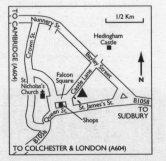

Colchester

52 BEDS **Open: 17.00hrs**

☏ 01206 867982 Fax: 01206 868628

Youth Hostel, East Bay House, 18 East Bay, Colchester, Essex CO1 2UE

Overnight Charges: Under 18 £5.00 Adult £7.45

⟨&⟩ P BABA

Feb 16 - Mar 30	Open X:Sun/Mon
Apr 1 - Sep 1	Open
Sep 2 - Oct 31	Open X:Sun
Nov 1 - Dec 21	Open Fr/Sat
Dec 27 - Dec 31	Open for New Year

The Hostel may be available for groups when otherwise closed - please contact Warden.

ACCOMMODATION 🛏2-4 3 🛏5-8 3 🛏9+ 2

This large Georgian house stands by the river Colne close to the centre of England's oldest recorded Roman town close to the port of Harwich. Cyclists will find many quiet lanes and roads, ideal for exploring Constable country. A Norman Keep, Saxon Church and Roman Wall are among the many historic attractions to be found in Colchester. It's also the origins of Humpty Dumpty and Old King Cole of nursery rhyme fame. Nearby attractions include Colchester Zoo, Fingrinhoe Nature Reserve and Clacton seaside resort.

TRAVEL INFO

🚌Frequent local services (☏ 0345 000 333)
🚉Hythe (Not Sun, except Jun-Sep) ½m; Colchester Town (Not Sun, except July/Aug) ¾m; Colchester North 1 ½m ⚓Harwich (21m) to Germany, Holland and Sweden
🛈 ☏01206 712920

NEXT HOSTELS

Castle Hedingham 18m, Blaxhall 32m, Saffron Walden 39m

ADDITIONAL INFO

Daytime access to simple shelter. Family rooms have access to all facilities.

HOW TO GET THERE

Opposite Periquito Hotel. ½m E of bus station and castle. 2m from Colchester Town train station (77 bus).
OS 168 GR 006252

Ely

Youth Hostel,

ACCOMMODATION
We regret that this Youth Hostel is now closed.
The nearest Youth Hostels are Cambridge (17m),
Brandon (21m) and Kings Lynn (24m).

Food for thought for Budget Travellers

Did you know that at most Youth Hostels you can now get scrummy, wholesome meals like home-made steak pie, vegetable au gratin, fresh salads and pizzas?

What's more, the prices take some topping too – with a full English breakfast costing just £2.80, freshly made lunchpacks £2.35 and three course evening meals from just £4.15. Vegetarian options are always available too.

So next time you go hostelling why not turn it into a real holiday and leave the cooking to us!

Epping Forest

📞 0181 508 5161 Fax: 0181 508 5161

Youth Hostel, Wellington Hall, High Beach, Loughton, Essex IG10 4AG

Overnight Charges: Under 18 £4.60 Adult £6.75

A P Cars at Hostel. Coaches by arrangement. BABA

Jan 1 - Feb 29	Rent-a-Hostel
Mar 1 - Sep 1	Open
Sep 2 - Nov 2	Open X:Sun
Nov 3 - Dec 31	Rent-a-Hostel

ACCOMMODATION 🛏5 🛏2
For fresh air, birdsong and forest walks all just 15km from central London, why not try this single storey simple self catering Hostel in a truly rural location. Walk freely and relax in 6000 acres of woodland, formerly a royal hunting forest. There is a well stocked shop at the Hostel but other shops are some distance away. As well as easy access to London, this area has lots to offer with Waltham Abbey, Conaught Water, Loughton Iron Age Camp and Queen Elizabeth Hunting Lodge all close by.

TRAVEL INFO
🚌 Townlink 250 BR Waltham Cross - Loughton Tube Station, alight Volunteer Inn, 1m (📞 0345 000 333). 🚇 Loughton (Underground) 2m; Chingford (BR) 3 ½m.
🛈 📞 01992 652295

NEXT HOSTELS
Hampstead Heath 13m, City of London 13m, Saffron Walden 29m

ADDITIONAL INFO
Daytime access to w.c. and simple shelter. Small shop at Hostel - milk must be ordered in advance.

HOW TO GET THERE
From junction 26 M25 take Epping/Loughton road. After ¼m turn right at Volunteer Inn. Right at next junction, left up Wellington Hill. Hostel on right after Duke of Wellington pub.
OS 167 GR 408983

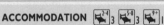 **40 BEDS**   Open: 17.00hrs

Great Yarmouth

☎ 01493 843991 Fax: 01493 843991

Youth Hostel, 2 Sandown Road, Great
Yarmouth, Norfolk NR30 1EY

Out of season contact: Regional Booking Service,
11B York Road, Salisbury, Wilts. SP2 7AP
☎ 01722 337494 Fax: 01722 414027

Overnight Charges: Under 18 £5.55 Adult £8.25

Family accommodation prices on p.10-13

P On roadside by Hostel. BABA

Jan 1 - Mar 28	Rent-a-Hostel
Mar 29 - Jun 30	Open X:Sun/Mon*
Jul 2 - Aug 31	Open
Sep 1 - Dec 31	Rent-a-Hostel

* Open Bank Hol Sun.

ACCOMMODATION 🛏²⁻⁴3 🛏⁵⁻⁸3 🛏⁹⁺1

This comfortable Victorian House is only minutes
from the coast, as well as the beautiful Broads
National Park. Not just a popular coastal resort,
Great Yarmouth is also steeped in history — for
instance, you can follow the medieval trail around
town (route available from Warden). Enjoy the
modern and medieval, coastal and cultural setting
of Yarmouth, one of Britain's favourite holiday
towns with its sandy beaches and huge range of
traditional seaside attractions and entertainment.
This is ideal cycling country along quiet lanes and
roads which link up the YHA network.

TRAVEL INFO
🚌Frequent from surrounding areas, also local
services (☎ 01603 613613) 🚂 Great Yarmouth
¾m
ℹ️ ☎ 01493 846345

NEXT HOSTELS
Norwich 21m, Sheringham 39m, Blaxhall 41m

ADDITIONAL INFO
Daytime access to simple shelter. Family rooms
have access to all facilities.

HOW TO GET THERE
OS 134 GR 529083

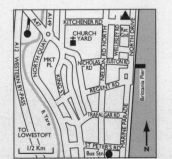

---

22 BEDS   Open: 17.00hrs

Harlow

☎ 01279 421702

Youth Hostel, Corner House, Netteswell
Cross, Harlow, Essex CM20 2QD

Overnight Charges: Under 18 £4.60 Adult £6.75

Ⓐ 🔍 ⌗ P Public car park (free) opposite.

ACCOMMODATION
This Hostel may not be open during 1996. Please
check availability with YHA South England
Regional Office. ☎ 01722 337494 Fax: 01722
414027.

NEXT HOSTELS
Epping Forest 11m, Saffron Walden 17m, City of
London 24m

ADDITIONAL INFO
This is a privately owned Hostel operated under an
agreement with YHA.

Hunstanton

48 BEDS | Open: 17.00hrs

☎ 01485 532061 Fax: 01485 532632

Youth Hostel, 15 Avenue Road, Hunstanton, Norfolk PE36 5BW

Overnight Charges: Under 18 £5.55 Adult £8.25

Seasonal Prices Jul 1 - Aug 31: Under 18 £6.15 Adult £9.10

Family accommodation prices on p.10-13

🅿 Road parking outside Hostel. BABA

Mar 1 - Apr 7	Open X:Sun/Mon
Apr 8 - Jun 30	Open X:Sun*
Jul 1 - Aug 31	Open
Sep 2 - Oct 31	Open X:Sun/Mon
Nov 1 - Dec 15	Open Fr/Sat

*Open Bank Hol Sun.

ACCOMMODATION 🛏2-4 6 🛏5-8 4

This Victorian town house in the heart of Hunstanton offers comfortable accommodation to suit families and individuals. With its Blue Flag beach and magnificent cliffs, Hunstanton is an ideal holiday resort. As well as good walking routes along Peddars Way and the Norfolk Coast path, there are many indoor activities on offer — visit Oasis, a large leisure complex, or the Sea Life Centre where you can view our coastal waters and what's lurking below.

TRAVEL INFO
🚌 Eastern Counties 410, 411 from Kings Lynn (passes close BR Kings Lynn) (☎ 01553 772343) 🚉 Kings Lynn 16m. ⛴ Harwich or Felixstowe 70m
🛈 ☎ 01485 532610

NEXT HOSTELS
Kings Lynn 16m, Sheringham 38m, Norwich 40m

ADDITIONAL INFO
Daytime access to room and w.c. Family rooms have access to all facilities.

HOW TO GET THERE
OS 132 GR 674406

King's Lynn

36 BEDS | Open: 17.00hrs

☎ 01553 772461 Fax: 01553 764312

Youth Hostel, Thoresby College, College Lane, Kings Lynn, Norfolk PE30 1JB

Out of season contact: Regional Booking Service, 11B York Road, Salisbury, Wilts. SP2 7AP
☎ 01722 337494 Fax: 01722 414027

Overnight Charges: Under 18 £5.00 Adult £7.45

Family accommodation prices on p.10-13

🅿 South quay 50yds from Hostel. BABA

Jan 1 - Mar 31	Rent-a-Hostel
Apr 4 - Jun 30	Open X:Tu/Wed
Jul 1 - Aug 31	Open
Sep 1 - Dec 31	Rent-a-Hostel

ACCOMMODATION 🛏2-4 2 🛏5-8 2 🛏9+ 2

This charming Hostel is located in a wing of the Chantry College and is perfectly sited on the quayside for exploring the historic town of King's Lynn. It offers good accommodation for families and individual travellers. Step straight out of the Hostel into the medieval streets of King's Lynn. Hunt for the treasure trove lost when King John's baggage train miscalculated the tide and disappeared into the Wash. Visit the Town Hall which houses the Tales of the Goal House — a new crime and punishment attraction.

TRAVEL INFO
🚌 Frequent from surrounding areas (☎ 01603 613613). 🚉 King's Lynn ¾m.
🛈 ☎ 01553 763044

NEXT HOSTELS
Hunstanton 16m, Brandon 25m

ADDITIONAL INFO
Family rooms have access to room and self catering facilities. We can cater for groups of 10 or more booked in advance.

HOW TO GET THERE
OS 132 GR 616199

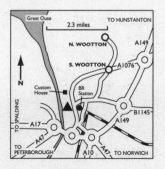

40 BEDS Open: 17.00hrs

Lincoln

☎ 01522 522076 Fax: 01522 567424

Youth Hostel, 77 South Park, Lincoln, Lincolnshire LN5 8ES

Overnight Charges: Under 18 £5.55 Adult £8.25

Family accommodation prices on p.10-13

⚟ P BABA

Feb 16 - Mar 31	Open X:Sun/Mon
Apr 1 - Jun 30	Open X:Sun*
Jul 1 - Aug 31	Open
Sep 3 - Oct 31	Open X:Sun/Mon
Nov 1 - Dec 21	Open Fr/Sat
Dec 27 - Dec 31	Open for New Year

* Open Bank Hol Sun.

ACCOMMODATION ⚟2-4 3 ⚟5-8 5

Stay at this fully modernised, comfortable Victorian Villa where you can take breakfast in the sunny conservatory with views over South Common where local ponies graze. Home of the Magna Carta, Lincoln is steeped in history and culture, with Tennyson Country, Land of the Pilgrim Fathers and nearby Robin Hood country. Take the challenge of cobbled 'Steep Hill' sampling a fine blend of curio shops and art galleries on the way. Your reward at the top is the medieval Cathedral and Norman Castle.

TRAVEL INFO
🚌 Frequent from surrounding areas (☎ 01522 532424). 🚆 Lincoln 1m.
ℹ ☎ 01522 529828

NEXT HOSTELS
Woody's Top 25m, Thurlby 35m, Cambridge 85m

ADDITIONAL INFO
Daytime access to shelter and w.c. Family rooms have access to all facilities. Ideal venue for conferences and special out of season/exclusive use.

HOW TO GET THERE
OS 121 GR 980700

---

68 BEDS Open: 17.00hrs

Norwich

☎ 01603 627647 Fax: 01603 629075

Youth Hostel, 112 Turner Road, Norwich, Norfolk NR2 4HB

Overnight Charges: Under 18 £5.55 Adult £8.25

Family accommodation prices on p.10-13

🔍 ⚟ P BABA

Feb 1 - Jun 30	Open X:Sun*
July 1 - Aug 31	Open
Sep 2 - Oct 31	Open X:Sun
Nov 1 - Dec 21	Open Fr/Sat
Dec 27 - Dec 31	Open for New Year

* Open Bank Hol Sun. The Hostel may be available for groups when otherwise closed - please contact Warden.

ACCOMMODATION ⚟2-4 9 ⚟5-8 6

This attractive Hostel offers comfortable facilities for families and individuals with a number of separate sitting rooms and it is perfectly sited in a quiet street with easy access to this ancient city. Renowned for its Norman Castle, awe-inspiring Cathedral, 33 medieval churches and fascinating specialist shops, Norwich is also an ideal base for exploring East Anglia with its unique broads and varied coastline.

TRAVEL INFO
🚌 Frequent from surrounding areas (☎ 01603 613613). 🚆 Norwich 2m.
ℹ ☎ 01603 666071

NEXT HOSTELS
Great Yarmouth 21m, Sheringham 25m, Brandon 36m

ADDITIONAL INFO
Daytime access to w.c. and day room. Family rooms have access to all facilities. Ideal conference and training venue.

HOW TO GET THERE
From outer ring road take A1074 heading to City Centre, take second left hand turn onto Turner Road.
OS 134 GR 213095

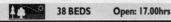

38 BEDS Open: 17.00hrs

Saffron Walden

☎ 01799 523117 Fax: 01799 523117

Youth Hostel, 1 Myddylton Place, Saffron Walden, Essex CB10 1BB

Overnight Charges: Under 18 £5.00 Adult £7.45

⊠ P 800yds to free car park. BABA

Mar 1 - Mar 31	Open Fr/Sat
Apr 1 - Jun 30	Open X:Sun/Mon*
Jul 1 - Aug 31	Open
Sep 17 - Oct 31	Open X:Sun/Mon
Nov 1 - Dec 21	Open Fr/Sat

* Open Bank Hol Sun. The Hostel may be available for groups when otherwise closed - please contact Warden.

ACCOMMODATION 🛏²⁻⁴1 🛏⁵⁻⁸2 🛏⁹⁺2

A former maltings, this 500 year old buiding retains many original features including an oak-wheeled sack hoist in one of the high roofed dormitories. Children will love the contoured floors, huge beams and courtyard garden while adults can unwind in the comfortable oak panelled lounge. Home cooked food always available. Continue your journey back in time with trails around the historic towns of Saffron Walden and Thaxted. Don't miss nearby Audley End House and Stansted Mount Fitchet Castle, while the gently rolling countryside makes cycling and easy rambling a pleasure. Popular with groups April to June. Useful stopover for Stansted Airport.

TRAVEL INFO

🚌 From surrounding areas, incl. link with BR Audley End by Hedingham/Viceroy 59 (☎ 0345 000333) 🚉 Audley End 2 ½m.
🛈 ☎ 01799 510444

NEXT HOSTELS

Cambridge 15m, Castle Hedingham 20m

ADDITIONAL INFO

Daytime access to simple shelter only.

HOW TO GET THERE

From the northbound M11 take junction 9, A11 and B184; from southbound M11 take junction 10, A505, A1301 and B184.
OS 154 GR 535386

109 BEDS Open: 13.00hrs

Sheringham

☎ 01263 823215 Fax: 01263 823215

Youth Hostel, 1 Cremer's Drift, Sheringham, Norfolk NR26 8HX

Overnight Charges: Under 18 £5.55 Adult £8.25

Seasonal Prices Jul 1 - Aug 31: Under 18 £6.15 Adult £9.10

Family accommodation prices on p.10-13

🛏 🔍 ♿ P Cars, mini-buses and small coaches. Alternative coach park (public) ¼m. BABA

Feb 16 - Mar 31	Open X:Sun
Apr 1 - Aug 31	Open
Sep 2 - Oct 31	Open X:Sun
Nov 1 - Dec 14	Open Fr/Sat
Dec 20 - Dec 29	Open for Christmas

The Hostel may be available for groups when otherwise closed - please contact Warden.

ACCOMMODATION 🛏²⁻⁴24 🛏⁵⁻⁸8

Set in its own tree-shaded flower garden, this former children's home offers spacious, comfortable accommodation with lots of small rooms for families and individuals — and its own licensed restaurant serving freshly cooked food. The Hostel is popular with groups April to June. Enjoy the spectacular scenery with gently rolling hills, sandy beaches and superb sunsets.

TRAVEL INFO

🚌 Eastern Counties 758/9, 761, Sanders Coaches from Norwich (☎ 01603 613613). 🚉 Sheringham ¼m.
🛈 ☎ 01263 824329

NEXT HOSTELS

Hunstanton 38m, Norwich 25m, Gt Yarm'th 39m

ADDITIONAL INFO

Open all day (reception closed 11.00 am to 1.00 pm). Late night access keys available. Conference and seminar facilities. Ask for leaflets on our special activity packages.

HOW TO GET THERE

Hostel is off the main A149 behind St Joseph's R.C. Church only 5mins on foot from railway and bus station.
OS 133 GR 159428

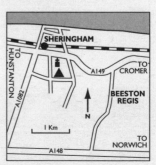

🚶🚶 34 BEDS   Open: 17.00hrs

Thurlby

☎ 01778 425588

Youth Hostel, 16 High St, Thurlby, Bourne, Lincolnshire PE10 0EE

Overnight Charges: Under 18 £5.00 Adult £7.45

Family accommodation prices on p.10-13

🅰 ⊠ ♿ 🅿 Cars and mini-buses. Coaches by prior arrangement.

Jan 1 - Mar 31	Rent-a-Hostel
Apr 1 - Oct 31	Open X:Th
Nov 1 - Dec 31	Rent-a-Hostel

ACCOMMODATION 🛏️2-4 1 🛏️5-8 2 🛏️9+ 2

Originally a forge with Georgian and Victorian additions, this charming self catering Hostel in its own beautiful grounds, is ideal for relaxing after a long day. South Lincolnshire is delightful for cyclists offering a choice of flatlands or gently rolling hills with pretty stone villages. Thurlby is surrounded by historic castles and cathedrals. Look out for the 'Woollen Churches' built by local sheep farmers. Stamford is worth visiting to see Burghley House, famous for its September horse trials. Watersports are on offer at Rutland Water — 15 miles, a lake created by flooding the Gwash Valley.

TRAVEL INFO

🚌 Delaine's service from Peterborough (passes close BR Peterborough) (☎ 01778 422866).
🚉 Peterborough 15m; Grantham 18m.
🛈 ☎ 01780 55611

NEXT HOSTELS

Lincoln 35m, Kings Lynn 38m, Copt Oak 50m

ADDITIONAL INFO

Daytime access to outside w.c. and shelter. Family rooms have access to all facilities.

HOW TO GET THERE

OS 130 GR 097168

🚶🚶 22 BEDS   Open: 17.00hrs

Woody's Top

☎ 01507 533323

Youth Hostel, Ruckland, Nr Louth, Lincolnshire LN11 8RQ

For advance bookings, contact: Regional Booking Service, 11B York Road, Salisbury, Wilts. SP2 7AP ☎ 01722 337494 Fax: 01722 414027. From Apr 1 - Aug 31, bookings for next night direct to Hostel.

Overnight Charges: Under 18 £4.15 Adult £6.10

⊠ 🅿 Cars and mini-buses.

Jan 1 - Mar 31	Rent-a-Hostel
Apr 1 - Aug 31	Open
Sep 1 - Sep 30	Open Sun to Th
	Fr\Sat Rent-a-Hostel only
Oct 1 - Dec 31	Rent-a-Hostel

ACCOMMODATION 🛏️2-4 4 🛏️5-8 1

This small self catering Hostel is a converted barn in the rolling Lincolnshire Wolds. It has recently been carefully extended and improved to provide small rooms and a cosy lounge/dining room with wood burning stove. The Hostel does have a small shop for basic items but other shops are some distance from the Hostel. The tranquil Lincolnshire Wolds offer good opportunities for walking and cycling. There are small market towns to explore, as well as the famous coastal resorts of Skegness and Mablethorpe. You can also visit the National Fishing Heritage Centre and the Cadwell Park Motor racing circuit.

TRAVEL INFO

🚌 Post Bus from Louth; Road Car/Stagecoach Grimsby- Cleethorpes/Blanchard 24/5, 51, X21 Grimsby - Louth, thence 6m (☎ 01522 553135)
🚉 Thorp Culvert (not Sun, except Jun - Sep) 18m; Grimsby Town 22m; Lincoln Central 25m.
🛈 ☎ 01507 609289

NEXT HOSTELS

Lincoln 25m, Thurlby 55m, Beverley 50m

ADDITIONAL INFO

Daytime access to w.c. and simple shelter. No credit cards accepted at Hostel.

HOW TO GET THERE

From A16 take minor road to Ruckland, turn left, Hostel 100yds from junction.
OS 122 GR 332786

Heart of England

Brimming with a turbulent past, the Heart of England is also rich in culture and closely associated with the Bard himself.

The rolling hills of the Cotswolds, the beechwoods of the Chilterns and ridges and valleys of the Marches – all designated Areas of Outstanding Natural Beauty – offer superb walking country.

The industrial revolution started in Ironbridge and its many relics form part of major visitor attractions in the area.

For culture, head straight for Stratford-upon-Avon where you'll find more attractions based around Shakespeare and his plays. Historic Oxford has much of architectural interest, including colleges, churches and museums.

Discounts are available to YHA members (on production of your membership card and discount booklet) at the Wildfowl and Wetlands Trust in Slimbridge, the Teddy Bear Museum in Stratford, and Salgrove Manor in Oxford among others.

Useful Publications

Individual Hostel leaflets are available at no charge – just specify which Hostel you're interested in and send a SAE to YHA South England Regional Office at the address opposite. Alternatively, leave a request on our YHA 24 hour literature line on 01426 951683 (local call charge).

Walking Routes Around Stow-on-the-Wold £1.00 Available from Stow-on-the-Wold Youth Hostel (see page 93).

For further information on The Ridgeway Long Distance Footpath contact: The Ridgeway Officer, Countryside Service, Department of Leisure and Arts, Holton, Oxford OX33 1QQ. Tel: 01865 810224.

Helping You to Book Ahead

If you are thinking of going to Shropshire, you can book any of the Youth Hostels there by contacting Ironbridge Youth Hostel. Seven Hostels – one telephone call! Just ring – 01952 433281.

For more information about hostelling in this area contact:

YHA South England Regional Office, 11b York Road, Salisbury, Wilts SP2 7AP

Tel: 01722 337494
Fax: 01722 414027

Badby

🏃🚴 **32 BEDS** **Open: 17.00hrs**

📞 01327 703883 Fax: 01327 703883

Youth Hostel, Church Green, Badby, Daventry, Northamptonshire NN11 3AS

Out of season contact: Regional Booking Service, 11B York Road, Salisbury, Wiltshire SP2 7AP
📞 01722 337494 Fax: 01722 414027

Overnight Charges: Under 18 £4.60 Adult £6.75

🅿 Very limited (not on village green). BABA

Jan 1 - Mar 31	Rent-a-Hostel
Apr 1 - May 31	Open X:Sun/Mon*
Jun 1 - Aug 31	Open X:Sun*
Sep 1 - Oct 26	Open X:Sun/Mon
Oct 27 - Dec 31	Rent-a-Hostel

*Open Bank Hol Sun.

ACCOMMODATION 🛏2-4 1 🛏5-8 3 🛏9+ 1

This 17th century country cottage is on the Church green in Badby village, one of the most picturesque villages in Northamptonshire and retains much of its original character with stone floors and wooden beams. A small comfortable and well furnished Hostel with no meals provided but good self catering facilities. The area offers sweeping landscape and a network of quiet lanes and footpaths — ideal for walkers and cyclists.

TRAVEL INFO
🚌 Stagecoach United Counties X64 Corby-Coventry; 41 from Northampton (both pass BR Northampton) (📞 01604 20077); Geoff Amos from BR Rugby (📞 01327 702181). On all, alight Daventry 2m. 🚉 Long Buckby 6m, Rugby 12m.
🛈 📞 01327 300277

NEXT HOSTELS
Bradwell 21m, Stratford 24m, Charlbury 29m

ADDITIONAL INFO
Daytime access to w.c. at rear of Hostel. Shelter at front of Hostel. Due to nature of this building smaller bedrooms adjoin larger ones.

HOW TO GET THERE
Badby village is just off the A361, Daventry - Banbury Road. Follow Main Street past both Pubs, turn left into Vicarage Hill, up to Church Green and turn left.
OS 152 GR 561588

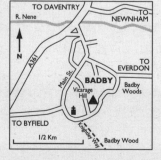

Birmingham

80 BEDS **Open: 17.00hrs**

Youth Hostel, Cambrian Halls, Brindley Drive, off Cambridge Street, Birmingham, West Midlands B1 2NB

♿ 🅿

ACCOMMODATION 🛏2-4 80

Due to refurbishment it is unlikely the Hostel will be open in 1996.
Please enquire to YHA Customer Services, Trevelyan House, 8 St Stephens Hill, St Albans, Herts AL1 2DY. 📞 01727 855215.

TRAVEL INFO
🚌 Frequent from surrounding areas (📞 0121 200 2700). 🚉 Birmingham New Street ½m.
🛈 📞 0121 643 2514

NEXT HOSTELS
Stratford-upon-Avon 20m, Ironbridge 25m, Malvern Hills 30m

HOW TO GET THERE
OS 139 GR 063870

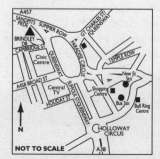

38 BEDS **Open: 17.00hrs**

Bradwell Village (Milton Keynes)

☎ 01908 310944 Fax: 01908 310944

Youth Hostel, Manor Farm, Vicarage Road, Bradwell Village, Milton Keynes, Bucks. MK13 9AG

Out of season contact: Regional Booking Service, 11B York Road, Salisbury, Wiltshire SP2 7AP
☎ 01722 337494 Fax: 01722 414027

Overnight Charges: Under 18 £4.60 Adult £6.75

🔲 🅿 At rear of Hostel. For coaches - contact Warden.
BABA

Jan 1 - Mar 31	Rent-a-Hostel
Apr 1 - Aug 31	Open X:Sun*
Sep 1 - Dec 31	Rent-a-Hostel

* Open Bank Hol Sun.

ACCOMMODATION 🛏️³ 🛏️¹ 🛏️²

A charming 18th century farmhouse with comfortable accommodation in the village of Bradwell close to the city of Milton Keynes — for a unique blend of old and new, city and countryside, real cows and concrete! Enjoy the extensive system of 'Redway' cycle paths or look and learn with the town art trail. Enjoy a picnic in one of the city parks, discover the ruins dating back to Roman times or follow the Grand Union Canal out into the beautiful Buckinghamshire countryside.

TRAVEL INFO
🚌 Frequent from surrounding areas (☎ 01908 668366). 🚉 Milton Keynes Central 1m. ☎ 01908 370883.
ℹ️ ☎ 01908 232525

NEXT HOSTELS
Ivinghoe 19m, Badby 21m, Oxford 38m

ADDITIONAL INFO
We can cater for groups of 10 or more booked in advance. Daytime access to simple outside shelter.

HOW TO GET THERE
OS 152 GR 831395

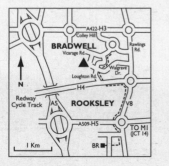

| 🚶🚴 | 35 BEDS | Open: 17.00hrs |

Bridges Long Mynd

☎ 01588 650656 Fax: 01588 650656

Youth Hostel, Ratlinghope, Shrewsbury, Shropshire SY5 OSP

Overnight Charges: Under 18 £4.60 Adult £6.75

🅰 ⬜ 🅿 For cars and coaches. BABA

Jan 1 - Feb 29	open for advance bookings only
Mar 1 - Nov 17	Open
Nov 18 - Dec 31	open for advance bookings only

ACCOMMODATION 🛏️²⁻⁸2 🛏️⁹⁺2

An old village school offering basic accommodation and set in the beautiful countryside between Lond Mynd and Stiperstones in the Shropshire Hills — an ideal base for walking, cycling, birdwatching and just getting away from it all! As well as the Long Mynd and the Stiperstones, the Shropshire Way passes close to the Hostel and there are many quiet lanes for cycling. This interesting geological area has some of Britain's oldest rocks. Other attractions include the Acton Scott Museum (8m) and Bishops Castle (8m).

TRAVEL INFO
🚌 Horrocks 551 from Shrewsbury (Tue only) (☎ 0345 056 785). 🚉 Church Stretton 5m.
🛈 ☎01734 350761

NEXT HOSTELS
Wilderhope 13m, Clun Mill 16m, Shrewsbury 14m.

ADDITIONAL INFO
Daytime access to simple shelter. Please make cheques payable to Bridges Youth Hostel. No credit cards accepted. This is a privately owned Hostel operated under an agreement with YHA. Access from Church Stretton can be difficult in winter.

HOW TO GET THERE
From Church Stretton, take 'The Burway' and take right fork at top of Long Mynd. From Shrewsbury take road via Longden and Pulverbatch, then left by Horseshoe Inn.
OS 137 GR 395965

| 🌲 | 50 BEDS | Open: 17.00hrs |

Charlbury

☎ 01608 810202

Youth Hostel, The Laurels, The Slade, Charlbury, Oxfordshire OX7 3SJ

Overnight Charges: Under 18 £5.00 Adult £7.45

Family accommodation prices on p.10-13

🔍 💻 ♿ 🅿 NO PARKING IN DITCHLEY ROAD.

Jan 1 - Jan 31	Open Fr/Sat/Sun
Feb 1 - Mar 31	Open X:Mon/Tu
Apr 1 - Jun 30	Open
Jul 1 - Aug 31	Open X:Sun*
Sep 4 - Oct 31	Open X:Mon/Tu

*Open Bank Hol Sun. The Hostel may be available for groups when other wise closed - please contact Warden.

ACCOMMODATION 🛏️²⁻⁴4 🛏️⁵⁻⁸6

Situated in a quiet Cotswold village between Oxford and Stratford-upon-Avon, this attractive 19th century stone house, a former glove factory, has been refurbished to a good standard. Enjoy home cooking and a friendly atmosphere too. You'll be ideally located for exploring the Cotswolds with cycling and walking routes available at the Hostel. Or make the most of the good public transport or cycle hire at the Hostel to visit Blenheim Palace, the Cotswold Wildlife Park and North Leigh Roman Villa.

TRAVEL INFO
🚌 Worths from Oxford, Witney, Woodstock, Chipping Norton, ☎ 01608 677322. 🚉 Charlbury 1m.
🛈 ☎01993 811038

NEXT HOSTELS
Oxford 15m, Stow 12m, Stratford 30m

ADDITIONAL INFO
Please make cheques payable to Charlbury Youth Hostel. This is a privately owned Hostel operated under an agreement with YHA. Daytime access to simple shelter and w.c.

HOW TO GET THERE
Turn off A44 Oxford-Evesham road at Enstone. Follow B4022 into village, turn left at first crossroads. Hostel 75yds on left.
OS 164 GR 361198

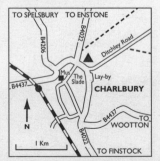

Cleeve Hill

Youth Hostel,

ACCOMMODATION
We regret that this Youth Hostel is now closed. The nearest Youth Hostels are Duntisbourne Abbots (14m), Stow-on-the-Wold (16m) and Malvern Hills (23m).

---

24 BEDS   **Open: 17.00hrs**

Clun Mill

☎ 01588 640582 Fax: 01588 640582

Youth Hostel, The Mill, Clun, Near Craven Arms, Shropshire SY7 8NY

Out of season contact: Ironbridge Youth Hostel, Paradise, Coalbrookdale, Telford, Shropshire TF8 7NR ☎ 01952 433281 Fax: 01952 433166

Overnight Charges: Under 18 £4.60 Adult £6.75

Ⓐ ⬚ Ⓟ BABA

Jan 1 - Mar 31	Rent-a-Hostel
Apr 1 - Sep 1	Open X:Wed
Sep 6 - Dec 31	Rent-a-Hostel

ACCOMMODATION
This charming self catering Hostel has been sympathetically upgraded and is now very comfortable. You can still see the workings of this former watermill. It is a haven of peace and tranquillity set in a stone built town unspoilt by modern development with its narrow 16th century humpback bridge and Norman castle. Centuries past echo through this area with its picturesque ruins and magnificent restorations of castles and abbeys. From the sinuous ridge of Offa's Dyke on the Welsh border to the elegance of the fortified manor at Stokesay, the very earth and stones breath intrigue.

TRAVEL INFO
🚌 Midland Red West 741-5 from Ludlow (pass close BR Ludlow), alight Clun, ¼m (☎ 0345 056 785). 🚉 Broome or Hopton both 7m; Craven Arms 10m.
🛈 ☎ 01584 875053

NEXT HOSTELS
Bridges 16m, Ludlow 18m, Wilderhope 20m

ADDITIONAL INFO
Daytime access to simple shelter and w.c. No drying room. Bread and milk only available if ordered in advance.

HOW TO GET THERE
From Clun High Street (B4368) go to the end of Ford Street, turn right and immediately left. Hostel 250yds on right.
⑳ 137 Ⓖ 303812

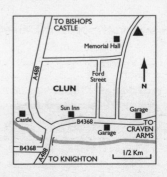

SHROPSHIRE EXPLORER

Enjoy a 2-day break based at Ironbridge Gorge, birthplace of the Industrial Revolution. Our "Shropshire Explorer" package includes:

▲ Full board accommodation at Ironbridge Gorge Youth Hostel

▲ Passport to all the Ironbridge Gorge Museum sites

▲ Entry to the Toy Museum, Ironbridge

▲ Return trip on the Severn Valley Railway

▲ Certificate for crossing the World's First Iron Bridge

all inclusive price:
£58.00 (adults) /
£50.00 (under 18's)

The Youth Hostel offers comfortable accommodation in family-sized bunk rooms.

Other facilities include:
• access during the day •
• large games room for children •
• quiet room •
• excellent meals •

Holder of "Heartbeat Award" for food and hygiene

See page 89 for Hostel details

---

 20 BEDS   **Open: 17.00hrs**

Copt Oak

☎ 01530 242661

The Youth Hostel, Whitwick Rd, Copt Oak, Markfield, Leicestershire LE67 9QB

Overnight Charges: Under 18 £4.15 Adult £6.10

Jan 1 - Mar 31	Rent-a-Hostel
Apr 1 - Oct 31	Open X:Tu
Nov 1 - Dec 31	Rent-a-Hostel

The Hostel may be available for groups when otherwise closed - please contact Warden.

ACCOMMODATION

This converted school house in the hills of north west Leicestershire has recently been modernised to provide a good standard of self catering accommodation — without losing any of its traditional appeal! The Hostel does have its own small shop but local shops are some 25 minutes walk away. It makes an ideal base for visiting the East Midlands. Nearby Charnwood Forest offers some superb countryside for walking and cycling, while the historic cities of Leicester and Nottingham are also well worth a visit. Other local attractions include Donington Race Circuit, the National Watersports Centre at Holme Peirpoint and Bosworth Battlefield.

TRAVEL INFO
Midland Fox/Barton/Kinchbus 121 Leicester-Loughborough; otherwise Midland Fox 117-9, 217-8 Leicester-Coalville (pass close BR Leicester), alight Flying Horse roundabout 1m (☎ 0116 2511411). Loughborough 7m.
☎ 0116 2511300

NEXT HOSTELS
Badby 42m, Stratford 45m, Matlock 35m

ADDITIONAL INFO
Daytime access to w.c., shower and shelter.

HOW TO GET THERE
OS 129 GR 482129

🏕 ☀ 59 BEDS Open: 17.00hrs

Duntisbourne Abbots

📞 01285 821682 Fax: 01285 821697

Youth Hostel, Duntisbourne Abbots, Cirencester, Gloucestershire GL7 7JN

Overnight Charges: Under 18 £5.00 Adult £7.45

Family accommodation prices on p.10-13

🅰 🔍 🖥 🅿 For cars, mini-buses and coaches. BABA

Jan 19 - Feb 10	Open Fr/Sat
Feb 16 - Nov 2	Open X:Sun*
Nov 8 - Dec 21	Open Fr/Sat

* Open Bank Hol Sun. The Hostel may be available for groups when otherwise closed - please contact Warden.

ACCOMMODATION 🛏2-4 2 🛏5-8 5 🛏9+ 2

The Old Rectory offers comfortable accommodation throughout and is set in 2 acres of its own grounds in a quaint Cotswold village at the heart of this Area of Outstanding Natural Beauty. The area is steeped in history, visit nearby Cirencester, the second largest Roman city with its museum, famous parish church, crafts market and leisure facilities. Other attractions include the Cotswold Countryside collection, Westonbirt Arboretum and nearby cities of Gloucester and Cheltenham, as well as picturesque Cotswold villages and market towns. The family accommodation and range of attractions make this an ideal family touring centre.

TRAVEL INFO
🚆No Service. 🚌Kemble 10m; Gloucester 14 ½m; Cheltenham Spa 14 ½m; Swindon 22m. 🛈 📞01285 654180

NEXT HOSTELS
Stow-on-the-Wold 20m, Slimbridge 23m

ADDITIONAL INFO
Daytime access to outside w.c. and limited shelter. Family rooms have access to all facilities.

HOW TO GET THERE
OS 163 GR 970080

🏠 97 BEDS Open: 17.00hrs

Ironbridge Gorge

📞 01952 433281 Fax: 01952 433166

Youth Hostel, Paradise, Coalbrookdale, Telford, Shropshire TF8 7NR

Overnight Charges: Under 18 £6.15 Adult £9.10

🔍 🖥 🅿 Small car park (coaches contact Warden) BABA

| Feb 2 - Nov 30 | Open |
| Dec 1 - Dec 31 | Open for groups only |

The Hostel may be available for groups when otherwise closed - please contact Warden.

ACCOMMODATION 🛏2-4 3 🛏5-8 6 🛏9+ 1

This imposing but friendly Hostel — built in the 19th century as the Literary and Scientific Institute for workers at the nearby Ironworks — is ideal for individuals or families, with lots of small rooms and speciality home cooking. 'Heartbeat Award' winner for healthy menus. Popular with groups from April to June. Set in the Severn Gorge close to the spectacular Iron bridge (the first in the world), the Hostel is at the centre of six square miles of World Heritage — including eight museums. There are also the chocolate factory, the famous Severn Valley Steam Railway and beautiful walks in the area.

TRAVEL INFO
🚌Frequent from Wellington & Telford (pass close BR Wellington Telford West & Telford Central) (📞 0345 056 785). 🚌Telford Central 5m; Wellington Telford West 5m. 🛈 📞01952 432166

NEXT HOSTELS
Shrewsbury 14m, Wilderhope 13m, Ludlow 26m

ADDITIONAL INFO
Daytime access to w.c. and simple shelter. Holiday packages available all year round. Conference facilities available. Shropshire Hostel booking service.

HOW TO GET THERE
Take major motorways to Telford centre, then follow signs for Ironbridge - with bridge on left, turn right at roundabout into Coalbrookdale. Hostel ½m on right.
OS 127 GR 671043

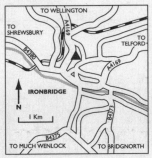

Ivinghoe

 67 BEDS   Open: 17.00hrs

☎ 01296 668251 Fax: 01296 662903

Youth Hostel, The Old Brewery House, Ivinghoe, Near Leighton Buzzard, Bedfordshire LU7 9EP

Overnight Charges: Under 18 £5.00 Adult £7.45

▲ P BABA

Feb 2 - Feb 10	Open Fr/Sat
Feb 16 - Mar 31	Open X:Sun/Mon
Apr 1 - Aug 31	Open X:Sun*
Sep 3 - Oct 31	Open X:Sun/Mon
Nov 1 - Dec 21	Open Fr/Sat

* Open Bank Hol Sun. The Hostel may be available for groups when otherwise closed - please contact Warden.

ACCOMMODATION 5-8 2 9+ 5

Former home of the local brewer, this attractive Georgian mansion — situated i the heart of the picturesque village of Ivinghoe — offers spacious public rooms and traditional dormitory arrangements. Ivinghoe village lies close to many places of interest. For instance, enjoy the dramatic scenery of Income Hole, discover the remains of an Iron Age Fort at Beacon Hill or explore the National Trust estate of Ashridge. Nearby Whipsnade Zoo and Woburn Abbey are also well worth a visit.

TRAVEL INFO
🚌 Luton & District 61 Aylesbury - Luton (passes close BR Aylesbury & Luton) (☎ 01296 84919). 🚂 Cheddington 2; Tring 3m. 🛈 ☎ 01582 471012

NEXT HOSTELS
Jordans 19m, Bradwell Village 19m, Windsor 28m

ADDITIONAL INFO
No daytime access facilities. Buckinghamshire Environmental Education centre available to visiting schools with full teaching service. Info pack available.

HOW TO GET THERE
In the centre of the village next to the church and opposite the village green on B489.
OS 165 GR 945161

Knighton

Youth Hostel

ACCOMMODATION
We regret that this Youth Hostel is now closed. The nearest Youth Hostels are Clun Mill (7m) and Ludlow (17m).

50 BEDS	Open: 17.00hrs

Ludlow

☎ 01584 872472 Fax: 01584 872095

Youth Hostel, Ludford Lodge, Ludford, Ludlow, Shropshire SY8 1PJ

Overnight Charges: Under 18 £4.60 Adult £6.75

Family accommodation prices on p.10-13

P Very limited. Free parking ¼m - ask Warden. BABA

Feb 16 - Sep 2	Open X:Sun*
Sep 3 - Nov 2	Open X:Sun/Mon
Nov 8 - Dec 21	Open Fr/Sat

* Open Bank Hol Sun. The Hostel may be available for groups when otherwise closed - please contact Warden.

ACCOMMODATION

This comfortable large house has a number of small bedrooms, two comfortable lounges and is ideally placed for touring the Shropshire Hills and Welsh Marches. Ludford Lodge stands on the banks of the River Teme facing the town across the medieval Ludford Bridge. Often praised as one of England's architectural gems, Ludlow is well worth visiting to view the blend of elegant Georgian town houses, the ruined castle and St Laurence's parish church. Excellent touring base for families and individuals.

TRAVEL INFO
Midland Red West 192, 292 Birmingham - Hereford to within ¼m (☎ 0345 212 555).
Ludlow ½m.
🛈 ☎ 01584 875053

NEXT HOSTELS
Wheathill 9m, Wilderhope Manor 15m, Clun Mill 18m

ADDITIONAL INFO
Family rooms have access to self catering kitchen, wcs and showers.

HOW TO GET THERE
OS 137 GR 513741

Malvern Hills

☎ 01684 569131 Fax: 01684 565205

Youth Hostel, 18 Peachfield Road, Malvern Wells, Malvern, Worcestershire WR14 4AP

Overnight Charges: Under 18 £5.00 Adult £7.45

🔍 P Cars and mini-buses (coach parking 600yds).
BABA

Feb 16 - Oct 31	Open
Nov 1 - Dec 21	Open Fr/Sat
Dec 27 - Dec 31	Open for New Year

The Hostel may be available for groups when otherwise closed - please contact Warden.

ACCOMMODATION

Nestling on the slopes of the beautiful Malvern Hills, this homely Youth Hostel offers a very warm welcome and good food, as well as spectacular view of the hills and Vale of Severn. The large enclosed garden makes a great play area and is an ideal place to relax. The majestic Malvern Hills and surrounding commons have been designated as an Area of Outstanding Natural Beauty. Great Malvern is a Victorian spa town. Inspiration for Elgar and home of the English String Orchestra, the Malverns have the unique atmosphere of an inland resort.

TRAVEL INFO
Frequent from surrounding areas (☎ 0345 125436). Great Malvern 1 ½m.
🛈 ☎ 01684 892289.

NEXT HOSTELS
Welsh Bicknor 28m, Ludlow 31m

ADDITIONAL INFO
Daytime access to w.c. and shelter.

HOW TO GET THERE
1 ½m S of Great Malvern on the Wells Road (A449). Turn opposite Railway Inn into Peachfield Road.
OS 150 GR 774440

5

HEART OF ENGLAND

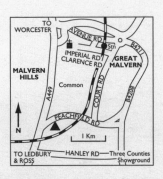

Oxford

🏙 112 BEDS   **Open: 24hrs**

📞 **01865 62997 Fax: 01865 69402**

Youth Hostel, 32 Jack Straw's Lane, Oxford, Oxfordshire. OX3 0DW

Overnight Charges: Under 18 £6.15 Adult £9.10

🅰 🔍 📷 ⑧ 🅿 Cars and mini-buses. Coach parking available nearby. BABA **IBN**

Open every day of the year.

ACCOMMODATION 🛏²⁻⁴ 6   🛏⁵⁻⁸ 6   🛏⁹⁺ 5

An attractive Victorian house set in it's own grounds with superb copper beech trees and redwoods in a quiet suburb. The Hostel provides comfortable dormitory accommodation, several rooms with washbasins. The Hostel is a favourite for international travellers both individuals and groups all year round. The city centre is just 1½m from the Hostel and is easily accessible by bus. There are a wealth of scenic attractions in Oxford including 35 colleges which are open to the public. The Ashmolean Museum and Pitt Rivers Museum are amongst some of the finest in the country. Add Oxford's famous bookshops and not even bad weather can spoil your visit.

TRAVEL INFO
� Frequent from city centre (📞 01685 711312). 13, 14, 14a from bus stop near to main Post Office in St Aldates. 🚉 Oxford 2½m.
🛈 📞 01865 726871

NEXT HOSTELS
Charlbury 15m, Ridgeway 17m, Streatley 19m

ADDITIONAL INFO
Bureau de change.

HOW TO GET THERE
Hostel is located approx. 1¼m along Marston Road from foot of Headington Hill. By road, keep on the ringroad until the Headington roundabout. Follow the London Road, turn right at the White Horse pub, Hostel on left ¼m.
OS 164 GR 533074

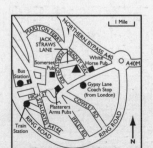

Shrewsbury

🏙 60 BEDS   **Open: 17.00hrs**

📞 **01743 360179 Fax: 01743 357423**

Youth Hostel, The Woodlands, Abbey Foregate, Shrewsbury, Shropshire SY2 6LZ

Out of season contact: Ironbridge Gorge Youth Hostel 📞 01952 433281

Overnight Charges: Under 18 £5.55 Adult £8.25

🔍 📷 ⑧ 🅿 BABA

Feb 16 - Jun 30	Open X:Sun
Jul 1 - Aug 31	Open
Sep 1 - Oct 31	Open X:Sun
Nov 1 - Dec 27	Open Fr/Sat Open for Christmas

The Hostel may be available for groups when otherwise closed - please contact Warden.

ACCOMMODATION 🛏²⁻⁴ 3   🛏⁵⁻⁸ 5   🛏⁹⁺ 2

A former Victorian Ironmasters house built in a distinct Red Stone, the Hostel is set in its own grounds just on the outskirts of Shrewsbury. Comfortable accommodation, friendly service and great home cooked meals. Shrewsbury, the county town of Shropshire, is built in a loop on the river Severn. As well as 500 listed buildings from all periods of history, this medieval market town is also the birthplace of Charles Darwin and home of Brother Cadfael. An ideal place to explore the Shropshire Hills.

TRAVEL INFO
🚍 Frequent from surrounding areas (📞 0345 056785). 🚉 Shrewsbury 1m.
🛈 📞 01743 350761

NEXT HOSTELS
Ironbridge 14m, Wilderhope 18m, Ludlow 28m

ADDITIONAL INFO
Daytime access to porch only. Good public transport links. Part of the Shropshire booking service.

HOW TO GET THERE
OS 126 GR 505120

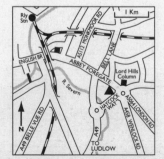

56 BEDS Open: 17.00hrs

Slimbridge

☎ 01453 890275 Fax: 01453 890625

Youth Hostel, Shepherd's Patch, Slimbridge, Gloucestershire GL2 7BP

Overnight Charges: Under 18 £6.15 Adult £9.10

Family accommodation prices on p.10-13

🔍 📷 🅿 Large car park with space for 2 coaches.
BABA

Jan 3 - Feb 29	Open X:Sun
Mar 1 - Sep 1	Open
Sep 2 - Nov 30	Open X:Sun

The Hostel may be available for groups when otherwise closed - please contact Warden.

ACCOMMODATION 🛏7 🛏5 🛏1

This comfortable purpose built Hostel has its own pond and wildfowl collection which can be enjoyed from an observation room. There is a good mix of bedroom accommodation and the five 2-bedded rooms are particularly popular with couples. Sir Peter Scott's Wildfowl and Wetlands Trust is 1/2m away. Other local attractions include the National Waterways Museum, the historic Gloucester Docks, Gloucester Cathedral, Berkeley Castle, Jenner Museum and the Severn Bore. With easy access to the Cotswold Way and Severn Way.

TRAVEL INFO
🚌 Badgerline 308 Bristol - Gloucester; Stagecoach Gloucester Citybus 91 Gloucester - Dursley (passes close BR Gloucester) (☎ 01452 425543). On both alight Slimbridge Cross Roads, 1 ½m. 🚉 Cam and Dursley 3m; Stonehouse 8 ½m
🛈 ☎01452 421188

NEXT HOSTELS
Duntisbourne 23m, Bristol 25m

ADDITIONAL INFO
Daytime access to w.c. and shelter. Family rooms have access to all facilities. Ideal for conferences.

HOW TO GET THERE
By road turn off A38 at Slimbridge crossroads, go through main village and after 1 ½m turn right at Tudor Arms.
OS 162 GR 730043

---

56 BEDS Open: 17.00hrs

Stow On The Wold

☎ 01451 830497 Fax: 01451 870102

Youth Hostel, Stow On The Wold, Cheltenham, Gloucestershire GL54 1AF

Overnight Charges: Under 18 £5.00 Adult £7.45

📷 🅿 In square. BABA

Feb 1 - Feb 29	Open Fr/Sat
Mar 1 - Apr 30	Open X:Sun*
May 1 - Sep 1	Open
Sep 2 - Nov 2	Open X:Sun
Nov 8 - Dec 15	Open Fr/Sat/Sun
Dec 24 - Dec 26	Open for Christmas

* Open Bank Hol Sun.

ACCOMMODATION 🛏2 🛏3

In this charming 16th century listed building, sample the comfortable accommodation and delicious home cooked food while watching local life drift through the historic market square of this beautiful Cotswold town. Standing 800ft above sea level in an Area of Outstanding Natural Beauty, the town is famous for its honey coloured stone buildings and many antique shops. As well as picturesque villages at Bourton and the Slaughters, the Cotswold Farm Park is well worth a visit to see the famous Cotswold sheep.

TRAVEL INFO
🚌 Pulhams Cheltenham Spa - Moreton-in-Marsh (passes close BR Cheltenham Spa & Moreton-in-Marsh) (☎ 01451 820369).
🚉 Kingham 4m; Moreton-in-Marsh 4m.
🛈 ☎01451 831082

NEXT HOSTELS
Duntisbourne Abbots 20m, Charlbury 12m, Stratford-upon-Avon 20m.

ADDITIONAL INFO
Daytime access to w.c. and self catering kitchen - please enquire when booking. Special meals available for celebrations. Try the Hostel cafe during July and August!

HOW TO GET THERE
OS 163 GR 191258

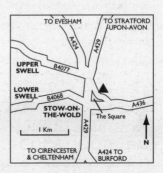

5

HEART OF ENGLAND

FOOD FOR THOUGHT

Why not turn your trip into a real holiday by taking advantage of the meals provided at the Hostel?

Menus vary between Hostels, but you'll usually find good home cooking using local, fresh produce where possible

Youth Hostel meals are also great value for money, so why not book your meals next time you book your stay?

YOUR GUIDE TO GOOD FOOD

---

 148 BEDS   Open: 24hrs

Stratford-Upon-Avon

☎ 01789 297093 Fax: 01789 205513

Youth Hostel, Hemmingford House, Alveston, Stratford-Upon-Avon, Warwickshire CV37 7RG

Overnight Charges: Under 18 £9.40 Adult £12.60 Bed & Breakfast included.

Family accommodation prices on p.10-13

🔍 📷 **P** Large car park with space for mini-buses and coaches. BABA **IBN**

Jan 4 - Dec 15	Open

ACCOMMODATION 🛏²⁻⁴ 13 🛏⁵⁻⁸ 12 🛏⁹⁺ 3

Set in 3 acres of grounds, Hemmingford House, a magnificent 200 year old Georgian mansion, is just 1 1/2m from the centre of town in a quiet village. Comfortable dormitory accommodation is provided, with several small rooms and the extensive gardens are ideal for games or just for relaxing in. The food shouldn't be missed either — with a tempting selection of dishes, you'll be spoilt for choice! Of course a visit to Stratford upon Avon wouldn't be complete without seeing all the Shakespeare properties and a play at one of the Royal Shakespeare Company theatres. Warwick Castle is just 8m. The Hostel is popular with school groups during term time and families visit during weekends and school holidays making the most of the value for money oasis.

TRAVEL INFO
🚌 Stratford Blue 18, 518 Leamington Spa - Stratford-upon-Avon - Coventry (pass close BR Leamington Spa) (☎ 01788 535555).
🚉 Stratford-upon-Avon 2 ½m.
ℹ ☎ 01789 293127

NEXT HOSTELS
Stow-on-the-Wold 20m, Badby 24m.

ADDITIONAL INFO
IBN booking centre. Excellent conference location.

HOW TO GET THERE
From M10 Jct 15 and town centre follow the one way system by the Leisure Centre. Take 1st left over Clopton Bridge. Take B4086 to the Hostel.
OS 151 GR 231562

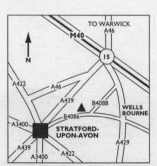

Wheathill

 28 BEDS   Open: 17.00hrs

☎ 01746 787236

Youth Hostel, Malthouse Farm, Wheathill, Bridgnorth, Shropshire WV16 6QT

Overnight Charges: Under 18 £3.75 Adult £5.50

Ⓐ Ⓧ Ⓟ Cars only (coaches nearby).

Jan 1 - Mar 31	Open X:Mon
Apr 1 - Jun 2	Open
Jun 18 - Sep 8	Open
Sep 24 - Dec 21	Open X:Mon
Dec 27 - Dec 31	Open for New Year

ACCOMMODATION 🛏²

Part of a Malthouse Farm dating from the 17th century, this simple self catering Hostel is in a truly rural setting in the Clee Hills. Sorry there are no showers here. This is excellent walking country with easy access to the Shropshire Way, Shropshire Challenge Walk and Shropshire Ring Walk. The Hostel is also close to many pleasant cycling routes along quiet country lanes.

TRAVEL INFO

🚌 Infrequent from Ludlow, alight Three Horseshoes 1m; otherwise Midland Red West 192, 292 Hereford - Birmingham (passes close BR Ludlow & Kidderminster), alight Hopton Bank, 5m (☎ 0345 056 785). 🚉 Ludlow 9m.
🛈 ☎ 01584 875053

NEXT HOSTELS

Ludlow 9m, Wilderhope Manor 12m, Bridges 23m

ADDITIONAL INFO

Daytime access to w.c. and simple shelter. No showers. No credit cards accepted. Hot snack meals available. Please make cheques payable to F. Powell. This is a privately owned Hostel operated under an agreement with YHA.

HOW TO GET THERE

Leave Bridgnorth or Ludlow on B4364, look out for Three Horse Shoes pub in Wheathill. Turn off adjacent to pub car park. Hostel 1m on right.
OS 138 GR 613818

Wilderhope Manor

58 BEDS   Open: 17.00hrs

☎ 01694 771363 Fax: 01694 771520

The John Cadbury Memorial Hostel, Easthope, Much Wenlock, Shropshire, TF13 6EG

Overnight Charges: Under 18 £5.55 Adult £8.25

Ⓐ Ⓠ Ⓧ Ⓟ BABA

Jan 1 - Feb 28	Open for groups booked in advance
Mar 1 - Aug 31	Open X:Sun*
Sep 16 - Oct 31	Open X:Sun
Nov 1 - Dec 31	Open for groups booked in advance

* Open Bank Hol Sun.

ACCOMMODATION 🛏²⁻⁴1 🛏⁵⁻⁸1 🛏⁹⁺4

Owned by the National Trust, this superb Elizabethan Manor House is idyllically situated on Wenlock Edge. Two wooden spiral staircases, the baronial banqueting room and original intricate plasterwork create a unique atmosphere. All the rooms have wonderful views of the Hope Valley and Corvedale. Many varied walks start directly from the Manor's front door, exploring the Edge and the surrounding countryside. Shropshire's timeless beauty is unique. Popular with groups April — June.

TRAVEL INFO

🚌 Go Whittle 152 from Bridgnorth (Tue only) or Horrocks 712 from Ludlow (Mon, Fri only); otherwise more frequent services from Ludlow or Bridgnorth to Shipton, thence 1 ½ mile walk (footpath) (☎ 0345 056 785). 🚉 Church Stretton 8m.
🛈 ☎ 01743 350761 Much Wenlock TIC 01952 727679

NEXT HOSTELS

Wheathill 12m, Bridges 13m, Ironbridge 13m

ADDITIONAL INFO

Daytime access to w.c. Banquets organised for groups.

HOW TO GET THERE

Coaches should come from Longville (B4371)
OS 137 GR 544928

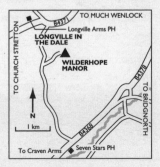

South and West Wales plus the Wye Valley

From the English borders across to the spectacular coastline of west Wales, there's a wealth of countryside, history and culture to explore in this beautiful area.

There are two National Parks; the Pembrokeshire Coast, with its wide sandy beaches, dramatic cliffs and 186 mile coastal footpath, and the Brecon Beacons, with mountains and moorland ideal for walking and pony trekking.

Cardiff, the capital city of Wales, is a vibrant cultural centre with the impressive Cardiff Castle at its heart and surrounded by museums, theatres and the developing Bay area.

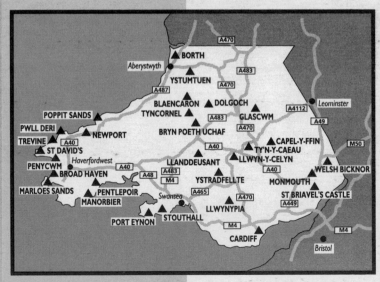

6

You can also experience the industrial heritage of the Welsh valleys in Rhondda Valley, explore the magical Wye Valley with its meandering river or surrender to the charms of the myriad castles which once defended the border and still stand today.

Don't forget to ask for your YHA discount (by showing your membership card) at various attractions including the Sherman Theatre and Techniquest.

Useful Publications

Offa's Dyke Strip Maps
£3.75 for set of 9 maps

Pembrokeshire Coast Footpath Booklet and Maps   £4.00

Wye Valley Waymarked Path Leaflets
  Highmeadow Woods
  Symonds Yat
60p each or 80p the two

Walkers Guide:
Tywi and Elan Valleys
£1.50

All of the above are available from the YHA Wales Regional Office at the address to the right. The prices include p&p, cheques should be made payable to YHA.

Helping You to Book Ahead

The West Wales Booking Bureau can book your stay at Poppit Sands, Newport (Pembs), Pwll Deri, Trevine, St David's, Penycwm (Solva), Broad Haven, Marloes Sands, Manorbier and Pentlepoir Youth Hostels – ideal for those walking the Pembrokeshire Coastal Path. Just send details of your requirements (at least 14 days prior to the first night of your visit), a fee of £2.50 per person (family rate available) and overnight and meal charges to:
YHA, Llaethdy, St David's, Haverfordwest, Pembs SA62 6PR
Tel: 01437 720345

The Elenith Discount Package gives you 7 nights for the price of 5 at any of the following Hostels: Blaencaron, Bryn Poeth Uchaf, Dolgoch, Glascwm, Tyncornel and Ystumtuen. Purchase your vouchers, in advance, from the YHA Wales Regional Office at the address below.

For more information about hostelling in this area contact:

**YHA Wales Regional Office,
1 Cathedral Road,
Cardiff CF1 9HA
Tel: 01222 396766/222122
Fax: 01222 237817**

16 BEDS   Open: 17.00hrs

Blaencaron

☎ 01974 298441

Youth Hostel, Blaencaron, Tregaron, Cardiganshire SY25 6HL

Overnight Charges: Under 18 £3.75 Adult £5.50

🅰 🅿 Cars/mini-buses nearby. Coaches-Tregaron 3m.

Apr 1 - Sep 7	Open

The Hostel may be available to open to advance bookings for groups during closed period.

ACCOMMODATION

This self catering Hostel is set in the unspoilt Afon Groes Valley, 3 miles E.N.E. of Tregaron. It provides basic accommodation in 3 dormitories, heating by wall mounted electric fire in the lounge, small drying room, combined lounge/kitchen/dining area. As well as the Cambrian Way Footpath and walks in the Elenith, the Elan Valley reservoirs form a lakeland with many scenic walks. Bird watching is particularly good in the area. There are many attractions to enjoy: Tregaron Bog/National Nature Reserve (4m), Strata Florida Abbey (10m), Dolaucothi Gold Mines (20m), Welsh Gold Centre (Tregaron 4m), Devil's Bridge Narrow Gauge Railway (17m) and a local pub (3m).

TRAVEL INFO
🚌 Bws Dyfed 516, 589 BR Aberystwyth - Tregaron, alight Tregaron, thence 2m (Highway & Transport Dept ☎ 01267 231817).
🚉 Aberystwyth 20m; Devil's Bridge 17m.
🛈 ☎ 01545 570602

NEXT HOSTELS
Dolgoch 12m, Tyncornel 14m, Ystumtuen 21m

ADDITIONAL INFO
Daytime access to shelter in stone cycle shed but no toilet. Credit cards not accepted. Mid-Wales Booking Bureau. On Cambrian Way footpath route.

HOW TO GET THERE
From Red Lion Inn, Tregaron, on road N (B4343. Take 1st right for 2m to phone box. Turn right - Warden's farm 1st right along rough track. Hostel 1m. New arrivals MUST book in at farm.
🆗 146 GR 713608

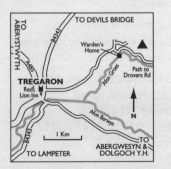

68 BEDS   Open: 17.00hrs

Borth

☎ 01970 871498 Fax: 01970 871827

Youth Hostel, Morlais, Borth, Cardiganshire SY24 5JS

Overnight Charges: Under 18 £5.55 Adult £8.25

Family accommodation prices on p.10-13

🔍 🅿 BABA

Feb 16 - Feb 25	Open
Feb 27 - Mar 30	Open X:Sun/Mon
Apr 2 - Aug 31	Open
Sep 1 - Oct 12	Open X:Sun/Mon
Oct 15 - Oct 27	Open

The Hostel is available for advance bookings by groups at any time throughout the year.

ACCOMMODATION

An Edwardian house overlooking the Dyfi Estuary with mountains as a backdrop. Rooms have heating and wash basins and many have sea views. Facilities include family rooms, TV/games room, small shop, good home cooking and a playroom during July/August. Popular with field study groups mid week and families and other travellers at weekends. The area has sandy beaches and is good for watersports. An exceptional location for bird watching with the Ynys Hir RSPB Reserve close by. Easy access to Snowdonia. Attractions close by: Animalarium; Fast Trax; Centre for Alternative Technology; Owain Glyndwr Museum; and Celtica.

TRAVEL INFO
🚌 Crosville Cymru 511/512, 520/524 from Aberystwyth (☎ 01970 617951) 🚉 Borth ¾m.
🛈 ☎ 01970 612125

NEXT HOSTELS
Corris 19m, Ystumtuen 18m, Blaencaron 29m

ADDITIONAL INFO
Daytime access to self catering kitchen, toilet, drying room and games room. Sand-yachting courses available all year. Wales Tourist Board approved.

HOW TO GET THERE
On the B4353 between Borth village and the Ynyslas golf links.
🆗 135 GR 608907

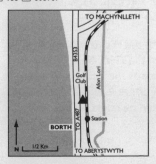

74 BEDS   Open: 17.00hrs

Broad Haven

☎ 01437 781688 Fax: 01437 781100

Youth Hostel, Broad Haven, Haverfordwest, Pembrokeshire SA62 3JH

Overnight Charges: Under 18 £5.55 Adult £8.25

Seasonal Prices Jul 1 - Aug 31: Under 18 £6.15 Adult £9.10

Family accommodation prices on p.10-13

🔍 🖂 ♿ 🅿 BABA

Feb 16 - Feb 24	Open
Feb 26 - Mar 30	Open X:Sun
Apr 1 - Aug 31	Open
Sep 2 - Nov 2	Open X:Sun

The Hostel is available for advance bookings by groups at any time throughout the year - please check with Warden.

ACCOMMODATION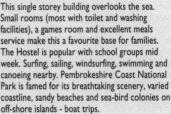

This single storey building overlooks the sea. Small rooms (most with toilet and washing facilities), a games room and excellent meals service make this a favourite base for families. The Hostel is popular with school groups mid week. Surfing, sailing, windsurfing, swimming and canoeing nearby. Pembrokeshire Coast National Park is famed for its breathtaking scenery, varied coastline, sandy beaches and sea-bird colonies on off-shore islands - boat trips.

TRAVEL INFO
🚌 Bws Dyfed 311 from Haverfordwest (passes close BR Haverfordwest) (☎ 01267 231817).
🚃 Haverfordwest 7m. ⛴ Pembroke Dock and Fishguard/Ireland
🛈 ☎ 01437 763110

NEXT HOSTELS
St David's 17m (25m by path), Marloes 10m (by path 13m), Penycwm (Solva) 8m

ADDITIONAL INFO
Main reception area open after noon with access to toilets, games machines and washing/drying facilities. WTB Disability Access Grade 1.

HOW TO GET THERE
From B4341 turn right into NP carpark, Hostel on left next to information centre.
OS 157 GR 863141

Bryn Poeth Uchaf

 22 BEDS   Open: 17.00hrs

☏ 01550 750235

Youth Hostel, Hafod-y-Pant, Cynghordy, Llandovery, Carmarthenshire SA20 0NB

Overnight Charges: Under 18 £3.75 Adult £5.50

Family accommodation prices on p.10-13

Ⓟ For cars and mini-buses only at farm (small charge). Coaches at Llandovery 8m.

Apr 1 - Sep 7	Open

The Hostel may be available to open to advance bookings for groups during the closed period.

ACCOMMODATION

A former farmhouse in an isolated location in the south of the Cambrian mountains. This self catering Hostel offers mountain hut type accommodation with lighting, heating and cooking by calor gas, as there is no electricity. Visitors should bring a torch and book in with the Warden at Hafod-y-Pant farm. A self-contained family annexe sleeping 4 is also available for weekly hire — advance booking is essential. Local attractions: Cambrian Way footpath, Twm Shon Catti's Cave (4m), RSPB Reserve (7m), Dolaucothi Gold Mines (11m), and Llyn Brianne Reservoir (7m). Shop and local pub one mile away (by steep footpath).

TRAVEL INFO

Postbus from Llandovery PO (passes close BR Llandovery) (☏ 01267 231817). Cynghordy 2m. ☏ 01550 20693 (seasonal)

NEXT HOSTELS

Dolgoch 15m, Tyncornel 10m by mountains

ADDITIONAL INFO

Daytime access to limited shelter/toilet. Mid-Wales Booking Bureau. Credit cards not accepted.

HOW TO GET THERE

From Llandovery take Rhandirmwyn Road N for 6m, turn right. Warden's farm 2m. From A483 turn west at N of village of Cynghordy and right at T junction (½m). Continue under railway viaduct, climbing steep hill, following Hostel signs. Access to Hostel by foot only ¾m uphill from Warden's farm. Torch essential after dark.

OS 146 GR 796439

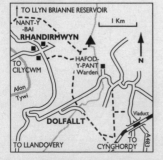

![] 40 BEDS Open: 17.00hrs

Capel-y-Ffin

☎ 01873 890650

Youth Hostel, Capel-y-Ffin, Abergavenny, NP7 7NP

Overnight Charges: Under 18 £4.60 Adult £6.75

🅰 🔲 🅿 Limited space in layby 30m N of Hostel gate for cars and mini-buses only.

Feb	Open Fr/Sat only (SC)
Mar 1 - Apr 2	Open X:Wed
Apr 4 - Apr 16	Open (SC Wed)
Apr 18 - Jun 30	Open X:Wed
Jul 1 - Sep 3	Open (SC Wed)
Sep 16 - Oct 29	Open X:Wed
Nov	Open Fr/Sat only (SC)

NB: SC = self-catering night. Also note that breakfast will not be served on the morning following the self-catering night.

ACCOMMODATION

A hillfarm in peaceful Llanthony Valley Black Mountains. Dormitory accommodation, large grounds, partial heating. Full board horse riding and trail riding holidays (2-7 nights) are run from the Hostel for anyone over 11 yrs. The Hostel is on the Cambrian Way and near the Offa's Dyke Footpath. Hay-on-Wye (7m) is renowned for its second hand bookshops. Abergavenny (16m) — market day Tuesdays.

TRAVEL INFO

🚌 Stagecoach Red & White 39, Yeomans Canyon 40 Hereford - Brecon (passes close BR Hereford), alight Hay-on-Wye, 8m (☎ 0345 125436).
🚉 Abergavenny 16m.
🛈 ☎ 01873 77588

NEXT HOSTELS

Ty'n-y-Caeau 23m (16m by mountain), Glascwm 20m, Monmouth 25m

ADDITIONAL INFO

Daytime access to simple shelter with w.c. Wales Tourist Board approved.

HOW TO GET THERE

Turn off the A465 at Llanfihangel Crucorney, follow signs to Llanthony and from there signs to Capel-y-Ffin.
OS 161 GR 250328

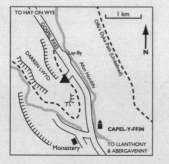

![] 68 BEDS Open: 15.00hrs

Cardiff

☎ 01222 462303 Fax: 01222 464571

Youth Hostel, 2 Wedal Road, Roath Park, Cardiff, CF2 5PG

Overnight Charges: Under 18 £6.15 Adult £9.10

🔲 🔲 ♿ 🅿 Cars and mini-buses. Street parking for coaches. BABA IBN

Jan 2 - Dec 1	Open

ACCOMMODATION

Only 2 miles from the city centre and near Roath Park and lake, Cardiff International Youth Hostel is readily accessible by public transport and provides a base for exploring Wales. Its name 'Ty Croeso' means 'Welcome House' and you are assured of a warm welcome here whether you are a UK or international visitor or part of a sports or social group. All dormitories have wash basins and individual reading lights. Coin operated laundry facilities and a late entry system are other bonuses for travellers. Cardiff, the lively capital of Wales, is packed with excellent entertainment and attractions: 7 superb Victorian/Edwardian shopping arcades, museums, theatres, National Ice Rink and many festivals throughout the year. Don't miss the Museum of Welsh Life, National Museum of Wales, Cardiff Castle, Castle Coch and Techniquest — Britain's largest hands-on science centre. Besides ice skating and ten pin bowling you can walk, sail and cycle!

TRAVEL INFO

🚌 Cardiff Bus 78/80/82 from BR Cardiff Central (☎ 01222 396521). 🚉 Cardiff Central Station 2 ½m 🚢 Swansea/Cork 50m, Fishguard/Rosslare 100m
🛈 ☎ 01222 668750

NEXT HOSTELS

Llwynypia 18m, Llwyn-y-Celyn 42m, Port Eynon 56m

ADDITIONAL INFO

Hostel opens at 3 pm. Wales Tourist Board approved. Laundry facilities.

HOW TO GET THERE

Follow signs from A470/A48 roundabout.
OS 171 GR 185788

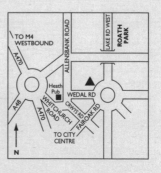

Dolgoch

☎ 01974 298680

Youth Hostel, Tregaron, Cardiganshire SY25 6NR

Advance bookings and enquiries to: YHA Wales Regional Office, 4th floor, 1 Cathedral Road, Cardiff, CF1 9HA ☎ 01222 222122
Fax: 01222 237817

Overnight Charges: Under 18 £3.75 Adult £5.50

🅿 Cars and mini-buses only. Coaches 9m.

Apr 1 - Sep 7	Open

The Hostel may be available to open to advance bookings for groups during the closed period.

ACCOMMODATION

This self catering remote farmhouse provides simple yet spacious mountain hut type accommodation. There is no electricity, but an open fire in the Common Room will keep you warm. Other facilities are a small shop, lighting and cooking by gas, pay telephone and car parking. Local attractions: Drygarn Fawr (6m), Twm Shon Catti's Cave (11m), Llyn Brianne Reservoir (2m), RSPB Reservoir (10m) and the Welsh Gold Centre. Birdwatching.

TRAVEL INFO
🚌 Bws Dyfed 516, 589 BR Aberystwyth - Tregaron, alight Tregaron, 9m (☎ 01267 231817).
🚉 Llanwrtyd Wells 10m. ⛴ Fishguard/Rosslare 66m
🛈 ☎01545 570602

NEXT HOSTELS
Tyncornel 19m (5m by mountains), Blaencaron 12m (9m by mountains), Bryn Poeth Uchaf 15m

ADDITIONAL INFO
Daytime access to limited shelter/toilet. Mid-Wales Booking Bureau. Pay telephone at the Hostel. Small Hostel shop.

HOW TO GET THERE
From Tregaron take Abergwesyn Mountain Road for 9m. From Beulah on A483 take road to Abergwesyn and then Tregaron Mountain Road 6m. Hostel ¾m S of Bridge in Tywi Valley along very rough and uneven forestry track.
OS 147 GR 806561

Glascwm

☎ 01982 570415

Youth Hostel, The School, Glascwm, Llandrindod Wells, Powys LD1 5SE

Overnight Charges: Under 18 £3.75 Adult £5.50

🅰 🅿 Nearby.

Apr 1 - Sep 7	Open

The Hostel may be available to open for advance bookings for groups during closed period.

ACCOMMODATION 3

This old stone built school is now a self catering Hostel in the centre of the quiet hamlet of Glascwm. It provides very basic accommodation. Three dormitories (two in an annexe), heating in the common room/kitchen only by coal fire, outside toilets, no shower and a small shop all add to the rustic feel of this building. The Radnorshire Hills are excellent for walking and cycling and the Hostel provides a link with the Offa's Dyke Path (4m) and Wye Valley Walk (5m). The area also offers the Radnor Forest and waterfalls (6m), Giants Grave and Mawn Pool (1m) and Welsh Crafts Centre at Llandrindod Wells. The second hand book capital of the world and market town of Hay-on-Wye is only 10 miles away.

TRAVEL INFO
🚌 Roy Brown Coaches from Builth Wells & BR Builth Road Mon only (☎ 01982 552597).
🚉 Builth Road 11m.
🛈 ☎01982 553307 (seasonal)

NEXT HOSTELS
Capel-y-Ffin 20m, Ty'n-y-Caeau 25m, Clun 25m

ADDITIONAL INFO
Daytime access to shelter in cycle shed and w.c. Credit cards are not accepted. Mid-Wales booking bureau. Pay telephone nearby.

HOW TO GET THERE
In centre of Glascwm village 10m from Kington and 4m from Hundred House.
OS 148 GR 158532

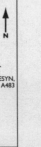

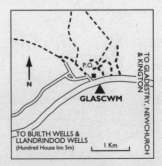

   28 BEDS   **Open: 17.00hrs**

Llanddeusant

☎ 01550 740634 & 740619

Youth Hostel, The Old Red Lion, Llanddeusant, Llangadog, Carmarthenshire SA19 6UL

For Rent-a-Hostel bookings contact YHA Wales Regional Office, 4th Floor, 1 Cathedral Road, Cardiff CF1 9HA ☎ 01222 222122 Fax: 01222 237817

Overnight Charges: Under 18 £4.15 Adult £6.10

Family accommodation prices on p.10-13

A P Cars/mini-buses ONLY. Coaches Llangadog 7m.

Apr 1 - Sep 7	Open

The Hostel is available for Rent-a-Hostel bookings when otherwise closed.

ACCOMMODATION 2-4 1 5-8 2 9+ 1

This self catering Hostel is a former Inn. Bedrooms have full central heating and washbasins. The large combined kitchen/dining room/lounge area has a log fire and a good social atmosphere. The area is excellent for ridgewalking and circular walks to nearby lakes. Horse riding, bird watching and rock climbing nearby. Local attractions: Carreg Cennen Castle, Craig-y-Nos Country Park, Castle Woods Nature Reserve, Dolaucothi Gold Mines and Dan-yr-Ogof Show Caves.

TRAVEL INFO
No Service. Llangadog 7m.
☎ 01550 20693 (seasonal)

NEXT HOSTELS
Bryn Poeth Uchaf 16m, Ystradfellte 23m, Llwyn-y-Celyn 25m, Port Eynon 44m.

ADDITIONAL INFO
Daytime access to hallway/corridor with toilet. Mid-Wales booking bureau. No Hostel shop. Cambrian Way Footpath route. Wales Tourist Board approved.

HOW TO GET THERE
From E, turn off A40 in Trecastle for 9m and turn left opposite Cross Inn. From W turn S off A40 for Llangadog, continue through village on A4069. Turn left opposite Three Horseshoes, then turn right and then left in Twynllanan.
OS 160 GR 776245

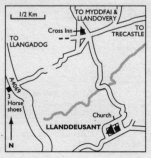

42 BEDS   Open: 17.00hrs

Llwyn-y-Celyn

☎ 01874 624261 Fax: 01874 624261

Youth Hostel, Libanus, Brecon, Powys LD3 8NH

Overnight Charges: Under 18 £5.00 Adult £7.45

⛺ 🅿 Cars & mini-buses. Coaches in layby 200yds.
BABA

Feb 16 - Jun 29	Open X:Sun*
Jul 1 - Aug 31	Open
Sep 2 - Sep 14	Open X:Sun
Sep 30 - Nov 30	Open X:Sun

*Open Easter Sun Apr 7, and Sun May 26. The Hostel may be available for advance bookings by groups when otherwise closed please contact Warden.

ACCOMMODATION 🛏5-8 1 🛏9+ 2

Welsh farmhouse in the heart of the Brecon Beacons National Park with 15 acres of grounds including a nature trail. Full central heating is a recent addition. Popular with walkers, cyclists and anyone wanting a mountain location that is not too remote. This area offers some of the best walking in Wales. Climbing, abseiling and caving are other favourite activities. Key attractions include the Dan-yr-Ogof Show Caves, Bit Pit Mining Museum and Brecon Mountain Railway.

TRAVEL INFO
🚃 Silverline Rail-Link 43 BR Merthyr Tydfil - Brecon (☎ 01685 382406). National Express daily to Brecon, twice daily May - Aug. 🚌 Merthyr Tydfil 11m; Abergavenny 28m.
🛈 ☎ 01874 625692

NEXT HOSTELS
Ty'n-y-Caeau 9m, Ystradfellte 12m, Llanddeusant 25m

ADDITIONAL INFO
Daytime access to simple shelter in wooden shed - no w.c. Wales Tourist Board approved.

HOW TO GET THERE
Hostel sign on main road A470 and 7m S of Brecon 12m N from Merthyr.
OS 160 GR 973225

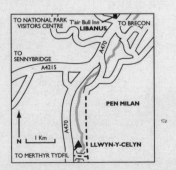

62 BEDS   Open: 17.00hrs

Llwynypia

☎ 01443 430859 Fax: 01443 423415

Youth Hostel, Glyncornel Centre, Llwynypia, Rhondda, CF40 2JF

For Rent-a-Hostel bookings: YHA Wales Regional Office, 4th Floor, 1 Cathedral Road, Cardiff CF1 9HA ☎ 01222 222122 Fax: 01222 237817

Overnight Charges: Under 18 £5.55 Adult £8.25

Family accommodation prices on p.10-13

♿ 🅿 Large car park. BABA

| Feb 16 - Feb 24 | Open |
| Mar 4 - Oct 25 | Open X:Sat/Sun* |

* Open Easter Sat/Sun 6/7 Apr and Bank Hols 5/6 & 26/27 May and 24/25 Aug. Available for advance bookings by groups at any time throughout the year - please contact Warden. Rent-a-Hostel Jan 1 - Feb 15, Feb 25-29, Oct 28 to mid Feb '97.

ACCOMMODATION 🛏2-4 1 🛏5-8 3 🛏9+ 3

Set in 75 acres of natural woodland with a variety of plant and wildlife and a nature trail, the Hostel provides comfortable accommodation. Ramp access makes it fully accessible to wheelchair users. Small museum with an interesting local history display in the building. Busy field study centre midweek. Within easy reach of the many attractions of Cardiff (18m) or the Brecon Beacons National Park. The local area is steeped in mining and industrial history. Don't miss a visit to the Rhondda Heritage Park or the 17th Century living history museum of Llancaiach Fawr. Bird watching, swimming and local walks nearby.

TRAVEL INFO
🚃 Local ½m. 🚌 Llwynypia ½m.
🛈 ☎ 01443 402077

NEXT HOSTELS
Cardiff 18m, Ystradfellte 18m, Llwyn-y-Celyn 30m

ADDITIONAL INFO
This YHA centre is ideal for small conferences, seminars. Wales Tourist Board approved.

HOW TO GET THERE
From M4 turn off at junction 34, follow signs for Rhondda Valley and Glyncornel Centre.
OS 170 GR 993939

Manorbier

🏠 68 BEDS   Open: 17.00hrs

📞 01834 871803 Fax: 01834 871101

Youth Hostel, Manorbier, Nr Tenby, Pembrokeshire SA70 7TT

For Rent-a-Hostel bookings: YHA Wales Regional Office, 4th Floor, 1 Cathedral Road, Cardiff CF1 9HA 📞 01222 222122 Fax: 01222 237817

Overnight Charges: Under 18 £5.55 Adult £8.25

Seasonal Prices Jul 1 - Aug 31: Under 18 £6.15 Adult £9.10

Family accommodation prices on p.10-13

🅰 🔍 📷 ♿ 🅿 BABA

Feb 17 - Aug 31	Open
Sep 16 - Oct 26	Open

The Hostel is available for advance bookings by groups at any time throughout the year - please contact Warden. Rent-a-Hostel available Jan 1 - Feb 15 and Oct 28 - mid Feb '97.

ACCOMMODATION

Situated within the Pembrokeshire Coast National Park, with a range of facilities including comfortable accommodation, TV/games room, picnic and sports grounds. Family rooms plus three self contained family annexes. The Hostel is popular with school groups mid week. Manorbier is only 5 miles from the seaside resort of Tenby with its narrow streets, shops, medieval walls and picturesque fishing harbour.

TRAVEL INFO
🚌 Bws Dyfed 358/9 Tenby - Haverfordwest, alight Manorbier 1m (📞 01267 231817) 🚉 Manorbier 2 ½m. ⛴ Pembroke/Rosslare 10m
🚲 📞 01834 842402

NEXT HOSTELS
Pentlepoir 13m, Marloes 20m, Broad Haven 28m

ADDITIONAL INFO
Daytime access to heated sitting room with drinks machine, public telephone, toilets and drying room. Wales Tourist Board approved and WTB Disability Access Grade 1.

HOW TO GET THERE
Off the B4585 from Manorbier village.
OS 158 GR 081975

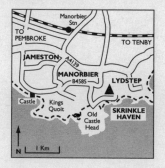

👣🏃 30 BEDS   Open: 17.00hrs

Marloes Sands

📞 01646 636667 (during open periods)

Youth Hostel, Runwayskiln, Marloes, Haverfordwest, Pembrokeshire SA62 3BH

When Hostel is closed bookings and enquiries: YHA Wales Regional Office, 4th Floor, 1 Cathedral Road, Cardiff CF1 9HA 📞 01222 222122 Fax: 01222 237817

Overnight Charges: Under 18 £4.60 Adult £6.75

Seasonal Prices Jul 1 - Aug 31: Under 18 £5.00 Adult £7.45

🏊 P Limited for 6 cars ONLY.

Apr 1 - Sep 28	Open

ACCOMMODATION 🛏️2-4 1 🛏️9+2

A cluster of farm buildings alongside the Pembrokeshire Coastal Path providing basic accommodation, self catering facilities, small shop, partial heating and limited parking for cars. Ideally placed for boat trips to Skomer Island, a famous bird sanctuary and marine reserve. The area has some very scenic walks as well as a superb watersports centre at Dale offering windsurfing, sailing, canoeing and waterskiing. Marloes Sands beach is one of the finest in Pembrokeshire.

TRAVEL INFO
🚌From Haverfordwest or Milford Haven (not daily), thence 1m (📞 01267 231817). 🚉Milford Haven 11m; Haverfordwest 14m.
⛴Pembroke/Ireland 7m
ℹ️📞01437 763110

NEXT HOSTELS
Broad Haven 13m by path, Pentlepoir 24m, St Davids 22m

HOW TO GET THERE
B4327 from Haverfordwest 11m, turn right to Marloes, then at village church turn L to Marloes Sands car park. Hostel down private track on left approx 200yds (coaches not allowed).
OS 157 GR 778080

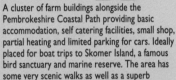

👣🏃 30 BEDS   Open: 17.00hrs

Monmouth

📞 01600 715116

Youth Hostel, Priory Street School, Priory Street, Monmouth, Monmouthshire NP5 3NX

Overnight Charges: Under 18 £4.60 Adult £6.75

P Parking opposite Hostel for cars. Coaches ¼m - but can unload at Hostel first.

Mar 1 - Oct 31	Open

The Hostel may be available for groups (self catering only) when otherwise closed - please contact Warden.

ACCOMMODATION 🛏️5-8 1 🛏️9+2

A simple self catering Hostel near the centre of a historic market town. There are wash basins in all dormitories. Storage heaters and a coal fire provide background heating. The large combined kitchen/lounge area provides an ideal social environment. Walkers take pleasure in the direct access to the Wye Valley Walk and Offa's Dyke Path. Canoeing, cycling and orienteering are other favoured activities. Monmouth town hosts many annual festivals in May — September. Places of interest include Raglan Castle, Tintern Abbey, Forest of Dean and the Wye Valley.

TRAVEL INFO
🚌Stagecoach Red & White 65/9 from Chepstow (pass close BR Chepstow); 60 from Newport (pass close BR Newport); Anslow 83, 416 from Hereford & Abergavenny (pass close BR Hereford & Abergavenny) No Sunday service (📞 01633 832478). 🚉Hereford 16m; Chepstow 16m; Abergavenny 17m. ⛴Fishguard/Rosslare 140m
ℹ️📞01600 713899

NEXT HOSTELS
Welsh Bicknor 8m, St Briavels Castle 8m, Capel-y-Ffin 25m

ADDITIONAL INFO
Daytime access to toilet but no shelter. Wales Tourist Board approved.

HOW TO GET THERE
Near the town centre adjacent to where the River Monnow runs along Priory Street.
OS 162 GR 508130

Newport (Pembs)

📞 01239 820080 Fax: 01239 820080

Youth Hostel, Lower St Mary's Street, Newport, Pembrokeshire, SA42 0TS

Overnight Charges: Under 18 £4.60 Adult £6.75

Seasonal Prices Jul 1 - Aug 31: Under 18 £5.00 Adult £7.45

Family accommodation prices on p.10-13

⛵ ♿ 🅿 Cars and mini-buses. BABA

Mar 1 - Jun 30	Open X:Tu/Wed*
Jul 1 - Aug 31	Open
Sep 1 - Oct 28	Open X:Tu/Wed

* Open Tu/Wed Easter 9/10 Apr and Bank Hol 28/29 May. Advance bookings for groups of 15 or more may be possible Nov to Feb - please contact Warden.

ACCOMMODATION 🛏5 🛏2

A new, modern, self catering Hostel in the centre of the enchanting town of Newport provides a fine base for individuals, families and small groups. The range of facilities include small dormitories (all with wash basins), family rooms, large kitchen/dining area and separate lounge. It is a convenient location for the Fishguard ferry service to Ireland and for exploring the Preseli Hills with burial chambers, iron age forts. As well as good walking country and nice beaches, flora and fauna abound. Newport village has many art galleries and craft shops to enjoy and the Fishguard Music Festival every July presents a variety of music and features the work of local artists. The Pottery and Kilgwen Candles.

TRAVEL INFO

🚌 412 Fishguard Harbour to Newport.

🚢 Fishguard-Ireland 8m

ℹ️ 📞01437 781412

NEXT HOSTELS

Pwll Deri 22m by coastal path (13 by road), Poppit Sands 11m by coastal path, Trevine 15m

HOW TO GET THERE

In the centre of the village of Newport. From A487 to Fishguard turn right on Lower St Mary's Street.
OS 145 GR 058393

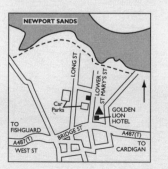

Pentlepoir

📞 01834 812333

Youth Hostel, The Old School, Pentlepoir, Saundersfoot, Pembrokeshire SA9 9BJ

Overnight Charges: Under 18 £4.60 Adult £6.75

⛵ 🅿 Cars ONLY. Coaches - Saundersfoot 1m.

Mar 29 - Jun 25	Open X:Wed/Th*
Jun 28 - Sep 3	Open
Sep 3 - Oct 29	Open X:Wed/Th

*Open Wed/Th Easter 10/11 Apr and Bank Hol 29/30 May.

ACCOMMODATION 🛏1 🛏2

A small, relaxed Hostel (once the village school) providing simple accommodation including a large common/dining room with plenty of games and a coal/wood burning stove. The quiet lanes in the area are good for walking, cycling and horse riding. The nearby seaside towns of Saundersfoot and Tenby are noted for their sandy beaches, attractive harbours, variety of watersports (windsurfing, sailing, canoeing, diving) and fishing. Attractions in the area include Oakwood Leisure Park, Folly Farm, Pembroke Castle, sightseeing cruises around Caldey Island.

TRAVEL INFO

🚌 Bws Dyfed 350-2, 361 from Tenby (📞 01267 231817). 🚂 Saundersfoot ¾m.

🚢 Pembroke/Rosslare 11m

ℹ️ 📞01834 811411

NEXT HOSTELS

Manorbier 13m, Broad Haven 21m, Marloes Sands 24m

ADDITIONAL INFO

Daytime access to covered area including outside toilet and wash basin at rear of Hostel. Meals operated privately by Warden - separate payment appreciated. Wales Tourist Board approved.

HOW TO GET THERE

Take A478 to Tenby from Kilgetty roundabout. Stay on main road to Tenby, past garage on left and old school on the right.
OS 158 GR 116060

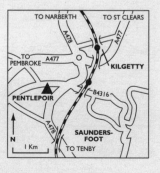

🚶🚶🚴 14 BEDS   Open: 17.00hrs

Penycwm (Solva)

📞 01437 720959 Fax: 01437 720959

Youth Hostel, Hafod Lodge, Whitehouse, Penycwm, Nr Solva, Haverfordwest, Pembrokeshire SA62 6LA

Overnight Charges: Under 18 £5.00 Adult £7.45

Seasonal Prices Jul 1 - Aug 31: Under 18 £5.55 Adult £8.25

Family accommodation prices on p.10-13

🔒 📶 🅿 BABA

Jan 1 - Feb 29	Advance bookings only
Mar 1 - Oct 31	Open
Nov 1 - Dec 31	Advance bookings only

ACCOMMODATION 🛏️2-4 2 🛏️5-8 1

Newly converted farm building now a small modern Hostel in a peaceful, rural setting. Comfortable accommodation (ensuite facilities) and home cooking make it a favourite place for visitors. 4 miles from the picturesque harbour village of Solva, Penycwm is ideal for walkers, nature lovers and watersports enthusiasts. St. David's Peninsula is an area of ancient history and legend with its magnificent cathedral, Bishop's Palace and beautiful beaches.

TRAVEL INFO

🚌 Richards/Summerdale 41½ BR Haverfordwest-Fishguard (passes close BR Fishguard Harbour), alight Penycwm, thence 1½m (📞 01276 231817) 🚉 Haverfordwest 10m.
⛴️ Fishguard/Rosslare 12m
🛈 📞 01437 763110

NEXT HOSTELS

Broad Haven 8m, St David's 9m (17m by path), Trevine 8m

ADDITIONAL INFO

Daytime access to conservatory and toilets. Credit cards not accepted. Wales Tourist Board approved. This is a privately owned Hostel operated under an agreement with YHA.

HOW TO GET THERE

Access via A487 Newgale to Solva road. At Penycwm take minor road N towards Letterston/Mathry and follow signs to Hostel.
📍 157 GR 857250

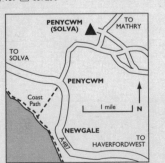

🚶🚶🚴 30 BEDS   Open: 17.00hrs

Poppit Sands

📞 01239 612936

Youth Hostel, Sea View, Poppit, Cardigan, SA43 3LP

Overnight Charges: Under 18 £4.60 Adult £6.75

Seasonal Prices Jul 1 - Aug 31: Under 18 £5.00 Adult £7.45

🅰 🅿 Coaches at bottom car park ½m below Hostel.

Mar 5 - Mar 31	Open X:Mon
Apr 2 - Apr 14	Open
Apr 16 - May 19	Open X:Mon
May 21 - Jun 2	Open
Jun 4 - Jun 23	Open X:Mon
Jun 25 - Sep 1	Open
Sep 3 - Oct 31	Open X:Mon
Nov 1 - Mar 2 '97	Open X:Sun/Mon advance bookings only

ACCOMMODATION 🛏️2-4 2 🛏️5-8 2 🛏️9+ 1

Former Inn now operating as a simple self catering Hostel, limited heating and a good shop. Set in five acres, the Hostel provides good views of the northern Pembrokeshire coastline. In the immediate area there are opportunities for bird watching, coastal walking, cycling and horse riding. St. Dogmael's 11th Century Abbey and working watermill, ancient burial chambers at Pentre Ifan, Castell Henllys — Iron Age village and Teiffi Nature Reserve nearby.

TRAVEL INFO

🚌 Bws Dyfed 407/9 from Cardigan to within ½m (Jul - Aug only), but to St. Dogmaels, 2m, at other times (📞 01267 231817). 🚉 Fishguard Harbour 20m; Carmarthen 26m; Aberystwyth 33m.
⛴️ Fishguard/Ireland 20m
🛈 📞 01239 613230

NEXT HOSTELS

Pentlepoir 25m, Pwll Deri 25m, Llanddeusant 43m

ADDITIONAL INFO

Daytime access to covered entrance way but no toilet. Wales Tourist Board approved.

HOW TO GET THERE

Turn right in village of St Dogmaels to Poppit Sands (1½m). Hostel sign posted from Lifeboat station - second set of buildings on right.
📍 145 GR 144487

🚶 🏃 🚴 32 BEDS   Open: 17.00hrs

Port Eynon

☎ 01792 390706 Fax: 01792 390706

Youth Hostel, The Old Lifeboat House, Port Eynon, Swansea, SA3 1NN

Overnight Charges: Under 18 £5.00 Adult £7.45

🅿 Use seafront car park ¼m. BABA

Feb 16 - Mar 30	Open Fr/Sat only
Apr 1 - Sep 28	Open X:Sun*
Oct 15 - Oct 26	Open X:Sun
Oct 28 - Nov 30	Open Fr/Sat only

*Open Easter Sun Apr 7 and Bank Hol Sun May 26 and Aug 25. The Hostel is available for advance bookings by groups when otherwise closed - please contact Warden.

ACCOMMODATION 🛏1 🛏2

A charming, self catering Hostel that is a converted Life Boat Station. Marvellous views from the lounge — often seals can be seen. Eating area outside allows visitors to enjoy the summer breezes and a barbeque is also available. Storage heaters provide heating and travellers should use the sea front car park as there is no parking at the Hostel itself. Port Eynon is a lively seaside village in the summer with safe swimming and watersports. The Hostel stands on the 25 miles long Gower Coastal Path. The Gower Peninsula has 34 miles of Heritage Coast with superb scenery, clean beaches, sea birds and rare flowers. Local sights: mysterious Culver Hole, Worms Head, Rhossili Beach and Three Cliffs Bay.

TRAVEL INFO

🚌 South Wales 18/A/C from Swansea (pass close BR Swansea) (☎ 01792 580580). 🚋 Swansea 16m
🚲 ☎ 01792 468321

NEXT HOSTELS

Ystradfellte 39m, Llwynypia 44m, Llanddeusant 44m

ADDITIONAL INFO

Daytime access to simple shelter (in shed), public toilets nearby. Wales Tourist Board approved.

HOW TO GET THERE

Footpath from Port Eynon car park or via beach.
OS 159 GR 468848

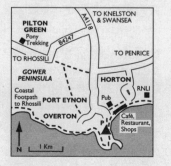

Arrangements have been made with Stouthall, 4m from Port Eynon, to take overflow bookings from families and individuals over the period Jul 20 - Sep 7, 1996.

👥 ❄ 60 BEDS   Open: 17.00hrs

Stouthall

☎ 01792 391086 Fax: 01792 391322

Youth Hostel, Reynoldston, Gower, Swansea SA3 1AP

Overnight Charges: Under 18 £6.15 Adult £9.10

🔍 ✉ ♿ 🅿 Ample for cars & mini-buses.

| Jul 20 - Sep 7 | Open |

ACCOMMODATION 🛏6 🛏7 🛏1

A fine Georgian mansion operating as a Youth Hostel during the summer only. A spacious, well equipped building with many small dormitories, providing a good base for families and individuals alike. Hostel shop can provide microwave meals. The Gower Peninsula is an Area of Outstanding Natural Beauty. For those wishing to experience beaches, bays and cliffs including the famous Worms Head, all are located nearby. The City of Swansea offers a maritime museum, art galleries and Plantasia — with 3 climatic zones and over 100 types of plants.

TRAVEL INFO

🚌 South Wales 18/A/C from Swansea (pass close BR Swansea) (☎ 01792 580580). 🚋 Swansea 13m.
🚢 Swansea-Cork 16m

NEXT HOSTELS

Port Eynon 4m

ADDITIONAL INFO

Wales Tourist Board approved. The grounds have outdoor barbecue facilities.

HOW TO GET THERE

Take the A4118 from Swansea, follow road through Upper Killay, Penmaen, past turnings to Reynoldston. Look for cream building on right - in its own grounds. Turn right over cattle grid. Hostel carpark 100 metres on right.
OS 159 GR 473892

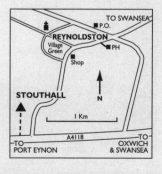

🚶🏃⛷ 32 BEDS   Open: 17.00hrs

Pwll Deri

📞 01348 891233

Youth Hostel, Castell Mawr, Tref Asser, Goodwick, Pembrokeshire SA64 0LR

Overnight Charges: Under 18 £4.60 Adult £6.75

Seasonal Prices Jul 1 - Aug 31: Under 18 £5.00 Adult £7.45

A **P** Nearby.

Mar 26 - Jun 29	Open X:Sun/Mon*
Jul 2 - Aug 31	Open
Sep 3 - Oct 26	Open X:Sun/Mon

*Open Bank Hol Sun/Mon Easter Apr 7-8 and Bank Hol May 26-27.

ACCOMMODATION 🛏1 🛏4

A small, self catering Hostel in an idyllic setting perched on the cliffs overlooking Pwll Deri Bay affording dramatic sunsets and superb views. Facilities include an open fire, simple dormitories, a cosy lounge and welcoming atmosphere. It is an excellent bird and seal watching location and is particularly popular with walkers and small groups. This peaceful part of the Pembrokeshire Coast National Park offers the chance to relax and enjoy the scenery. The Llangloffan Cheese Farm and Woollen Mill are 4 miles away. Closest Hostel to Fishguard Harbour for the ferry service to Ireland.

TRAVEL INFO
🚌 Bws Dyfed 410 Fishguard - Goodwick (connections from BR Haverfordwest), alight Goodwick, thence 4m (📞 01267 231817). 🚉 Fishguard Harbour 4½m. 🚢 Ireland 4½m. 🛈📞 01348 873484

NEXT HOSTELS
Trevine 9m by path, St David's 21m, Poppit Sands 37m by path, Newport 13m (22m by path)

ADDITIONAL INFO
Daytime access to entrance hallway and toilet. Wales Tourist Board approved.

HOW TO GET THERE
Take Strumble Head road out of Goodwick, follow signs for Strumble Head, then Pwll Deri. From St Davids-Fishguard road, approach via St Nicholas.
🗺 157 GR 891387

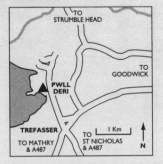

St Briavels Castle

70 BEDS Open: 17.00hrs

☎ 01594 530272 Fax: 01594 530849

Youth Hostel, The Castle, St. Briavels, Lydney, Gloucestershire GL15 6RG

Overnight Charges: Under 18 £5.55 Adult £8.25

🛗 P BABA

Feb 2 - Oct 26	Open
Oct 28 - Dec 12	Open X:Fri/Sat/Sun*
Dec 23 - Dec 27	Christmas Event

*Group bookings for special events especially welcome on weekends Oct 28 - Dec 14 - please contact Warden.

ACCOMMODATION 🛏5-8 5 🛏9+ 4

A unique moated Norman castle that was originally King John's hunting lodge. His bed chamber is now the lounge, and you can sleep in a room that was once a prisoner's cell. The Hostel features a 'hanging room' plus it's own oubliette (a 30ft deep dungeon into which prisoners where thrown and forgotten). All dormitories are heated and the rest of the building is supplemented by open fires. Popular with school groups mid week; other groups, families and individuals at weekends. Many marked trails in the Forest of Dean and Wye Valley. Attractions nearby: Chepstow Castle, Tintern Abbey and Clearwell Caves.

TRAVEL INFO

🚌 Stagecoach Red & White 69 from Chepstow (passes close BR Chepstow), alight Bigsweir Bridge, 2m (☎ 01633 266336). Local services very infrequent - ask Warden. 🚉 Lydney 7m.
🛈 ☎01600 713899

NEXT HOSTELS

Monmouth 8m, Welsh Bicknor 12m, Slimbridge 30m

ADDITIONAL INFO

Daytime access to toilet. Medieval banquets every Wed and Sat night in August priced £5.50 (ordinary Hostel meals are NOT available on these nights). Guided tours of the Castle 60p.

HOW TO GET THERE

In centre of village follow signs from A466.
OS 162 GR 558045

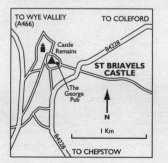

St David's

40 BEDS Open: 17.00hrs

☎ 01437 720345 Fax: 01437 721831

Youth Hostel, Llaethdy, St David's, Haverfordwest, Pembrokeshire SA62 6PR

Overnight Charges: Under 18 £4.15 Adult £6.10

Seasonal Prices Jul 1 - Aug 31: Under 18 £5.00 Adult £7.45

Family accommodation prices on p.10-13

A P Cars & minibuses ONLY. BABA

Mar 29 - Jul 3	Open X:Th*
Jul 5 - Sep 4	Open
Sep 6 - Sep 28	Open X:Th

*Open Th Easter 4 and 11 Apr & Bank Hol 30 May.

ACCOMMODATION 🛏2-4 1 🛏9+ 3

A farmhouse and outbuildings nestled at the foot of a rocky outcrop (2 miles from the centre of St. David's) offering simple, self catering accommodation with limited heating, open fire and well stocked shop. St. David's is very popular with walkers for its magnificent clean beaches, spring flowers and seabirds. Take a boat trip to Ramsey Island RSPB Reserve and don't miss St. David's Cathedral and Bishops Palace.

TRAVEL INFO

🚌 Richards/Summerdale 411 BR Haverfordwest-Fishguard (passes close BR Fishguard Harbour), alight St David's, thence 2m (☎ 01267 231817). 🚉 Fishguard Harbour 15m; Haverfordwest 18m. ⛴ Fishguard/Rosslare (Ireland) 15m
🛈 ☎01437 763110

NEXT HOSTELS

Trevine 11m by path, Pwll Deri 21m by path, Penycwm (Solva) 9m by road

ADDITIONAL INFO

Daytime access to room and w.c. Good Hostel shop. Wales Tourist Board approved.

HOW TO GET THERE

Leave Fishguard Road just outside St Davids, follow signs to White Sands Bay. Hostel signs from golf club.
OS 157 GR 739276

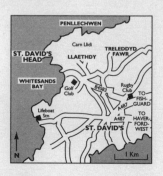

Trevine (Trefin)

📞 01348 831414

Youth Hostel, 11 Ffordd-yr-Afon, Trefin, Haverfordwest, Pembrokeshire SA62 5AU

Overnight Charges: Under 18 £4.60 Adult £6.75

Seasonal Prices Jul 1 - Aug 31: Under 18 £5.00 Adult £7.45

Family accommodation prices on p.10-13

🅿 30yds

Mar 5 - Jun 29	Open X:Sun/Mon*
Jul 2 - Aug 31	Open
Sep 3 - Oct 26	Open X:Sun/Mon

*Open Sun/Mon Easter Apr 7-8, and Bank Hol 26-27 May.

ACCOMMODATION 🛏 2-4 5 🛏 5-8 1

Recently refurbished, this former school in the centre of a friendly village offers comfortable accommodation in small rooms (all with wash basins), full carpeting and good self catering facilities — but the local pub also serves food. An ideal family holiday centre with a public children's play area adjacent. Good access by bus from St. David's, Fishguard and Haverfordwest. It is an excellent area for spotting seabirds, peregrine falcons and choughs. The magnificent Pembrokeshire coastline comprises rugged cliffs, secluded bays and picturesque harbour villages. Visit the Hand Weaving Centre in the village.

TRAVEL INFO

🚌 Richards/Summerdale 411 BR Haverfordwest-Fishguard (passes close BR Fishguard Harbour) (📞 01267 231817).
🚉 Fishguard Harbour 12m; Haverfordwest 18m.
⛴ Fishguard/Rosslare (Ireland) 12m
🏛 📞 01437 763110

NEXT HOSTELS

Pwll Deri 9m, St David's 11m, Penycwm (Solva) 8m

ADDITIONAL INFO

Daytime access to family rooms only. Nearest pub (serving food) is 200yds away. Wales Tourist Board approved.

HOW TO GET THERE

In centre of village near pub.
OS 157 GR 840324

Tyncornel

Youth Hostel, Llanddewi - Brefi, Tregaron, Cardiganshire SY25 6PH

All correspondence, bookings and enquiries to YHA Wales Regional Office, 4th Floor, 1 Cathedral Road, Cardiff. CF1 9HA 📞 01222 222122 Fax: 01222 237817

Overnight Charges: Under 18 £3.75 Adult £5.50

🅰 🅿 Limited. Coaches in layby 9m.

Apr 1 - Sep 7	Open

The Hostel may be available to open to advance bookings for groups during the closed period.

ACCOMMODATION 🛏 5-8 2

An isolated farmhouse in a valley in Mid Wales that offers basic, self catering mountain hut type accommodation. Heating is by cosy open fire in the lounge. There is no electricity; lighting and cooking by gas. The nearest shop and telephone call box is 7m. The area offers fine mountain walking. Local attractions include the Welsh Gold Centre (Tregaron 10m), Soar-y-Mynydd Chapel (2½m) and Llyn Brianne Reservoir (3m), Tregaron National Nature Reserve (10m).

TRAVEL INFO

🚌 Bws Dyfed 516, 589 BR Aberystwyth - Tregaron, some calling, some with connections by Bws Dyfed 588 to Llanddewi Brefi, thence 7m or alight Tregaron on others, thence 10m (📞 01267 231817). 🚉 Aberystwyth 28m.
🏛 📞 01545 570602

NEXT HOSTELS

Blaencaron 14m (8m by mountains), Dolgoch 19m (5m by mountains), Bryn Poeth 37m (10m by mountains)

ADDITIONAL INFO

Day time access to limited shelter/toilet. Mid-Wales Booking Bureau.

HOW TO GET THERE

From Llanddewi-Brefi follow road S E up Brefi valley (not S W to Farmers). Fork left at 4¾m. At signpost at 6m continue on rough track. Hostel 1m.
OS 146 GR 751534

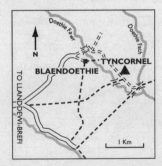

Ty'n-y-Caeau (Nr Brecon)

☎ 01874 665270 Fax: 01874 665278

Youth Hostel, Groesffordd, Brecon, Powys. LD3 7SW

Overnight Charges: Under 18 £4.60 Adult £6.75

🅿 Cars and mini-buses only. Coaches 1 mile. BABA

Apr 1 - Jun 29	Open X:Sun*
Jul 1 - Aug 31	Open
Sep 16 - Oct 26	Open X:Sun

*Open Sundays Easter 7 Apr and Bank Hol 26 May.

ACCOMMODATION 🛏2-4 2 🛏5-8 5 🛏9+ 1

This country house has background heating, an open fire, well stocked shop and extensive grounds with a flat area for outdoor games. Enjoy splendid views of the Brecon Beacons mountains and sample the beautiful local countryside with walks to the top of Pen-y-Fan (2907ft) or along the Brecon — Monmouth Canal. As well as an International Jazz Festival, Brecon boasts a wealth of listed properties, narrow streets, a lively market and a local natural history museum. The Hostel is well situated to reach many places of interest and a variety of activities such as walking, horse riding, cycling, caving and fishing.

TRAVEL INFO
🚌 Stagecoach Red & White 21 Newport - Brecon (passes close BR Abergavenny), alight Llanfrynach turn, 1m; 39 and Yeomans Canyon 40 from Hereford (passes close BR Hereford), alight Llanddew turn, ¾m (☎ 01633 266336 for Red & White, ☎ 0345 125436 Yeomans); Silverline Rail-Link 43 BR Merthyr Tydfil - Brecon, alight Brecon, thence 1¾m by bridle-path (☎ 01685 382406). 🚉 Merthyr Tydfil 20m; Abergavenny 19m. 🛈 ☎ 01874 623366

NEXT HOSTELS
Llwyn-y-Celyn 9m, Capel-y-Ffin 23m.

ADDITIONAL INFO
Daytime access to porch with pay telephone. Wales Tourist Board approved.

HOW TO GET THERE
½m N of Groesffordd village.
OS 160 GR 074388

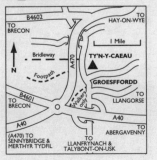

Welsh Bicknor

☎ 01594 860300 Fax: 01594 861276

Youth Hostel, Welsh Bicknor Rectory, Nr Goodrich, Ross-on-Wye, Herefordshire HR9 6JJ

Overnight Charges: Under 18 £5.55 Adult £8.25

Family accommodation prices on p.10-13

  Coaches - contact Warden. BABA

Feb 16 - Feb 24	Open
Mar 2 - Mar 30	Open Fr/Sat only
Apr 1 - Jun 29	Open X:Sun*
Jul 1 - Sep 1	Open
Sep 23 - Oct 26	Open X:Sun
Nov 1 - Dec 15	Open Fr/Sat/Sun only
Dec 23 - Jan 4 '97	Open self catering only

* Open Sun Easter 7 Apr and Bank Hol 26 May. The Hostel is available for advance bookings by groups at any time throughout the year.

ACCOMMODATION 🛏2-4 7 🛏5-8 7 🛏9+ 1

The Hostel renowned for its idyllic setting on the River Wye, delicious home cooking, magnificent views across to the Forest of Dean and Symonds Yat. The Hostel is popular with school groups mid week during spring/summer terms and enjoyed by families and all other travellers the rest of the year. Countless footpaths criss-cross the area. The area is rich in castles with Raglan, Skenfrith, Goodrich, St. Briavel's and Chepstow.

TRAVEL INFO
🚌 Stagecoach Red & White 34 Gloucester - Ross-on-Wye, alight Goodrich Village 1 ½m (☎ 01345 125436) 🚉 Lydney 12m.
🛈 ☎ 01989 65057

NEXT HOSTELS
Monmouth 8m, St Briavel's Castle 12m

ADDITIONAL INFO
Daytime access to simple shelter - no toilet. Separate self-contained cottage sleeps 14. Ideal for families and groups. Own river landing stage.

HOW TO GET THERE
Cars and mini-buses follow lane from Goodrich.
OS 162 GR 591177

Ystradfellte

🚶 🚶 🚶 **28 BEDS** **Open: 17.00hrs**

☎ 01639 720301

Youth Hostel, Tai'r Heol, Ystradfellte, Aberdare, CF44 9JF

Overnight Charges: Under 18 £4.15 Adult £6.10

🅿 Cars and mini-buses ONLY.

Jan 12 - Mar 27	Open Fr/Sat nights for advance bookings
Mar 29 - Apr 24	Open
Apr 26 - May 22	Open X:Th
May 24 - Jun 5	Open
Jun 7 - Jul 17	Open X:Th
Jul 19 - Sep 4	Open
Sep 6 - Oct 30	Open X:Th
Nov 1 - Dec 14	Open Fr/Sat nights for advance bookings

Hostel may open to groups of 15 or more booking in advance during closed periods.

ACCOMMODATION

Self catering Hostel with background heating. This part of the Brecon Beacons National Park is unique waterfall and caving country. Key places to visit are Penscynor Wildlife Park, Dan-yr-Ogof Show Caves and National Park Centres.

TRAVEL INFO

🚌 From Aberdare (passes close BR Aberdare), alight Penderyn, 3 ½m (☎ 01443 409966). SWT X5, 160/1 Swansea-Glyn Neath (passes close BR Neath), thence 5m (☎ 01792 580580).
🚉 Aberdare 10m.
🛈 ☎ 01639 721795

NEXT HOSTELS

Llwyn-y-Celyn 12m, Ty'n-y-Caeau 21m.

ADDITIONAL INFO

Daytime access to shelter in adjoining garage but no w.c. Wales Tourist Board approved. Mid-Wales Booking Bureau. No Hostel shop, local shop 1 ½m.

HOW TO GET THERE

From A4059 turn left 1m N of Penderyn. At fork go left and left again in Ystradfellte village. Hostel 1m. From Glyn Neath proceed to Pont Nedd Fechan, then left to Ystradfellte. Hostel 4m.
📍 160 GR 925127

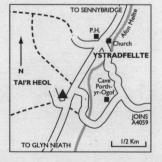

Ystumtuen

🚶 🚶 🚶 **24 BEDS** **Open: 17.00hrs**

☎ 01970 890693

Youth Hostel, Glantuen, Ystumtuen, Aberystwyth, Cardiganshire SY23 3AE

Overnight Charges: Under 18 £3.75 Adult £5.50

🅿 Cars and mini-buses nearby. Coaches Ponterwyd 2m.

| Apr 1 - Sep 7 | Open |

The Hostel may be available to open to advance bookings for groups during the closed period.

ACCOMMODATION

A basic self catering Hostel in an old lead mining village. It was formerly a village school in what is now a somewhat deserted village. Facilities include simple dormitories, combined lounge/dining area with heating by coal fire, shower, drying room and outside toilets. The nearest shop is in Ponterwyd two miles away. The Devil's Bridge area is a series of spectacular waterfalls. Magnificent chasms have been carved into the rock by the water's force. The Vale of Rheidol Narrow Gauge Railway is worth a ride and Llywernog silver and lead mines are only 2 miles from the Hostel. Nant-y-Moch Reservoir (5m) and Plynlimon Fawr (2468') are of particular interest. In easy reach is Aberystwyth with its Victorian seaside, castle ruins and Ceredigion Museum.

TRAVEL INFO

🚌 Crosville Cymru 501 from Aberystwyth (passes BR Aberystwyth), alight 1m W of Ponterwyd, thence 1½m (☎ 01970 617951). 🚉 Rhiwfron (Vale of Rheidol Rly - seasonal) 2m; Aberystwyth 12m.
🛈 ☎ 01970 612125

NEXT HOSTELS

Borth 18m, Blaencaron 21m, Tyncornel 28m

ADDITIONAL INFO

Daytime access to outside w.c. Cambrian Way footpath route. Mid-Wales booking bureau. Small Hostel shop at Warden's house.

HOW TO GET THERE

From A44 turn S 1m W of Ponterwyd. Hostel 1 ½m. From A4120 Devil's Bridge via Parson's Bridge - unsuitable for cyclists and dangerous after dark.
📍 135 GR 735786

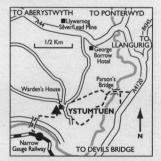

SOUTH AND WEST WALES PLUS THE WYE VALLEY

North Wales & Chester

For some great contrasts in scenery, a wide range of historical attractions and the distinctive Welsh culture, North Wales is definitely worth a visit.

Sandy beaches, sheltered coves, impressive castles and beach resorts combine to make up the dramatic North Wales coastline while Snowdonia National Park has the most spectacular mountains and lakes in Wales.

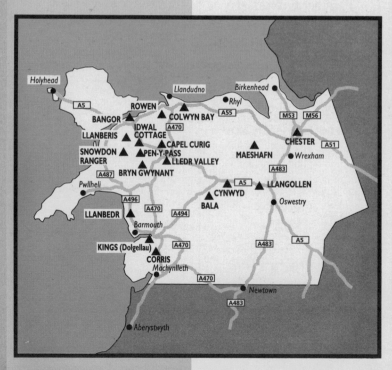

The Park encompasses 15 peaks over 3,000 feet, wooded valleys, shimmering lakes and waterfalls. There are exhilarating walks and climbs, and opportunities for fishing, horse riding and water sports.

The SHERPA bus service operates late May to mid-September from Llanberis to Caernarfon serving Pen-y-Pass, Bryn Gwynant and Snowdon Ranger Youth Hostels.

To the east of Snowdonia at Llangollen, you'll find one of the YHA's Activity Centres. Here qualified instructors take care of you on a wide range of activity holidays.

With its Roman walls and cathedral, the ancient city of Chester has a fascinating architectural heritage. It's also an ideal starting point from which to discover the dramatic scenery and commanding castles of North Wales.

And as a YHA member you will be entitled to discounts at many attractions and outlets including the Centre for Alternative Technology, Conwy Butterfly Jungle, Norton Priory and Gardens, and the Welshpool and Llanfair Light Railway.

For more information about hostelling in this area contact:

YHA Wales Regional Office,
1 Cathedral Road,
Cardiff CF1 9HA
Tel: 01222 396766/222122
Fax: 01222 237817

NORTH WALES & CHESTER

Bala

📞 01678 520215

Youth Hostel, Plas Rhiwaedog, Rhos-y-Gwaliau, Bala, Merionethshire, LL23 7EU

Overnight Charges: Under 18 £5.00 Adult £7.45

🔍 Ⓟ Coaches - contact Warden.

Apr 2 - May 31*	Open X:Sun/Mon
Jun 1 - Aug 31	Open
Sep 3 - Sep 14	Open X:Sun/Mon
Oct 1 - Oct 26	Open X:Sun/Mon

* Open Bank Hol Sun Apr 7, May 5, 26. Available for advance bookings by groups at any time throughout the year. This Hostel may NOT remain open throughout 1996 - check with Hostel or Wales Regional Office (01222 222122).

ACCOMMODATION 2-4 2 5-8 3 9+ 2

A 17th century manorhouse with partial heating and common room. A superb location for undisturbed walking in the Aran, Arenig and Berwyn Mountains. Bala Lake is only 1m and the River Tryweryn is well known for whitewater canoeing and rafting while the quiet local lanes are ideal for cycling. Nearby local attractions worth visiting are the Bala Lake Railway, Chirk Castle, Lake Vyrnwy RSPB Reserve and the Centre for Alternative Technology.

TRAVEL INFO
🚌 Crossville Cymru 94 Wrexham-Barmouth (passes close BR Ruabon & Barmouth), alight Bala 2m (📞 01286 679535). 🚉 Blaenau Ffestiniog 21m.
ℹ️ 📞 01678 521021

NEXT HOSTELS
Cynwyd 12m, Kings 24m, Llangollen 24m, Lledr Valley 28m.

ADDITIONAL INFO
Daytime access to ground floor room in Gatehouse with w.c. opposite. Barbecue in grounds.

HOW TO GET THERE
From Bala take B4391 for ¾ mile - turn right to hamlet of Rhos-y-Gwaliau (signposted as to Lake Vyrnwy) over narrow bridge and left along farm road.
OS 125 GR 947348

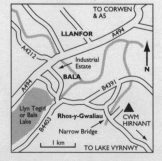

Bangor

📞 01248 353516 Fax: 01248 371176

Youth Hostel, Tan-y-Bryn, Bangor, Caernarfonshire LL57 1PZ

Overnight Charges: Under 18 £5.55 Adult £8.25

🔍 🖥️ Ⓟ BABA

Jan 1 - Nov 24	Open
Dec 27 - Dec 31	Open

ACCOMMODATION 2-4 3 5-8 6 9+ 3

This friendly Hostel only 10 minutes from the city centre provides comfortable accommodation and excellent facilities including a games room and extensive lawns. Brilliant views of the Snowdonia mountains, friendly staff and good transportation links by rail and coach make it a popular location with all types of travellers as well as school groups mid week during term time. Bangor is a gateway to Snowdonia, Anglesey and onward to Ireland. The city boasts a restored Victorian Pier, cathedral, theatre and maritime centre. The well visited castles of Penrhyn, Beaumaris and Caernarfon are easily reached. Other convenient sites worth a visit are Anglesey Sea Zoo, Greenwood Centre and Plas Newydd.

TRAVEL INFO
🚌 Frequent from surrounding areas (📞 01286 679535). 🚉 Bangor 1 ¼m. 🚢 Holyhead/Dublin, Ireland (17m)
ℹ️ 📞 01248 351915

NEXT HOSTELS
Idwal Cottage 9m, Llanberis 11m, Colwyn Bay 20m, Snowdon Ranger 17m

ADDITIONAL INFO
Daytime access to covered rear porch and w.c. Stay in the same room as Vivien Leigh or Lawrence Olivier who were regular visitors in the 40s when the building was a private home! Wales Tourist Board approved.

HOW TO GET THERE
On A5122 50yds before sharp bend into Bangor. From railway station, go along High Street onto A5122. Hostel on right.
OS 114 GR 590722

67 BEDS   Open: 17.00hrs

Bryn Gwynant

☎ 01766 890251 Fax: 01766 890479

Youth Hostel, Bryn Gwynant, Nantgwynant, Caernarfon, Caernarfonshire LL55 4NP

For Rent-a-Hostel bookings contact YHA Wales Regional Office, 4th Floor, 1 Cathedral Road, Cardiff CF1 9HA ☎ 01222 222122 Fax: 01222 237817

Overnight Charges: Under 18 £5.55 Adult £8.25

Family accommodation prices on p.10-13

🚶 🔍 P Cars and mini-buses. BABA

Jan 4 - Mar 30	Open Th/Fr/Sat only
Mar 31 - Sep 1	Open
Sep 16 - Nov 3	Open

The Hostel is available for advance bookings by groups at any time throughout the year - please contact the Warden. The annexe is available for Rent-a-Hostel bookings mid Sept to end March.

ACCOMMODATION 🛏️ 2-4 8 🛏️ 5-8 3 🛏️ 9+ 2

This beautiful stone mansion and annexe with fantastic views overlooking Llyn Gwynant has an excellent range of facilities, friendly atmosphere and good accessibility. It is a prime location for exploring the lofty peaks and the magnificent surrounding scenery, many of Snowdonia's popular attractions are easily reached. During Spring/Summer terms it is well used by school groups mid week.

TRAVEL INFO

🚌 Bws Gwynedd 11 Caernarfon-Llanberis; 95 to Beddgelert from Porthmadog or from Caernarfon, thence 4m (☎ 01286 679535). 🚂 Betws-y-Coed 13m; Bangor 13m. ⛴️ Holyhead/Dublin 35m

ℹ️ ☎ 01766 512981

NEXT HOSTELS

Pen-y-Pass 4m, Capel Curig 8m, Snowdon Ranger 9m, Llanberis 11m.

ADDITIONAL INFO

Daytime access to limited shelter in main house and outside toilets. Wales Tourist Board approved.

HOW TO GET THERE

On the A498 8m west of Capel Curig.

OS 115 GR 641513

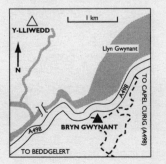

60 BEDS   Open: 17.00hrs

Capel Curig

☎ 01690 720225 Fax: 01690 720270

Youth Hostel, Plas Curig, Capel Curig, Betws-y-Coed, Aberconwy LL24 0EL

Overnight Charges: Under 18 £5.55 Adult £8.25

Family accommodation prices on p.10-13

P For cars only. Coaches - contact Warden. BABA

| Feb 16 - Dec 15 | Open |

ACCOMMODATION 🛏️ 8 🛏️ 5-8 6

Conveniently situated in Snowdonia National Park with good access by all modes of transport, the Hostel overlooks a river and forest with inspiring views of Moel Siabod. There are plenty of small dormitories and it is popular with couples, families, walkers and cyclists. It is a good location for riverside walks, forest tracks and waterfalls leading to Betws-y-Coed — a bustling mountain town. Attractions are Swallow Falls (3m), Ugly House (2m), Gwydyr Forest and Penmachno Woollen Mill. The area provides opportunities for most outdoor sports especially walking, climbing and abseiling. Plas-y-Brenin Outdoor Pursuits Centre offers half and full day courses.

TRAVEL INFO

🚌 Bws Gwynedd 19 Llandudno - Llanberis (pass BR Betws-y-Coed & Llandudno Junction) (☎ 01286 679535). 🚂 Betws-y-Coed 5m. ⛴️ Holyhead/Ireland, Dublin 40m

ℹ️ ☎ 01690 710426

NEXT HOSTELS

Lledr Valley 10m (5m by mountain), Pen-y-Pass 5m, Idwal Cottage 6m, Bryn Gwynant 8m.

ADDITIONAL INFO

Daytime access to outside toilet only. Family rooms have access all day.

HOW TO GET THERE

Road access from Betws-y-Coed difficult. Proceed to junction with A4086, turn around and return to Hostel. Steep driveway.

OS 115 GR 726579

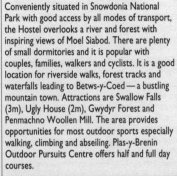

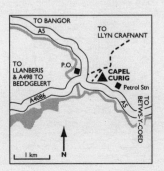

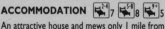

| 130 BEDS | Open: 15.00hrs |

Chester

☎ 01244 680056 Fax: 01244 681204

Youth Hostel, Hough Green House, 40 Hough Green, Chester, Cheshire CH4 8JD

Overnight Charges: Under 18 £6.15 Adult £9.10

🔍 📷 🛁 🅿 Cars only - coaches ½m BABA IBN

| Jan 5 - Dec 22 | Open |

ACCOMMODATION 🛏️⁻⁴7 🛏️⁵⁻⁸8 🛏️⁹⁺5

An attractive house and mews only 1 mile from the city centre with quality accommodation and outstanding facilities including many small rooms (some ensuite), with individual bedlights, comfortable lounges, games room and good access. It is a convenient base for exploring Liverpool's attractions and a gateway to North Wales. Chester is a fascinating Roman city with a complete circuit of city walls, a beautiful 900 year old cathedral, 'Rows' two-tiered mediaeval shopping arcades, Roman amphitheatre, Chester Zoo, Grosvenor Museum and the Deva Roman Experience. Other facilities include a selection of pubs, cinemas, theatre and interesting guided city tours on foot or by bus. Frequent services by rail, coach, bus in addition to excellent links with motorways and main roads makes this a desirable and easy to get to destination with plenty available to keep all visitors satisfied.

TRAVEL INFO
🚌 Frequent from surrounding areas (☎ 01244 602666). 🚉 Chester 1 ½m.
ℹ️ ☎ 01244 313126

NEXT HOSTELS
Llangollen 22m, Colwyn Bay 41m, Maeshafn 14m, Manchester 39m

ADDITIONAL INFO
Daytime access to left luggage, toilets, telephone, hot/cold drinks machine, comfortable seating and booking system. Good venue for residential meetings, seminars and workshops.

HOW TO GET THERE
SW of city centre on A5104 (signposted to Saltney) 350yds from traffic lights on right-hand side.
OS 117 GR 397651

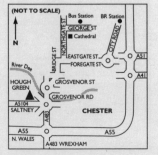

| 75 BEDS | Open: 17.00hrs |

Colwyn Bay

☎ 01492 530627 Fax: 01492 535518

Youth Hostel, Foxhill, Nant-y-Glyn, Colwyn Bay, Aberconwy and Colwyn LL29 6AB

Overnight Charges: Under 18 £4.60 Adult £6.75

🔍 🅿 Cars and mini-buses BABA

Apr 2 - Apr 27	Open X:Sun/Mon*
Apr 30 - Aug 31	Open
Sep 3 - Oct 26	Open X:Sun/Mon

* Open Easter Sun/Mon Apr 7 & 8. The Hostel is available for advance bookings by groups at any time throughout the year - please contact the Warden.

ACCOMMODATION 🛏️⁵⁻⁸5 🛏️⁹⁺3

One mile inland from the busy north Wales coast in a peaceful valley, this Hostel is surrounded by woodland and provides a relaxing atmosphere, meals and snack service, partial heating, pool table and large, secluded grounds. It is popular with international backpackers during the summer as a base for visiting the north Wales coastal resorts and Snowdonia, as well as a stopping point to or from Ireland (via Holyhead). Attractions in the area include Welsh Mountain Zoo, Conwy Castle and Town Walls, Bodnant Gardens, Rhyl Sun Centre and the Great Orme Mine. Cycling, horse riding, sailing, swimming and rock sports can be found within five miles.

TRAVEL INFO
🚌 Frequent from surrounding areas (☎ 01492 596969). 🚉 Colwyn Bay 2m. ⛴️ Ireland 35m.
ℹ️ ☎ 01492 530478

NEXT HOSTELS
Rowen 11m, Bangor 20m, Chester 41m, Capel Curig 20m.

ADDITIONAL INFO
Daytime access to garage with chairs and w.c. Wales Tourist Board approved.

HOW TO GET THERE
Turn off A55 Old Colwyn exit to join A547 (Colwyn Bay). At Park Hotel, turn left up Nant-y-Glyn road. Carry on across crossroads. Hostel is ½m on right.
OS 116 GR 847776

Corris

46 BEDS Open: 17.00hrs

☎ 01654 761686 Fax: 01654 761686

Youth Hostel, Canolfan Corris, Old School, Old Road, Corris, Machynlleth, SY20 9QT

Overnight Charges: Under 18 £5.00 Adult £7.45

Family accommodation prices on p.10-13

🖥 🔟 ⊠ P Small car park 30 metres. BABA

Feb 2 - Mar 31	Advance bookings
Apr 1 - Apr 30	Open X:Mon*
May 1 - Aug 31	Open
Sep 1 - Nov 2	Open X:Mon
Nov 3 - Dec 21	Advance bookings
Dec 27 - Jan 2 '97	Open

* Open Easter Bank Hol Mons Apr 1 and 8. The Hostel may be available for groups when otherwise closed.

ACCOMMODATION 🛏²⁻⁴2 🛏⁵⁻⁸1 🛏⁹⁺2

A former village school that was imaginatively renovated to create an ambience in keeping with its educational heritage. It has an energy efficiency and conservation theme. Popular with cyclists and families. The Centre for Alternative Technology, 'Celtica', Talyllyn Narrow Gauge Railway, Welsh Gold and King Arthur's Labyrinth within easy reach. The peak of Cader Idris is 3 miles away providing challenging hikes and good scenery.

TRAVEL INFO
🚌 34 Machynlleth - Aberllefenni. 94A Aberystwyth - Dolgellau (passes BR Machynlleth). 30 Machynlleth - Tywyn. Trawscambria 701 🚉 Machynlleth 6m.
🛈 ☎ 01654 702401

NEXT HOSTELS
Kings (Dolgellau) 15m, Borth 19m, Bala 27m, Llanbedr 28m

ADDITIONAL INFO
Day shelter, public wc's in village. WTB. Cheques payable to 'Canolfan Corris'. Credit cards not accepted. This is a privately owned Hostel operated under an agreement with YHA.

HOW TO GET THERE
Turn off A487 into Corris village. At Slaters Arms Pub, turn left, Hostel is 150metres on the right.
OS 124 GR 753080

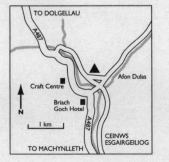

Cynwyd

30 BEDS Open: 17.00hrs

☎ 01490 412814

Youth Hostel, The Old Mill, Cynwyd, Corwen, Denbighshire LL21 0LW

Overnight Charges: Under 18 £3.75 Adult £5.50

Family accommodation prices on p.10-13

🔼 ⊠ P

Apr 3 - Apr 9	Open
May 1 - May 7	Open
May 22 - May 28	Open
Jun 1 - Sep 28	Open

The Hostel is available for advance booking by groups at any time throughout the year - please contact Warden.

ACCOMMODATION 🛏²⁻⁴2 🛏⁵⁻⁸2 🛏⁹⁺1

A self catering Hostel in a tranquil village setting, that once was a watermill has retained some of the original character with its lovely wooden beams. It offers simple accommodation in 5 dormitories with limited heating, a small shop and parking for a few cars. A separate, simple self contained cottage sleeping 5 plus a baby is available for advance bookings from April to October. As well as fine walking in the Berwyn Mountains and good cycling country, you'll also find Bala Lake (12 miles) excellent for sailing, canoeing and windsurfing. The Pistyll Rhaeadr Falls (tallest in Wales) are also worth visiting.

TRAVEL INFO
🚌 Bws Gwynedd 94 Wrexham - Barmouth (passes close BR Ruabon & Barmouth) (☎ 01286 679535).
🚉 Ruabon 18m. ⛴ Liverpool or Holyhead 40m
🛈 ☎ 01978 860828

NEXT HOSTELS
Llangollen 14m, Bala 11m, Maeshafn 18m, Lledr Valley 26m

ADDITIONAL INFO
Daytime access to shelter on small back porch and w.c. Wales Tourist Board approved.

HOW TO GET THERE
On B4401 from Corwen, bear left before bridge and follow road for 100 metres. From Bala turn right before bridge then 2nd right.
OS 125 GR 057409

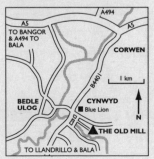

Ffestiniog

Youth Hostel,

ACCOMMODATION
We regret that this Youth Hostel is now closed. The nearest Youth Hostels are Lledr Valley (10m), Bryn Gwynant (14m) and Llanbedr (17m).

56 BEDS Open: 17.00hrs

Idwal Cottage

☎ 01248 600225 Fax: 01248 602952

Youth Hostel, Nant Ffrancon, Bethesda, Bangor, Caernarfonshire LL57 3LZ

Overnight Charges: Under 18 £4.60 Adult £6.75

Ⓐ Ⓟ BABA

Jan 4 - Mar 30	Open Th/Fr/Sat only
Mar 31 - Aug 31	Open
Sep 3 - Oct 26	Open X:Sun/Mon
Dec 24 - Dec 26	Open Xmas

The Hostel is available for advance bookings by groups at any time through the year - please contact Warden.

ACCOMMODATION 🛏2-4 2 🛏5-8 1 🛏9+ 3
With an impressive setting below the Glyder mountains and near Llyn Ogwen, this Hostel is very popular with climbers and walkers. Open fire in the winter and a large selection of board games for relaxing evening entertainment. A cafeteria style meals service operates 17.00-20.45 offering 1, 2 or 3 course meals. The Hostel stands in a small wood with access to the Cwm Idwal Nature Reserve just above it for bird watching. Spectacular lake and mountain scenery. It provides a base for climbing or rambles of all grades. Many mountain activities are available in the area. Ask the staff for details.

TRAVEL INFO
🚌 Bws Gwynedd 95 Bangor - Llanrwst (passes BR Betws-y-Coed); otherwise Purple Motors 6/7 from Bangor (pass BR Bangor), alight Bethesda, 4m (☎ 01286 679535) 🚉 Bangor 12m; Betws-y-Coed 11m. ⛴ Holyhead/Dublin 30m
🛈 ☎ 01690 710426

NEXT HOSTELS
Pen-y-Pass 10m (5m by mountain), Capel Curig 6m, Llanberis 12m (7m by mountain), Bangor 10m

ADDITIONAL INFO
Daytime access to covered way with bench seating. Public toilets next door. Wales Tourist Board approved.

HOW TO GET THERE
On the A5, 5m S of Bethesda.
OS 115 GR 648603

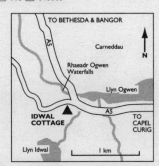

🏕 56 BEDS	Open: 17.00hrs

Kings (Dolgellau)

📞 01341 422392 Fax: 01341 422477

Youth Hostel, Kings, Penmaenpool, Dolgellau, Merionethshire LL40 1TB

Overnight Charges: Under 18 £4.60 Adult £6.75

Family accommodation prices on p.10-13

 P Cars and mini-buses. BABA

Feb 1 - Feb 29	Open Th/Fr/Sat only
Mar 1 - Apr 30	Open X:Sun/Mon*
May 1 - Aug 31	Open
Sep 17 - Oct 26	Open X:Sun/Mon
Oct 31 - Nov 23	Open Th/Fr/Sat only
Dec 27 - Jan 1 '97	Open New Year

* Open Easter Sun/Mon Apr 7 & 8. The Hostel is available for advance bookings by groups at any time - please contact Warden.

ACCOMMODATION 🛏️7

Country house and annexe set in a beautiful wooded valley with captivating views up to Cader Idris and the Rhinog mountain ranges. Family rooms, central heating and a bonfire/barbecue site in attractive riverside grounds. High and low level walking and other activities available locally. Attractions include Mawddach Estuary, Cymer Abbey, Talyllyn Railway, Centre for Alternative Technology, forest trails and gold panning at Bontddu.

TRAVEL INFO

🚌 Bws Gwynedd 28 Dolgellau - Tywyn (passes close BR Fairbourne), alight 1m W of Penmaenpool, thence 1m (📞 01286 679535). 🚉 Morfa Mawddach 5m.
ℹ️ 📞 01341 422888

NEXT HOSTELS

Corris 15m, Llanbedr 17m, Bala 24m, Lledr Valley 31m

ADDITIONAL INFO

Wales Tourist Board approved.

HOW TO GET THERE

Follow A493 1m W Penmaenpool, turn uphill opposite Abergwynant Trekking Centre, then 1m along lane situated on right hand river bank
OS 124 GR 683161

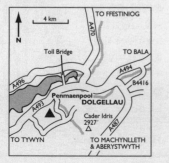

🏕 47 BEDS	Open: 17.00hrs

Llanbedr (nr. Harlech)

📞 01341 241287 Fax: 01341 241389

Youth Hostel, Plas Newydd, Llanbedr, Barmouth, Merionethshire LL45 2LE

Overnight Charges: Under 18 £5.00 Adult £7.45

Family accommodation prices on p.10-13

 P Cars and mini-buses. Coaches ½m. BABA

Jan 5 - Feb 18	Open Fr/Sat/Sun only
Feb 19 - May 1	Open X:Tu/Wed
May 2 - Sep 2	Open
Sep 5 - Oct 28	Open X:Tu/Wed
Dec 27 - Jan 1 '97	Open New Year

The Hostel is open for advanced bookings on all other dates.

ACCOMMODATION 🛏️4 🛏️6

This comfortable and homely Hostel in the centre of a village is well placed for exploring sandy seashores and unspoilt mountain wilderness. It now has full central heating (plus an open fire in the winter), plenty of family rooms and a public children's playground adjacent. With excellent rail and bus links, it is accessible throughout the year. Visitors can walk along the river valley into the heart of the majestic Rhinog mountain range or along the farm and nature trails. Pony trekking is also available. Shell Island (2m) offers a great variety of wildlife and walks for everyone. Other popular sites are Roman Steps (6m), Ffestiniog Railway, Portmeirion and Harlech Castle.

TRAVEL INFO

🚌 Bws Gwynedd 38 Dolgellau-Blaenau Ffestiniog (📞 01286 679535) 🚉 Llanbedr ½m.
ℹ️ 📞 01766 780658

NEXT HOSTELS

Kings 17m, Bryn Gwynant 31m, Snowdon Ranger 33m, Borth 48m.

ADDITIONAL INFO

Wales Tourist Board approved. No daytime access but pub and shops in village.

HOW TO GET THERE

On A496 in centre of village beside river.
OS 124 GR 585267

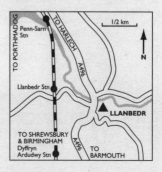

Llanberis

67 BEDS   Open: 17.00hrs

☎ 01286 870280 Fax: 01286 870936

**Youth Hostel, Llwyn Celyn, Llanberis,
Caernarfon, Caernarfonshire LL55 4SR**

Overnight Charges: Under 18 £5.55 Adult £8.25

🔍 🅿 Cars and mini-buses. Coaches, ask Warden. BABA

Jan 5 - Mar 31	Open Fr/Sat/Sun only
Apr 1 - Aug 31	Open
Sep 3 - Oct 26	Open X:Sun/Mon
Dec 27 - Jan 1	Open New Year
'97	

The Hostel is available for advance bookings by
groups at any time throughout the year - please
contact Warden.

ACCOMMODATION 2 5-8 1 9+ 3

On the hillside overlooking the lakes of Llyn
Padarn and Llyn Peris, this Hostel provides
panoramic views with the summit of Snowdon
being visible. It provides an excellent base for
sightseeing, mountain hikes, low level walks in
Padarn Country Park and all that Snowdonia
National Park has to offer. Climbing, abseiling and
fishing are also popular. Tourist attractions
include the Snowdon Mountain Railway, Power of
Wales Exhibition, Llechwedd Slate Caverns, Sygun
Copper Mines and Caernarfon Castle.

TRAVEL INFO
🚌 KMP 88 from Caernarfon; Williams 76/7 from
Bangor (pass close BR Bangor), on both alight ½m
NW of Llanberis, thence ½m (☎ 01286 679535)
🚉 Bangor 11m ⛴ Holyhead/Ireland 30m
ℹ ☎ 01286 870765

NEXT HOSTELS
Snowdon Ranger 11m (4m by mountain),
Pen-y-Pass 6m, Bangor 11m, Bryn Gwynant 11m

ADDITIONAL INFO
Daytime access to shelter in wooden shed but no
w.c. Hostel is especially suitable for annual club
re-unions. Wales Tourist Board approved.

HOW TO GET THERE
½m S W of Llanberis. From High Street take Capel
Coch Road, keep left at fork in road. Half way up
hill. Hostel on left through gate.
OS 115 GR 574596

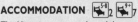 **124 BEDS** **Open: All Day**

Llangollen

📞 01978 860330 Fax: 01978 861709

YHA Study and Activity Centre, Tyndwr Hall, Tyndwr Road, Llangollen, Denbighshire LL20 8AR

Overnight Charges: Under 18 £5.55 Adult £8.25

🚿 🍴 🔥 **P** BABA

Mar 29 - Nov 2	Open

The Hostel is available for pre-booked groups when otherwise closed - please contact Centre Manager.

ACCOMMODATION 🛏️5-8 2 🛏️9+ 7

This Victorian manor and coach house provides comfortable accommodation, a good quality meals service with a restaurant license and extensive grounds. A wide selection of activities are offered for all ages: multi-activity, climbing, canoeing, caving and mountain biking are just a few. All specialist equipment is provided. The emphasis is on safety and adventure while having fun. Enjoy a 2, 3, 4 or 7 night activity break to suit your interest. The Hostel is also popular with school groups mid week in spring/summer terms. The Vale of Llangollen is a superb base for exploring north Wales and the border country.

TRAVEL INFO

🚌 Crosville Cymru 5, 94, Bryn Melyn X5 Wrexham-Llangollen (pass BR Ruabon), alight Llangollen, thence 1 ½m (📞 01352 704035)
🚉 Chirk 6m; Ruabon 6m.
ℹ️ 📞 01978 860828

NEXT HOSTELS

Cynwyd 14m, Bala 22m, Maeshafn 16m, Chester 23m

ADDITIONAL INFO

Daytime access to facilities except self catering kitchen. Wales Tourist Board accredited activity centre.

HOW TO GET THERE

From A5 E of Llangollen, follow Hostel signs. From town follow A5 towards Shrewsbury, bear right up Birch Hill. Right at Y junction in ½m.
OS 117 GR 232413

---

  60 BEDS **Open: 17.00hrs**

Lledr Valley (Betws-y-Coed)

📞 01690 750202

Youth Hostel, Lledr House, Pont-y-Pant, Dolwyddelan, Aberconwy LL25 0DQ

Overnight Charges: Under 18 £5.00 Adult £7.45

🅰️ **P** Cars and one coach.

Feb 16 - Mar 30	Open Fr & Sat only
Mar 31 - Aug 30	Open
Sep 2 - Oct 31	Open X:Sat/Sun

The Hostel is available for advance bookings by groups at any time throughout the year - please contact Warden.

ACCOMMODATION 🛏️2-4 5 🛏️5-8 2 🛏️9+ 3

A pleasant Hostel in a quiet valley in Snowdonia National Park with many small dormitories, partial heating, amiable atmosphere and large play area opposite. Only 4 1/2m from the busy town of Betws-y-Coed. This Hostel is well used by field study groups mid week during the spring/summer terms and popular on weekends and during the summer with visitors who want a more relaxing stay in the Snowdonia area. Valley and forest walks as well as walking routes to Capel Curig and Bryn Gwynant Youth Hostels. The rich industrial heritage can be seen at the slate quarries, copper mines and woollen mills. Visit the great Welsh Castles at Caernarfon, Conwy and Dolwyddelan.

TRAVEL INFO

🚌 No Service. 🚉 Pont-y-Pant ¾m.
⛴️ Holyhead/Ireland 50m
ℹ️ 📞 01690 710426

NEXT HOSTELS

Capel Curig 10m (5m by track), Bryn Gwynant 18m (10m by path), Idwal Cottage 16m, Llanbedr 25m

ADDITIONAL INFO

Daytime access to toilet and shelter in drying room. Wales Tourist Board approved.

HOW TO GET THERE

On A470 1m north west of Dolwyddelan. From Pont-y-Pant railway station turn left along road, then left across bridge and left along main road.
OS 115 GR 749534

Maeshafn

 31 BEDS   Open: 17.00hrs

☎ 01352 810320 (during opening dates)

Holt Hostel, Maeshafn, Mold, Denbighshire CH7 5LR

For Rent-a-Hostel bookings or any bookings/enquiries when Hostel is closed: YHA Wales Regional Office, 4th Floor, 1 Cathedral Road, Cardiff CF1 9HA ☎ 01222 222122 Fax: 01222 237817

Overnight Charges: Under 18 £4.60 Adult £6.75

A P

Apr 3 - Apr 9	Open
Apr 12 - Jun 29	Open Fr/Sat only*
Jun 30 - Aug 31	Open

* Open Bank Hol Sun May 5, 26. The Hostel is available for Rent-a-Hostel/sole usage bookings during closed periods.

ACCOMMODATION 🛏²

A Swiss chalet style self catering Hostel in peaceful surroundings providing moderate facilities with 3 tier bunks, a small shop and a combined dining/common room for a good social atmosphere. There are ample cycling routes in the beautiful countryside and ideal walking opportunities in the Clwydian Range or on Offa's Dyke Path just 3 miles away. Attractions in the area include Loggerheads Country Park, hill forts, Wrexham Geological and Industrial museums and castles: Ewloe, Flint and Howarden.

TRAVEL INFO

🚌 Crosville Cymru from Mold, with connections from BR Flint and Chester. Alight Maeshafn Road end, 1 ½m (☎ 01352 704035). 🚉 Buckley 8m; Flint 10m; Chester 16m. ⛴ Holyhead/Dublin 70m
ℹ ☎ 01352 759331

NEXT HOSTELS

Llangollen 16m, Chester 14m, Cynwyd 20m, Colwyn Bay 33m

ADDITIONAL INFO

Good Hostel shop. Wales Tourist Board approved.

HOW TO GET THERE

From Mold take A494 for Ruthin, then follow Maeshafn sign. Left at village. Hostel ½m on left.
OS 117 GR 208606

Pen-y-Pass

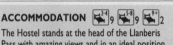 104 BEDS   Open: 13.00hrs

☎ 01286 870428 Fax: 01286 872434

Youth Hostel, Pen-y-Pass, Nant Gwynant, Caernarfon, Caernarfonshire LL55 4NY

Overnight Charges: Under 18 £6.15 Adult £9.10

Family accommodation prices on p.10-13

🔍 ♿ P Public car park opposite - permits from Warden. BABA

Jan 1 - Oct 27	Open
Dec 27 - Jan 1	Open
'97	

ACCOMMODATION 🛏²⁻⁴9 🛏⁵⁻⁸9 🛏⁹⁺2

The Hostel stands at the head of the Llanberis Pass with amazing views and in an ideal position to explore the marvellous Snowdonia National Park. A wide selection of facilities is provided including many small dormitories, TV/games room, good drying room, family rooms, plenty of information leaflets and often tea/coffee making facilities. It is a good centre for groups, walkers, families and mountain sports lovers. Being central to a ring of Youth Hostels, Pen-y-Pass offers a choice of walking routes from one to another. Both the Miner's and Pig Tracks to Snowdon Summit begin at the Hostel's front door. The Llanberis Pass with its 'three cliffs' is known as a prime area for rock climbing. The Hostel runs full board walking, climbing, navigation and photography weekends throughout the year.

TRAVEL INFO

🚌 Bus Gwynedd 19 Llandudno-Llanberis; 11 Caernarfon-Llanberis, also 96 from Llanberis (pass BR Llandudno Junction & Betws-y-Coed) (☎ 01286 679535) 🚉 Bangor 18m; Betws-y-Coed 12m. ⛴ Holyhead/Dublin 30m
ℹ ☎ 01286 870765

NEXT HOSTELS

Bryn Gwynant 4m, Capel Curig 5m, Llanberis 6m, Idwal Cottage 11m (5m by mountain)

ADDITIONAL INFO

Daytime access after 1 pm. Wales Tourist Board approved.

HOW TO GET THERE

On the A4086, 5m West of Capel Curig.
OS 115 GR 647556

| 👫 🚶 | **24 BEDS** | **Open: 17.00hrs** |

Rowen

☎ 01492 650089 (during opening dates)

Youth Hostel, Rhiw Farm, Rowen, Conwy, Aberconwy LL32 8YW

During closed periods bookings and enquiries:
Colwyn Bay Youth Hostel, Foxhill, Nant-y-Glyn,
Colwyn Bay, Aberconwy and Colwyn LL29 6AB
☎ 01492 530627 Fax: 01492 535518

Overnight Charges: Under 18 £3.75 Adult £5.50

Ⓐ Ⓟ Cars and mini-buses - coaches 1 ½m.

| Apr 3 - Apr 9 | Open |
| May 4 - Aug 31 | Open |

The Hostel may be available for advance bookings
by groups when otherwise closed - please contact
Warden.

ACCOMMODATION

This self catering, remote Welsh farmhouse on a
hill provides very basic accommodation with open
fires, no showers and only a small shop. It offers
panoramic views of the Conwy Valley and a
perfect chance to enjoy a relaxing break away
from modern conveniences. Many country lanes
are ideal for cycling where visitors can enjoy
quietness and solitude. The Hostel is only 5 miles
south of the north Wales coastline and handy for
Aber Falls, Conwy Castle, Welsh Mountain Zoo
and Bodnant Gardens.

TRAVEL INFO
🚌 Bws Gwynedd 19 Llandudno-Llanberis (pass
close BR Llandudno Junction & Conwy) (☎ 01286
679535). 🚆 Tal-y-Cafn 3m. ⚓ Ireland 38m
🛈 ☎ 01492 592248

NEXT HOSTELS
Colwyn Bay 11m, Bangor 12m by mountain, Idwal
Cottage 17m by mountain

ADDITIONAL INFO
Access to Hostel up very steep hill, unsuitable for
some vehicles. Advance booking recommended.

HOW TO GET THERE
From B5106 follow signs for Rowen to P.O.
Continue along main street for 500yds. Turn right
at Youth Hostel sign. Continue straight up hill.
Hostel is ¾m further on left.
ⓄⓈ 115 ⒼⓇ 747721

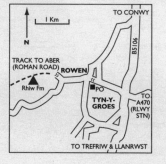

| 👫 ☀ | **67 BEDS** | **Open: 17.00hrs** |

Snowdon Ranger

☎ 01286 650391 Fax: 01286 650093

Youth Hostel, Rhyd Ddu, Caernarfon, Caernarfonshire LL54 7YS

Overnight Charges: Under 18 £5.55 Adult £8.25

🔍 Ⓟ BABA

Feb 16 - Mar 31	Open Fr/Sat/Sun only
Apr 1 - Aug 31	Open
Sep 1 - Oct 31	Open X:Mon/Tu
Nov 1 - Dec 22	Open Fr/Sat/Sun only
Dec 24 - Dec 26	Open Xmas

The Hostel is available for advance bookings by
groups at any time throughout the year - please
contact Warden.

ACCOMMODATION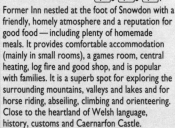

Former Inn nestled at the foot of Snowdon with a
friendly, homely atmosphere and a reputation for
good food — including plenty of homemade
meals. It provides comfortable accommodation
(mainly in small rooms), a games room, central
heating, log fire and good shop, and is popular
with families. It is a superb spot for exploring the
surrounding mountains, valleys and lakes and for
horse riding, abseiling, climbing and orienteering.
Close to the heartland of Welsh language,
history, customs and Caernarfon Castle.

TRAVEL INFO
🚌 Bws Gwynedd 95 Caernarfon-Beddgelert
(connections from BR Bangor and BR Porthmadog)
(☎ 01286 679535). Bus connections to Llanberis,
Pen-y-Pass and Bryn Gwynant Youth Hostels.
🚆 Bangor 16m, Porthmadog 13m ⚓ Ireland 30m
🛈 ☎ 01286 672232

NEXT HOSTELS
Llanberis 11m (4m by path), Bryn Gwynant 9m (7m
by path), Pen-y-Pass 14m (10 by path), Bangor 17m

ADDITIONAL INFO
Daytime access to shelter under porch/covered
way, no w.c. Wales Tourist Board approved.

HOW TO GET THERE
On A4085 between Caernarfon and Beddgelert
(8m from Caernarfon)
ⓄⓈ 115 ⒼⓇ 565550

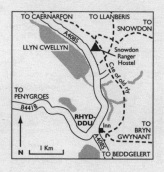

The Peak District and Manchester

Beautiful limestone dales, wild moorland and soaring gritstone edges all combine to make this some of the most stunning scenery in the country. Beloved of walkers, climbers and cyclists, the Peak District is easy to reach from all parts of the country.

The landscape is ideal for a wide range of adventure activities. Why not try one of the activity holidays or courses at the YHA Activity Centre at Edale?

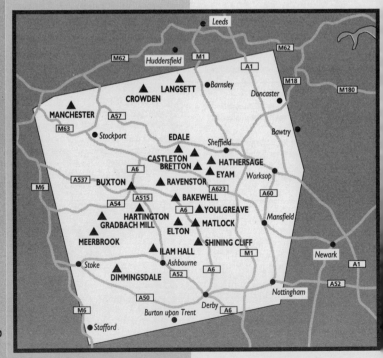

You can explore the area's many spa towns, villages and stately homes and its industrial heritage brought to life at a variety of museums and visitor centres. Then complete the formula for a great break with a trip to Alton Towers Theme Park, a show cave or a cable car ride.

Your YHA membership card and discount booklet will get you reduced rates at Jodrell Bank Science Centre and the National Tramway Museum, among others.

Useful Publications

'England's North Country'

Peak District Inter-Hostel Walks

'Cycle and See' the Staffordshire Moorlands

'Walking Holidays in England's North Country'

Holidays and courses at Edale YHA Activity Centre Tel: 01433 670302.

Helping You to Book Ahead

Pennine Way Central Booking Service – to make it easy to organise a holiday walking the Pennine Way, the booking office can organise your accommodation for all or part of the route.

A similar booking service operates for the White Peak Way, a 90-mile circular walk connecting 7 Youth Hostels.

All the above are available from the Northern Regional Office, address below (send s.a.e.)

For more information about hostelling in this area contact:

YHA Northern England Regional Office, PO Box 11 Matlock Derbys DE4 2XA

Tel: 01629 825850
Fax: 01629 824571

| 🌲 ☀ | **36 BEDS** | **Open: 17.00hrs** |

Bakewell

☎ 01629 812313 Fax: 01629 812313

Youth Hostel, Fly Hill, Bakewell, Derbyshire DE45 1DN

Overnight Charges: Under 18 £4.60 Adult £6.75

🅿 Small car park - parking in town centre. BABA

Jan 2 - Apr 4	Open Fr/Sat
Apr 5 - Oct 26	Open X:Sun*
Oct 27 - Dec 22	Open Fr/Sat
Dec 31 - Jan 1	Open for New Year
'97	

* Open Bank Hol Sun, closed Bank Hol Mon. The Hostel may be available for families and groups when otherwise closed - please contact the Warden.

ACCOMMODATION 🛏5-8 2 🛏9+ 2

Perched on a hill overlooking the lovely Wye Valley, Bakewell Hostel is a modern building close to the town centre. Small and friendly, it is an ideal choice for exploring the Peak District while enjoying the atmosphere of a traditional market town. Famous for its 'Bakewell Pudding' the town is centred around the River Wye and its medieval bridge. The surrounding countryside offers excellent walks in limestone dales and along gritstone edges. Nearby are two famous historic houses — Chatsworth House and Haddon Hall, open to the public in summer.

TRAVEL INFO
🚌 Frequent from surrounding areas (☎ 01332 292200). 🚉 Matlock 8m.
ℹ ☎ 01629 813227

NEXT HOSTELS
Youlgreave 3 ½, Matlock 8m, Buxton 12m

ADDITIONAL INFO
Daytime access to shelter. Bakewell offers guided walks, map and guidebook hire. On 'White Peak Way' and 'Three Rivers Way'.

HOW TO GET THERE
From Rutland Square take Buxton Road turning. Turn left up North Church Street, then second turning on right after 450yds.
OS 119 GR 215685

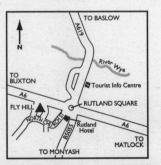

| 🚶 🚴 | **18 BEDS** | **Open: 17.00hrs** |

Bretton

Youth Hostel, near Eyam

Bookings c/o John and Elaine Whittington, 7 New Bailey, Crane Moor, Sheffield, S30 7AT. ☎ 0114 2884541.

Overnight Charges: Under 18 £4.15 Adult £6.10

🅿 For cars and mini-buses only. Coaches nearby, ask booking secretary.

| Jan 1 - Dec 31 | Open Sat/Bank Hol Sun X:Xmas |

Available for Rent-a-Hostel from Jan 1 - Feb 29 and Oct 27 - Dec 31 but not Sat when volunteer Wardened. Groups and families welcome mid-week when booked in advance.

ACCOMMODATION 🛏2-4 1 🛏5-8 2

Bretton is a small, self catering Hostel 1250ft high on Eyam Edge with breathtaking views over the moors and edges of the Dark Peak area of the National Park. A secluded location in a tiny hamlet, close to several interesting Peak District villages. The Hostel is less than 2 miles from the historic plague village of Eyam, with its fascinating church and monuments. Surrounded by unspoilt countryside, it offers a superb base for walking and exploring. Gliding available nearby (2m), riding (4m) and cycle hire (7m).

TRAVEL INFO
🚌 Various services from Sheffield, Buxton & Chesterfield (passing close BR Sheffield, Buxton Chesterfield), alight Foolow, 1m (☎ 01298 23098). 🚉 Grindleford 4m; Hathersage 4m.

NEXT HOSTELS
Eyam 1 ½m, Hathersage 5m, Ravenstor 6m

ADDITIONAL INFO
Resident Warden on Sat and Bank Hol Sun only. No shop - all food must be brought. Credit card payments are not accepted at the Hostel.

HOW TO GET THERE
1 ¾m N W of Eyam
OS 119 GR 200780

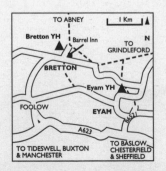

55 BEDS   **Open: 17.00hrs**

Buxton

☎ **01298 22287 Fax: 01298 22287**

Youth Hostel, Sherbrook Lodge, Harpur Hill Road, Buxton, Derbyshire SK17 9NB

Overnight Charges: Under 18 £4.60 Adult £6.75

[icons] **P** BABA

Feb 9 - Mar 28	Open Fr/Sat
Mar 29 - Dec 22	Open X:Sun*
Dec 27 - 1 Jan '97	Open

* Open Bank Hol Sun, closed Bank Hol Mon. The Hostel may be available for groups when otherwise closed - please contact Warden.

ACCOMMODATION [icons] 2 4 2

A large house in its own wooded grounds (with spacious car parking) on the outskirts of the town. Buxton is a gateway to the Peak National Park with the amenities of a busy market town — shops, indoor swimming pool, Pavilion Gardens, arts festival (July/August) etc. The Hostel is within easy walking distance of the railway station. Surrounded by the gritstone moorland, with pretty limestone villages and dales to the south, Buxton is a spa town with many attractions. The town centre has some fine buildings — don't miss the Crescent and the Opera House. Pooles Cavern is a fascinating show cave. Days out from Buxton include Alton Towers, Chatsworth House and Granada Studios.

TRAVEL INFO
🚌 Frequent from surrounding areas. Many different operators. (☎ 01298 23098). On the route of the R1 Trans Peak bus between Manchester and Nottingham. 🚉 Buxton 1¼m.
ℹ️ ☎ 01298 25106

NEXT HOSTELS
Gradbach 7m, Ravenstor 7m, Castleton 12m

ADDITIONAL INFO
Daytime access to shelter. Car parking space for long-stay circular walks.

HOW TO GET THERE
¾m S of Market Place on junction between A515 Ashbourne Road and Harpur Hill Road.
OS 119 GR 062722

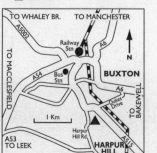

---

 150 BEDS   **Open: All Day**

Castleton

☎ **01433 620235 Fax: 01433 621767**

Youth Hostel, Castleton Hall, Castleton, Sheffield, Derbyshire S30 2WG

Overnight Charges: Under 18 £5.55 Adult £8.25
Beds in adjacent Vicarage may also be booked: Under 18 £7.45 Adult £10.90

Family accommodation prices on p.10-13

[icons] **P** Nearby. BABA

| Feb 9 - Dec 23 | Open |

32 bed annexe available for Rent-a-Hostel Nov-Feb. The Hostel may be available for groups when otherwise closed - please contact the Warden.

ACCOMMODATION [icons] 16 11 3

Historic Castleton Hall dates from the 15th century and, together with the former Vicarage, offers all the comforts of a modern Youth Hostel. Situated in the heart of the village below the ruins of Peveril Castle, the Hostel is popular with groups midweek during the school summer term, and individuals and families throughout the year. The spectacular 'Winnats Pass' and Mam Tor (the 'Shivering Mountain') overlook Castleton, a village with many craft shops and tea rooms. Close by are several famous show caves and caverns — Treak Cliff, Blue John, Speedwell and Peak. A good centre for walking (start of the Limestone Way), climbing and caving. Easily accessible from Sheffield and Manchester.

TRAVEL INFO
🚌 Mainline/Hulleys/Chesterfield Transport 272/4, East Midland 280 from Sheffield (passes BR Hope). (☎ 01298 23098). 🚉 Hope 3m. 🚢 Hull 60m
ℹ️ ☎ 01433 620679

NEXT HOSTELS
Edale 4m, Hathersage 6m, Eyam 7m

ADDITIONAL INFO
Mountain bike hire nearby.

HOW TO GET THERE
OS 110 GR 150828

Crowden-In-Longdendale

50 BEDS **Open: 17.00hrs**

☎ 01457 852135 Fax: 01457 852135

Peak National Park Hostel, Crowden, Hadfield, Hyde, Cheshire, SK14 7HZ

Overnight Charges: Under 18 £4.60 Adult £6.75

P Cars and coaches. BABA

Jan 1 - Mar 7	Rent-a-Hostel
Mar 8 - Apr 3	Open Fr/Sat
Apr 4 - Oct 26	Open X:Wed
Oct 27 - Nov 30	Open Fr/Sat
Dec 1 - Dec 31	Rent-a-Hostel

The Hostel may be available for groups when otherwise closed - please contact Warden.

ACCOMMODATION 4 2 2

Crowden-in-Longdendale is surrounded by the high moors of Bleaklow and Blackhill, the most remote and unspoilt areas of the Peak National Park. Overlooking the reservoirs of the Longdendale Valley, the Hostel was converted from a row of railwaymen's cottages. Situated on the Pennine Way and surrounded by varied walking country, the Hostel is particularly popular with walkers and climbers. It also offers a convenient rural base for visiting the many attractions of Manchester (Museum of Science and Industry, Castlefields, Granada Studios, etc).

TRAVEL INFO
National Express Sheffield - Manchester (passes close BR Sheffield) 350. Hadfield (not Sun) 5m.
☎ 01457 855920

NEXT HOSTELS
Edale 15m via Pennine Way, Mankinholes 24m via Pennine Way, Langsett 10m

ADDITIONAL INFO
Daytime access to shelter. Hostel also open to non-members.

HOW TO GET THERE
On N side of Manchester - Barnsley Road (A628) marked 'Crowden' on map.
OS 110 GR 073993

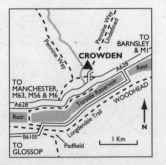

Dimmingsdale

26 BEDS **Open: 17.00hrs**

☎ 01538 702304

Youth Hostel, Little Ranger, Dimmingsdale, Oakamoor, Stoke on Trent, Staffordshire ST10 3AS

Overnight Charges: Under 18 £4.15 Adult £6.10

P For cars and mini-buses (coaches at Oakamore 1m)

Jan 1 - Mar 7	Rent-a-Hostel
Mar 8 - Oct 26	Open X:Sun*
Oct 27 - Jan 1	Rent-a-Hostel

* Open Bank Hol Sunday. The Hostel may be available for groups and parties when otherwise closed - please contact Warden.

ACCOMMODATION 2

A simple Hostel in secluded woods overlooking the Churnet Valley. Less than 2 miles from Alton Towers Leisure Park, the Hostel has basic facilities (self catering only and no showers). It makes an ideal base for exploring this relatively undiscovered corner of the Staffordshire Moorlands. Alton Towers is Britain's premier theme park, set in the grounds of magnificent mansion with lovely gardens and woodland. Visit the restored canal and barge at Froghall (5m), Cheddleton Flint Mill and the pottery museums and visitor centres at Stoke-on-Trent.

TRAVEL INFO
PMT 238 from Uttoxeter (passes close BR Uttoxeter), alight Oakamoor, ¾m (☎ 01785 223344). Blythe Bridge 6m.
☎ 01538 381000

NEXT HOSTELS
Ilam 12m, Meerbrook 14m, Gradbach 17m

ADDITIONAL INFO
Limited shop. Discounted tickets for Alton Towers on sale at reception.

HOW TO GET THERE
From Oakamoor off B5417, take road S end of Bridge past Admiral Jervis. Take right fork to top of hill, turn left up farm track to Hostel.
OS 119 GR 052436

139 BEDS   Open: All Day

Edale

☎ 01433 670302 Fax: 01433 670243

Youth Hostel and Activity Centre, Rowland Cote, Nether Booth, Edale, Derbyshire S30 2ZH

Overnight Charges: Under 18 £6.15 Adult £9.10

🛁 🔍 🖨 P Coaches - ring Hostel for best route into valley. Coach parking at bottom of drive. All other vehicles adjacent to centre. BABA

Jan 4 - Dec 1	Open*

* Open New Year for Activity Package.

ACCOMMODATION 🛏2-4 10 🛏5-8 13 🛏9+ 2

A lively Hostel with holidays and courses in a wide range of outdoor activities throughout the year (see adjacent advert). A large country house in extensive grounds in the lovely Edale Valley. Woodland, pasture and moorland extend up to the skyline — the edge of Kinder Scout plateau. Popular with school groups midweek during the summer terms. Edale marks the start of the Pennine Way and the wild moorland and heather that form the northern backbone of England. Explore gritstone edges, limestone caves, cycle trails and reservoirs. Splendid views from the Hostel tempt walkers to explore footpaths in every direction.

TRAVEL INFO
🚌 No Service. 🚆 Edale 2m. On Friday evenings (16.00-20.00 hrs) all trains are met to take you to the Hostel.
🛈 ☎01433 670207

NEXT HOSTELS
Castleton 4m, Hathersage 12m, Crowden 15m (Pennine Way over moors)

ADDITIONAL INFO
Ideal venue for conferences, seminars and group workshops. Activity holidays and courses for all levels of ability. Residents ☎ 01433 670225. Reception open all day. Small groups (up to 30) may have exclusive use of 'Kinder Cottage'.

HOW TO GET THERE
1m E of Edale village marked 'Rowland Cote' on OS. Good road and rail access.
OS 110 GR 139865

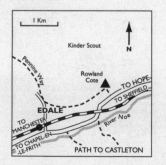

EDALE YHA ACTIVITY CENTRE for
a weekend, mini-break or longer holiday. Try lots of different sports on our multi-activity breaks. Learn or improve new skills on our specialist courses.

Abseiling	**Kayaking**
Archery	**Mountain Biking**
Adventure Course	
	Navigation
Caving	**Orienteering**
Climbing	**Pony Trekking**
Canoeing	
Hang Gliding	**Walking**

Qualified, experienced Instructors. All specialist equipment provided.

Approved by Mountain Leader Training Board, British Canoe Union, British Orienteering Federation. Member of British Activity Holiday Association. Affiliated to National Caving Association.

For details contact:
Edale YHA-Activity Centre
Rowland Cote, Nether Booth,
Edale, Derbyshire S30 2ZH

Tel (01433) 670302
Fax (01433) 670243

Elton

👣🚶🚴 32 BEDS   Open: 17.00hrs

📞 01629 650394

Youth Hostel, Elton Old Hall, Main Street, Elton, Matlock, Derbyshire DE4 2BW

Overnight Charges: Under 18 £4.15 Adult £6.10

🅿 Main Street

| Mar 1 - Oct 26 | Open |
| Dec 24 - Dec 26 | Open for Xmas |

The Hostel may be available for groups when otherwise closed - please contact Warden.

ACCOMMODATION

The Old Hall is a 17th century listed building on the main street of the village. It is a simple Hostel, retaining its old-world character, cosy and friendly. A limited meals service is available (continental breakfasts, evening snacks and packed lunches). Surrounded by a network of lanes and trails, Elton is popular with cyclists. Bicycles are available for hire at several centres. The nearby towns of Bakewell and Matlock offer many attractions for all the family and there is a wealth of industrial heritage sites to visit.

TRAVEL INFO
🚌 Hulleys 170 Matlock-Bakewell (passes close BR Matlock) (📞 01298 23098). 🚉 Matlock (Not Sun, except Apr-Oct) 6m.
ℹ 📞 01629 813227

NEXT HOSTELS
Youlgreave 2 ½m, Bakewell 7m, Matlock 6m

ADDITIONAL INFO
Daytime access to shelter. Snacks served up to 8pm.

HOW TO GET THERE
The Hostel is at the E end of Elton village on the main street.
🆗 119 GR 224608

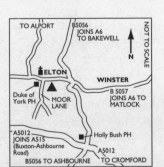

Eyam

🌲☀ 60 BEDS   Open: 17.00hrs

📞 01433 630335 Fax: 01433 630335

Youth Hostel, Hawkhill Road, Eyam, Sheffield, Derbyshire S30 1QP

Overnight Charges: Under 18 £5.00 Adult £7.45

🔍 🅿 BABA

Feb 9 - Apr 4	Open X:Sun
Apr 5 - Sep 7	Open
Sep 8 - Oct 27	Open X:Sun
Oct 28 - Nov 30	Open Fr/Sat

The Hostel may be available for groups when otherwise closed - please contact Warden.

ACCOMMODATION

A large Victorian house perched on a wooded hillside overlooking the village and with extensive views across the countryside. Popular with school parties midweek during the summer term and with walkers and climbers at weekends and holidays. Eyam is famous as the 'plague village' — with many historic reminders of 1665 when the Great Plague of London reached Derbyshire. Here and in the neighbouring villages, colourful well dressings are held throughout the summer. Eyam's annual carnival is held at the end of August. Historic houses to visit include Eyam Hall, Chatsworth and Haddon Hall.

TRAVEL INFO
🚌 As for Bretton, but alight Eyam. 🚉 Grindleford 3 ½m; Hathersage 4m.
ℹ 📞 01629 813227

NEXT HOSTELS
Hathersage 6m, Bakewell 7m, Ravenstor 7m

ADDITIONAL INFO
Daytime access to shelter and toilet.

HOW TO GET THERE
Follow signs to the public/coach park and continue up the hill - Hostel 600yds on the left past 'The Edge' and 'Windward House'.
🆗 119 GR 219769

Gradbach Mill

☎ 01260 227625 Fax: 01260 227334

Youth Hostel, Gradbach, Quarnford, Buxton, Derbyshire SK17 0SU

Overnight Charges: Under 18 £5.55 Adult £8.25

Family accommodation prices on p.10-13

🔍 📷 ♿ Ⓟ BABA

Feb 9 - Oct 26	Open
Oct 27 - Dec 7	Open X:Sun
Dec 24 - Dec 30	Open for Xmas

ACCOMMODATION 🛏2-4 11 🛏5-8 7 🛏9+ 1

A former mill on the banks of the River Dane in a quiet, unspoilt corner of the Peak District. Set in its own secluded grounds with playing field, the Hostel is popular with families and walkers exploring this relatively unknown part of the Staffordshire Moorlands. Nearby are the Roaches, gritstone crags offering superb climbing. Buxton (spa town with shops, indoor swimming pool, theatre, etc) is 6m away, Manchester only 30m. Alton Towers theme park is 14m, Quarry Bank Mill at Styal (National Trust) is 20m.

TRAVEL INFO
🚌 PMT X23 Sheffield - Hanley (passes close BR Sheffield & Buxton), alight Flash, 2 ½m (☎ 01298 23098). 🚉 Buxton 7m; Macclesfield 9m.
🚹 ☎ 01538 381000

NEXT HOSTELS
Buxton 7m, Hartington 12m, Ravenstor 12m

ADDITIONAL INFO
Ground floor accommodation suitable for people with disabilities. Discounted tickets for Alton Towers on sale at reception.

HOW TO GET THERE
OS 118 GR 993661

Hartington Hall

☎ 01298 84223 Fax: 01298 84415

Youth Hostel, Hartington, Buxton, Derbyshire SK17 0AT

Overnight Charges: Under 18 £5.55 Adult £8.25

Beds in courtyard barn with en-suite showers may also be booked: Under 18 £7.45 Adult £10.90

Family accommodation prices on p.10-13

🔍 📷 Ⓟ Limited with some roadside parking too.
BABA

Feb 9 - Dec 23	Open
Dec 27 - Jan 1	Open for New Year

The Hostel may be available for groups when otherwise closed - please contact Warden.

ACCOMMODATION 🛏2-4 8 🛏5-8 3 🛏9+ 6

This magnificent 17th century manor house — complete with a room where Bonnie Prince Charlie slept — retains many period features including oak panelling and open fires. A converted barn overlooking the courtyard offers good family accommodation with some ensuite facilities. Popular with school groups midweek during the summer term. Surrounded by a patchwork of limestone walls, Hartington is one of Derbyshire's prettiest villages. Numerous walks centre on the Dove Valley, and bikes can be hired to explore the Tissington, Manifold and High Peak Trails. Alton Towers and the American Adventure theme park are within easy reach.

TRAVEL INFO
🚌 Bowers 442 from BR Buxton; also from other areas on Sun & Bank Holidays only (☎ 01298 23098). 🚉 Buxton 12m, Matlock (Not Sun, except Apr - Oct) 13m

NEXT HOSTELS
Youlgreave 6m, Ilam 9m, Buxton 11m

ADDITIONAL INFO
Paddock for ponies available. Discounts for Alton Towers available for Hostel residents. Tickets on sale at reception.

HOW TO GET THERE
OS 118 GR 131603

THE WHITE PEAK WAY

A 90-mile circular walk in the Peak National Park.

Explore the hills and dales of the limestone "White Peak".

The YHA offers:

▲ A Booking Bureau - the easy and convenient way to book your accommodation

▲ Fully inclusive 1-week guided walking holidays with luggage transfer. Starting dates: 26 May, 4 August, 1 September £225.

For details send s.a.e. to:
**YHA Northern Region
PO Box 11 Matlock,
Derbyshire DE4 2XA
Tel: 01426 939215
(calls at local rate, 24 hrs)**

---

 42 BEDS   Open: 17.00hrs

Hathersage

☎ 01433 650493 Fax: 01433 650493

Youth Hostel, Castleton Road, Hathersage, Sheffield S30 1AH

Overnight Charges: Under 18 £5.00 Adult £7.45

🅿 In village 300yds. BABA

Jan 4 - Apr 2	Open Fr/Sat
Apr 3 - Oct 27	Open X:Sun*
Oct 28 - Nov 30	Open Fr/Sat
Dec 24 - Dec 26	Open for Xmas

* Open Bank Hol Sun, closed Bank Hol Mon. The Hostel may be available for groups when otherwise closed - please contact Warden.

ACCOMMODATION 🛏3 🛏5

A Victorian house on the edge of this popular village, the Hostel is just a few minutes walk from the railway station (Manchester-Sheffield line) and a good starting point for exploring the Peak National Park or the 'White Peak Way' circular walk. Overlooked by Stanage and Millstone Edge (two impressive gritstone edges) Hathersage attracts climbers of all abilities. The village has associations with Little John (buried here) and Charlotte Bronte who based 'Jane Eyre' on the area. Outdoor heated swimming pool open in summer. Sheffield is 10m.

TRAVEL INFO
🚌Mainline/Hulleys 272, East Midland 280 from Sheffield (☎ 01298 23098). 🚉Hathersage ½m.
🛈☎01433 620679

NEXT HOSTELS
Castleton 6m, Edale 12m, Eyam 4m

ADDITIONAL INFO
Daytime access to shelter/drying room. Booking bureau for 'White Peak Way' (sae for details). Mountain bike hire in village. Horse riding 6m.

HOW TO GET THERE
The Hostel is 100yds on right past the George Hotel on the road to Castleton.
OS 110 GR 226814

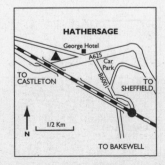

Ilam Hall

☎ 01335 350212 Fax: 01335 350350

Youth Hostel, Ilam Hall, Ashbourne, Derbyshire, DE6 2AZ

Overnight Charges: Under 18 £6.15 Adult £9.10
Family accommodation prices on p.10-13

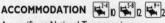 NT car park (NT charge). BABA

| Jan 5 - Feb 8 | Open Fr/Sat |
| Feb 9 - Nov 16 | Open |

The Hostel may be available for groups and parties when otherwise closed.

ACCOMMODATION 10 12 2

A magnificent National Trust mansion surrounded by a Country Park on the banks on the River Manifold near Dovedale. Beautifully decorated, it retains the atmosphere of a large country house while offering all modern comforts. Popular with school groups midweek during the summer term, and with families, individuals and other groups at weekends and holiday times. Family rooms with ensuite showers are available in the 'Brewhouse Wing'. This is a favourite area of the National Park for many walkers and hang gliders (courses available). Alton Towers is only 9m, watersports at Carsington Water (10m), cycle hire nearby.

TRAVEL INFO
Infrequent from Ashbourne; otherwise from Derby, Manchester (passing close BR Derby & Macclesfield), alight Ilam Cross Roads, 2 ½m (☎ 01332 292200). Derby 20m; Uttoxeter 15m. ☎ 01335 343666

NEXT HOSTELS
Hartington 9m, Dimmingdale 12m, Matlock 20m

ADDITIONAL INFO
ETB Grade 1 facilities for people with disabilities. Residents call box ☎ 01335 350379. Ideal venue for conferences. Discounts for Alton Towers available for Hostel residents (tickets on sale at reception).

HOW TO GET THERE
OS 119 GR 131506

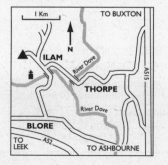

Langsett

Youth Hostel, Nr Penistone

Bookings to: c/o John and Elaine Whittington, 7 New Bailey, Crane Moor, Sheffield, S30 7AT. ☎ 0114 2884541.

Overnight Charges: Under 18 £4.15 Adult £6.10

P Coaches contact Bookings Secretary

Jan 1 - Jul 26	Open every Sat and Bank Hol Sun
Jul 27 - Aug 31	Open
Sep 1 - Dec 31	Open every Sat and Bank Hol Sun X:Xmas

Available for Rent-a-Hostel all year. Voluntary Warden on Sat, Bank Hol Sun and during August. (14 bed unit not available for Rent-a-Hostel during these periods).

ACCOMMODATION 4 1 1

Overlooking Langsett village and reservoir and the superb heather moorland beyond, this self catering Hostel is in the north east of the Peak District. Popular with small groups, both the main Hostel (22 beds) and the annexe (14 beds, but not Saturdays) are available for exclusive use all year. The northern moorland of the National Park, Bleaklow, Margery Hill and the Derwent valleys are easily accessible from Langsett, as well as the gentler terrain to the north east. Holmfirth ('Summer Wine' country) is only 8m away. Sheffield with its superb leisure facilities, museums and shops is 12m.

TRAVEL INFO
Globe/Barnsley & District/Yorkshire Traction 381 from BR Barnsley (pass close BR Penistone) (☎ 01742 768688). Penistone 3m.

NEXT HOSTELS
Crowden 10m, Hathersage 18m, Edale 20m

ADDITIONAL INFO
Daytime access to simple porch. No shop - all food must be brought. Credit card payments are not accepted at the Hostel.

HOW TO GET THERE
OS 110 GR 211005

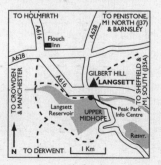

Manchester

☎ 0161 839 9960 Fax: 0161 835 2054

Youth Hostel, Potato Wharf, Castlefield, Greater Manchester M3 4NB

Overnight Charges: Under 18 £8.20 Adult £11.60

Family accommodation prices on p.10-13

Open every day of the year.

ACCOMMODATION

State of the art architecture makes this new Youth Hostel part of the vibrant Castlefield area of Manchester. The Hostel offers modern and comfortable accommodation in mostly 4 bedded rooms (some twins) all with ensuite facilities. Premium rooms are available for an extra charge and include the added facility of a TV, a table and chairs and tea and coffee making facilities. The Hostel is fully accessible to people with disabilities. The Canalside Restaurant serves delicious meals with adventurous daily menus. Everything is on the Hostels doorstep — quite literally! The Granada Studios Tour, the Museum of Science and Industry, Manchester United Football Club Tour and Museum, as well as numerous pubs, clubs and of course shops are never more than 15 minutes away! What's more we're open 24 hours a day so you can enjoy the city at night time too! The Hostel is very popular with groups during the school term time and when sporting events are taking place.

TRAVEL INFO
📞 ☎ 0161 234 3157\8

NEXT HOSTELS
Crowden 20m, Castleton 30m, Edale 30m

ADDITIONAL INFO
Conference and meeting rooms facilities. Bureau de change.

HOW TO GET THERE
From Picadilly and Victoria train stations and the bus station - take the metrolink to the G-Mex station. From the Airport - take the rail link to Picadilly station and then the metro to G-Mex. By Road - follow signs for Castlefield/Museum of Science and Industry. Hostel opposite the Museum and next door to the Castlefield Hotel.

OS 109 GR 978834

Matlock

☎ 01629 582983 Fax: 01629 583484

Youth Hostel & Training Centre, 40 Bank Road, Matlock, Derbyshire DE4 3NF

Overnight Charges: Under 18 £6.15 Adult £9.10

Family accommodation prices on p.10-13

🛏 🔍 🖥 🅿 For cars only (coaches 300yds). BABA

Jan 2 - Mar 1	Open X:Sun
Mar 2 - Dec 23	Open

The Hostel may be available for groups when otherwise closed - please contact Warden.

ACCOMMODATION 🛏2 🛏1 🛏1

This handsome Victorian building overlooks the town across to the hills beyond. Only 2 mins walk from the town centre, it is close to all amenities — shops, indoor swimming pool, bus and rail stations (with connections to London) and the M1. The Derbyshire Dales offer many places to visit for all the family: the Heights of Abraham (cable cars), the Peak District Lead Mining Museum, the National Tramway Museum and the new watersports centre at Carsington Water. The American Adventure and Alton Towers theme parks are within easy reach.

TRAVEL INFO

🚌 Frequent from surrounding areas (☎ 01332 292200). 🚆 Matlock (not Sun, except Apr-Oct) ¼m.

🚲 ☎01629 55082

NEXT HOSTELS

Bakewell 8m, Youlgreave 10m, Hartington 13m

ADDITIONAL INFO

Excellent training and conference facilities available for all to use. Includes one conference room (25max) and two seminar rooms (8-10max). Cot and high chair available for families.

HOW TO GET THERE

From Crown Square, the Hostel is 200yds up Bank Road on right.

OS 119 GR 300603

Meerbrook

Youth Hostel, Old School, Meerbrook, Leek, Staffordshire ST13 8SJ

Bookings c/o Mrs I Carlile, Elton Youth Hostel, Elton Old Hall, Main Street, Elton, Matlock, Derbyshire DE4 2BW. ☎ 01629 650394.

Overnight Charges: Under 18 £4.15 Adult £6.10

🔲 🅿 For cars only - coaches on outskirts of village.

Jan 1 - Apr 3	Rent-a-Hostel
Apr 4 - Jun 13	Open Fr/Sat*
Jun 14 - Sep 14	Open
Sep 15 - Oct 26	Open Fr/Sat*
Oct 27 - Jan 1	Rent-a-Hostel

* Available for Rent-a-Hostel (Sun-Th). Open Bank Hol Sun.

ACCOMMODATION 🛏2 🛏1 🛏1

Popular with walkers exploring this quiet corner of the Staffordshire Moorlands, this simple self catering Hostel — a former school house in the centre of Meerbrook village — has a cosy common/dining room which retains the original beamed roof. The Roaches, a long ridge of millstone grit enjoyed by climbers, is within sight of the Hostel. For birdlife and fishing Tittesworth Reservoir is on the edge of the village. The museums, factory shops and potteries of Staffordshire are all within easy reach, as well as Alton Towers theme park.

TRAVEL INFO

🚌 PMT X23 Shefield - Hanley (passes close BR Stoke-on-Trent & Buxton), alight Blackshaw Moor, 2m (☎ 01298 23098). 🚆 Stoke-on-Trent 15m.

NEXT HOSTELS

Gradbach 5m, Buxton 11m, Hartington 12m

ADDITIONAL INFO

Credit cards can only be accepted for bookings made in advance. No shop - all foodstuff must be brought.

HOW TO GET THERE

OS 119 GR 989608

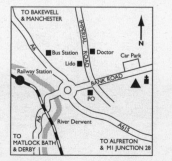

WALKING THE PENNINE WAY

Use the YHA booking service. The easy and convenient way to plan your walk.

▲ From Edale to Kirk Yetholm

▲ All accommodation booked for you

▲ Meals provided or self catering

For details send large s.a.e.
to
YHA Northern Region
PO Box 11, Matlock,
Derbyshire DE4 2XA
Tel: 01426 939215
(calls at local rate, 24 hrs)

---

84 BEDS　　**Open: 17.00hrs**

Ravenstor

☎ 01298 871826 Fax: 01298 871275

Youth Hostel, Millers Dale, Buxton, Derbyshire SK17 8SS

Overnight Charges: Under 18 £6.15 Adult £9.10

🛏 🔍 P BABA

Feb 9 - Apr 4	Open X:Sun
Apr 5 - Oct 26	Open
Oct 27 - Dec 23	Open Fr/Sat
Dec 24 - Dec 30	Open for Xmas

The Hostel may be available for groups when otherwise closed - please contact Warden.

ACCOMMODATION 🛏3 🛏2 🛏4

A large Hostel standing high above the limestone dales of the River Wye. Owned by the National Trust, it offers modern comforts in a 'country house' atmosphere — with log fires, a grand staircase and stained glass windows. Children can enjoy a nail trail and treasure hunts in the extensive wooded grounds. The White Peak around Ravenstor is a beautiful area of little fields bounded by limestone walls. Walkers follow the Monsal Trail with its famous viaduct and bike hire is available nearby. Don't miss the summer village well dressings or a visit to the market towns of Bakewell and Buxton (7m).

TRAVEL INFO

🚌 From Sheffield, Buxton (passes close BR Sheffield & Buxton) (☎ 01298 23098). 🚉 Buxton 8m.
ℹ ☎ 01298 25106

NEXT HOSTELS

Eyam 7m, Buxton 7m, Bakewell 7m

ADDITIONAL INFO

Daytime access to drying room/games room/toilet. Special meals for groups and meetings. 'Sunship Earth' children's holidays. Residents ☎ 01298 871204

HOW TO GET THERE

From A6 between Bakewell and Buxton take the B6049 to Tideswell. The Hostel is 1m past Millers Dale.
OS 119 GR 152732

Shining Cliff

Youth Hostel, Shining Cliff Woods, Nr Ambergate, Derbyshire

Bookings c/o Mrs I Carlile, Elton Youth Hostel, Main Street, Elton, Matlock, Derbyshire DE4 2BW.
📞 01629 650394.

Overnight Charges: Under 18 £3.75 Adult £5.50

🅿 Cars 10min walk (coaches by arrangement).

Jan 1 - Apr 4	Rent-a-Hostel
Apr 5 - Jul 20	Open Sat*
Jul 21 - Sep 6	Open
Sep 7 - Oct 26	Open Sat*
Oct 27 - Dec 31	Rent-a-Hostel

* Available for Rent-a-Hostel (Sun-Fr). Open Bank Hols.

ACCOMMODATION

A secluded little Hostel in the middle of a wood, offering basic self catering accommodation — ideal for small groups and families. The simple nature of the building means that there are outside toilets and no showers. Shining Cliff Woods is a Site of Special Scientific Interest in the Derwent Valley. Nearby is Matlock Bath with its attractions, Cromford's former water mill open to the public and the villages and dales of the Peak District.

TRAVEL INFO

🚌 Trent 123, 124, R1 from Derby, alighting ½m NW of Ambergate on some, thence ¾m, or at Ambergate, 1m, on others (📞 01332 292200). 🚉 Ambergate (Not Sun, except Apr-Oct).
ℹ 📞 01629 55082

NEXT HOSTELS

Matlock 8m, Elton 10m, Youlgreave 12 ½m

ADDITIONAL INFO

No shop or resident Warden. Bring torch. Credit cards accepted for advance bookings only.

HOW TO GET THERE

From Ambergate cross river by church. Cyclists up hill, turn R into woods by 3rd farm. Walkers turn R by river, through works yard and up path through woods. From Wirksworth-Belper road, turn L at pack crossroad, L into woods and R at fork.
OS 119 GR 335522

Youlgreave

📞 01629 636518 Fax: 01629 636518

Youth Hostel, Fountain Square, Youlgreave, Nr Bakewell, Derbyshire DE4 1UR

Overnight Charges: Under 18 £5.00 Adult £7.45

🅿 For cars on street and in village car park (100yds). Coaches by arrangement. BABA

Feb 9 - Apr 4	Open Fr/Sat
Apr 5 - Oct 26	Open X:Sun
Oct 27 - Dec 23	Open Fr/Sat
Dec 24 - Dec 26	Open for Xmas

The Hostel may be available for groups when otherwise closed - contact the Warden.

ACCOMMODATION

Youlgreave Youth Hostel is a unique and impressive building — the former village Co-op. Externally it retains fascinating features from its days as the village store, internally it offers all the facilities of a traditional Youth Hostel. The village is just 3m south of Bakewell, close to the limestone dales of the rivers Bradford and Lathkill with their numerous footpaths. Cycles can be hired at Parsley Hay (4m) with safe cycling along former railway lines. Chatsworth House and Haddon Hall are both close by.

TRAVEL INFO

🚌 Hulleys 170/1 from Bakewell (with connections from BR Chesterfield & Matlock) (📞 01298 23098). 🚉 Matlock (Not Sun, except Apr-Oct) 11m.
ℹ 📞 01629 813227

NEXT HOSTELS

Bakewell 3½m, Elton 2½m, Matlock 10m

ADDITIONAL INFO

Daytime access to shelter.

HOW TO GET THERE

Hostel in centre of village on main street opposite the Fountain Well.
OS 119 GR 210641

The Yorkshire Dales and South Pennines

The Yorkshire Dales offer mile after mile of wild fells, green upland pastures and valleys cut by sparkling rivers and waterfalls. Criss-crossed by a network of footpaths, this is superb walking country. 'The Herriot Way' is a popular 55-mile circular walk, taking in the best parts of Swaledale and Wensleydale (see p171)

The beautiful scenery of the National Park has impressive limestone features like Malham

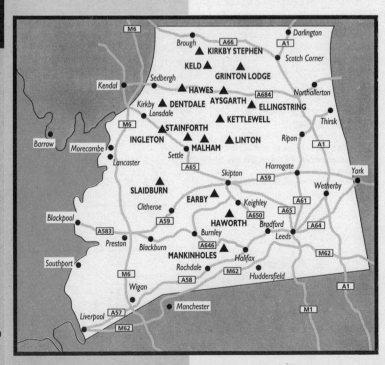

Cove and Kilnsey Crag – making it an ideal area for caving and climbing.

The South Pennines have a different kind of beauty where the peat-clad moorlands are based on sand and gritstone. The area is closely linked with the Brontë sisters and there are many associated attractions.

Also within easy reach is the city of Bradford where you'll find museums and industrial heritage to explore.

Discounts for YHA members are available at a variety of attractions in the area including National Museum of Photography, Film and Television, Tetleys Brewery Wharf and the Brontë Parsonage Museum.

Camping Barns

For simple friendly accommodation try YHA Camping Barns in North Yorkshire and the Forest of Bowland (see pages 188-193). Tel. 01200 28366 (Forest of Bowland) or 01426 939215 (North Yorks) for further details and a booking form.

Travel Information

'Dales Connections' is a free guide to getting around the Yorkshire Dales by bus and train. Send large s.a.e. to Yorks Dales National Park Centre, Hebden Road, Grassington, N. Yorks BD23 5LB. (Summer timetable available end of May).

Useful Publications

'England's North Country' – free
'Walking Holidays in England's North Country' – free
Send a SAE to the YHA Regional Office listed below

The Yorkshire Dales Cycleway Telephone 01729 830363 for your information pack.

Helping You to Book Ahead

Pennine Way Central Booking Service
Coast to Coast Central Booking Service
Herriot Way Central Booking Service & Route Maps (£1)
– to make it easy to organise a holiday walking any of the above routes, the booking office can organise your accommodation for all or part of the route – send a large SAE to the Regional Office listed below, for more details,

For more information about hostelling in this area contact:

YHA Northern England Regional Office,
PO Box 11
Matlock
Derbys DE4 2XA

Tel: 01629 825850
Fax: 01629 824571

Aysgarth Falls

 65 BEDS   **Open: 17.00hrs**

☎ 01969 663260 Fax: 01969 663110

Youth Hostel, Aysgarth, Leyburn, North Yorkshire DL8 3SR

Overnight Charges: Under 18 £5.00 Adult £7.45

Family accommodation prices on p.10-13

🔍 P Cars and mini-buses only. Coaches next door at Falls Country Club. BABA

Jan 12 - Mar 31	Open Fr/Sat
Apr 1 - Jun 30	Open X:Sun*
Jul 1 - Aug 31	Open
Sep 1 - Oct 31	Open X:Sun
Nov 1 - Nov 30	Open Fr/Sat

* Open Bank Hol Sun April 7, May 5, May 26. This Hostel may be available for groups when otherwise closed - please contact Warden.

ACCOMMODATION 🛏6 🛏6

Built of mellow sandstone, the Hostel is just 1 minute's walk from Aysgarth's famous falls. Here the foaming waters of the River Ure plunge over a series of broad rocky steps creating one of Yorkshire's most popular beauty spots. A good base for exploring Wensleydale. An excellent choice of circular walks start from Aysgarth, including the 55 mile long 'Herriot Way'. See Bolton Castle (where Mary Queen of Scots was imprisoned), visit the Yorkshire Carriage Museum (300yds) or follow the Aysgarth Falls and Woodland Trail.

TRAVEL INFO
🚌United 26 from Richmond (infrequent) (connections from BR Darlington) (☎ 01325 468771). Dales Bus (☎ 01423 566061). Also Postbus service from Northallerton (weekdays). 🚉Garsdale (not Sun, except Apr-Oct) 16m; Northallerton 24m; Darlington 34m.
🛈 ☎01969 663424

NEXT HOSTELS
Hawes 9m, Grinton Lodge 8m, Kettlewell 13m

ADDITIONAL INFO
Daytime access to porch and cycle shed.

HOW TO GET THERE
¹/₂m E of Aysgarth on the A684.
OS 98 GR 012884

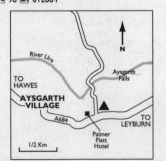

Dentdale

 40 BEDS   **Open: 17.00hrs**

☎ 015396 25251

Youth Hostel, Cowgill, Dent, Sedbergh, Cumbria LA10 5RN

Overnight Charges: Under 18 £5.00 Adult £7.45
P

Feb 2 - Feb 29	Open Fr/Sat
Mar 1 - Mar 31	Open X:Wed/Th
Apr 1 - Aug 31	Open X:Th
Sep 1 - Oct 31	Open X:Wed/Th
Nov 1 - Dec 21	Open Fr/Sat
Dec 27 - Jan 4	Open
'97	

The Hostel may be available for groups when otherwise closed - please contact the Warden.

ACCOMMODATION 🛏1 🛏3

An attractive whitewashed building on the banks of the River Dee, the Hostel is a former shooting lodge, now a listed building. Situated in the upper reaches of lovely Dentdale, on the Dales Way Path, the Hostel is popular with cavers and walkers alike. The cobbled streets and tiny cottages of Dent evoke the days of the 17th century. Step back in time to enjoy the surrounding landscape of meadows and hedges; then walk to the top of Whernside (2424ft) for truly outstanding views. Or take a trip on the historic Settle to Carlisle Railway.

TRAVEL INFO
🚌As for Hawes, but alight Hawes, thence 8m.
🚉Dent 2m (not Sun except Apr-Oct)
🛈 ☎015396 20125

NEXT HOSTELS
Hawes 8m, Ingleton 11m, Stainforth 15m

HOW TO GET THERE
On Dentdale road N.E. of Whernside, about 2m from junction with Hawes - Ingleton road about 6m E. of Dent. 7'6' width restriction at Cowgill; large vehicles approach via Newby Head.
OS 98 GR 773850

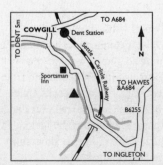

Earby

23 BEDS   Open: 17.00hrs

☎ 01282 842349

Katherine Bruce Glasier Memorial Hostel, Glen Cottage, Birch Hall~Lane, Earby, Colne, Lancs BB8 6JX

Overnight Charges: Under 18 £4.15 Adult £6.10

🅿 Limited.

Jan 1 - Mar 31	Rent-a-Hostel
Apr 3 - Sep 30	Open X:Tu
Oct 1 - Dec 31	Rent-a-Hostel

ACCOMMODATION 🛏2-4 1 🛏5-8 3

A small cottage on the outskirts of the town, the Hostel offers simple self catering accommodation just 1 mile from the Pennine Way. The pretty garden complete with waterfalls is adjacent to the local open park, providing plenty of space for outdoor recreation. Look across from Earby to Pendle Hill, home of Lancashire's witches, and beyond to the edge of the Forest of Bowland. Explore the area's rich industrial heritage with a wealth of fascinating places to visit — museums, railways and historic houses. Or browse around the many mill shops and markets.

TRAVEL INFO
🚌 Various services from Burnley, Skipton (passing close BR Colne & Skipton), alight Earby, ½m (☎ 01257 241693). 🚆 Colne 5m; Skipton 8m.
🛈 ☎01756 817046

NEXT HOSTELS
Haworth 15m (via Pennine Way), Linton 15m, Malham 16m (via Pennine Way)

ADDITIONAL INFO
Daytime access to shelter and toilet. No Hostel shop and limited heating.

HOW TO GET THERE
The Hostel is 300yds beyond the Red Lion public house.
OS 103 GR 915468

Ellingstring

20 BEDS   Open: 17.00hrs

☎ 01677 460216 (Warden's phone)

Youth Hostel, Lilac Cottage, Ellingstring, Masham, Nr Ripon, North Yorkshire HG4 4PW

Or book via: Mrs A C Wright, Hollybreen, Ellingstring, Ripon, North Yorks HG4 4PW.

Overnight Charges: Under 18 £3.75 Adult £5.50

🅿 Cars and mini-buses.

Jan 1 - Mar 31	Rent-a-Hostel
Apr 1 - Jun 30	Open X:Wed/Th
Jul 1 - Aug 31	Open
Sep 1 - Oct 31	Open X:Wed/Th
Nov 1 - Dec 31	Rent-a-Hostel

ACCOMMODATION 🛏2-4 1 🛏5-8 2

The Hostel — a stone built detached cottage surrounded by pretty gardens in the tiny hamlet of Ellingstring — offers basic self catering accommodation, just outside the Yorkshire Dales National Park. The ancient town of Middleham is close by, famous for its castle and racehorses. Follow the road and Yorkshire Dales Cycle Way down secret Coverdale, the longest of Wensleydale's many side-valleys, to Kettlewell in Wharfedale. Or visit the splendid monastic ruins of Fountains Abbey and Jervaulx Abbey. Pony trekking available 3m.

TRAVEL INFO
🚌 United 159 (infrequent) from Ripon to within 1m (☎ 01325 468711); otherwise postbus from Ripon (☎ 01325 447470) or Dales Bus (☎ 01423 566061). 🚆 Thirsk 16m; Northallerton 17m.
🛈 ☎01765 4625

NEXT HOSTELS
Grinton 12m, Aysgarth 14m, Osmotherley 25m

ADDITIONAL INFO
Credit card bookings are not accepted. Limited supplies are available from Hostel shop. No showers.

HOW TO GET THERE
OS 99 GR 176835

Grinton Lodge

70 BEDS **Open: 17.00hrs**

☎ 01748 884206 Fax: 01748 884876

Youth Hostel, Grinton, Richmond, North Yorkshire DL11 6HS

Overnight Charges: Under 18 £4.60 Adult £6.75

🔍 📷 Ⓟ BABA

Jan 5 - Mar 31	Open X:Sun/Mon
Apr 1 - Aug 31	Open
Sep 1 - Nov 2	Open X:Sun
Dec 27 - Jan 4 '97	Open

The Hostel may be available when otherwise closed - please enquire.

ACCOMMODATION 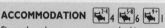 4 6 1

Situated on the grouse moor overlooking Swaledale and Arkengarthdale, this former shooting lodge retains much of its original character. Complete with turret, log fires, courtyard and tiled game larder (now the cycle shed!), this is an excellent location for exploring 'Herriot Country'. Coast to Coast route 3/4m. The swift flowing river, green meadows and drystone walls of Swaledale give this dale a unique character. Further down the valley is the market town of Richmond, with its narrow alleys steeped in history and dominated by its castle.

TRAVEL INFO
🚌 United 30 Richmond - Keld (infrequent) (connections from BR Darlington), alight Grinton, ¾m (☎ 01325 468771); West Yorkshire Dales Bus (☎ 01423 566061). 🚆 Kirkby Stephen (not Sun, except Apr - Oct) 24m; Darlington 25m.
ℹ ☎ 01748 825994

NEXT HOSTELS
Aysgarth 8m, Keld 13m, Ellingstring 13m

ADDITIONAL INFO
Daytime access to kitchen, sitting area and toilets. On the 'Herriot Way'. Barbecue and grounds for games. Fishing in River Swale. Mountain bike hire from Hostel.

HOW TO GET THERE
¾m from Grinton due S on Reeth-Leyburn Road
OS 98 GR 048975

Hawes

58 BEDS **Open: 17.00hrs**

☎ 01969 667368 Fax: 01969 667368

Youth Hostel, Lancaster Terrace, Hawes, North Yorkshire DL8 3LQ

Overnight Charges: Under 18 £5.55 Adult £8.25

🔍 📷 📶 Ⓟ Cars & coaches 300yds. BABA

Mar 1 - Mar 31	Open X:Wed/Th
Apr 1 - Jun 30	Open X:Su*
Jul 1 - Aug 31	Open
Sep 1 - Dec 22	Open X:Mon/Tu
Dec 23 - Dec 28	Open

* Open Bank Hol Sun Apr 7, May 5, May 26. The Hostel may be available for group when otherwise closed - please contact Warden.

ACCOMMODATION 7 5

This modern, comfortable Hostel overlooks the lovely village of Hawes and Wensleydale beyond. Its friendly atmosphere and small bedrooms make this a popular base for families, plus walkers on the Pennine Way and Herriot Way. Hawes is at the heart of the Yorkshire Dales surrounded by heather clad fells. Don't miss Hardraw Force waterfall (the highest single fall in England) or a glimpse of a steam train crossing the magnificent Ribblehead viaduct. Visit the factory where Wensleydale's famous cheese is made.

TRAVEL INFO
🚆 BR Harrington from BR Garsdale (☎ 01969 50682); United 26 from Richmond (infrequent) (connections from BR Darlington) (☎ 01325 468771); National Park bus from BR Garsdale in summer (☎ 01423 566061). Also Postbus service. 🚆 Garsdale (not Sun, exc. Apr-Oct) 6m.
ℹ ☎ 01969 667450

NEXT HOSTELS
Dentdale 8m, Keld 9m, Aysgarth 10m

ADDITIONAL INFO
Daytime access to entrance hall and drying room. Gayle Institute 10mins walk from Hostel available for classroom/workshop. 'Heartbeat Award' for catering.

HOW TO GET THERE
W of Hawes on the Ingleton Road.
OS 98 GR 867897

Haworth

90 BEDS | Open: All day

☏ 01535 642234 Fax: 01535 643023

Youth Hostel, Longlands Hall, Longlands Drive, Lees Lane, Haworth, Keighley, West Yorkshire BD22 8RT

Overnight Charges: Under 18 £5.55 Adult £8.25

P Cars & coaches. BABA

Feb 2 - Mar 31	Open X:Sun
Apr 1 - Sep 30	Open
Oct 1 - Dec 21	Open X:Sun
Dec 23 - Dec 28	Open

The Hostel may be available for groups when otherwise closed - please contact Warden.

ACCOMMODATION 🛏2-4 2 🛏5-8 4 🛏9+ 5

This impressive Victorian mansion in its own grounds overlooks the famous Bronte village of Haworth. Built in the grand style for a wealthy mill owner, it boasts a grand sweeping staircase and oak panelling. Popular with groups midweek during the school summer term and other visitors throughout the year. Explore the village and surrounding moors which provided inspiration for novels like 'Wuthering Heights'. Visit the Bronte Museum; Worth Valley Steam Railway; the National Museum of Film, Photography and Television (at Bradford 8m); Saltaire Victorian village or the 'Eureka' childrens museum at Halifax.

TRAVEL INFO
🚌 Frequent from surrounding areas (☏ 01535 603284). 🚉 Keighley 4m; Haworth (Worth Valley Rly) ½m.
🛈 ☏ 01535 642329

NEXT HOSTELS
Mankinholes 12m, Earby 18m, York 45m

ADDITIONAL INFO
Ideal for conferences. Special menus available.

HOW TO GET THERE
OS 104 GR 038378

Ingleton

66 BEDS | Open: 17.00hrs

☏ 015242 41444 Fax: 015242 41854

Youth Hostel, Greta Tower, Sammy Lane, Ingleton, Carnforth, Lancashire LA6 3EG

Overnight Charges: Under 18 £4.60 Adult £6.75

Family accommodation prices on p.10-13
🖥 P BABA

Jan 5 - Jan 31	Open Fr/Sat/Sun
Feb 1 - Mar 31	Open X:Sun/Mon
Apr 1 - Jun 30	Open X:Sun
Jul 1 - Aug 31	Open
Sep 1 - Sep 30	Open X:Sun
Oct 1 - Nov 2	Open X:Sun/Mon
Dec 23 - Jan 4 '97	Open

* Open Bank Hol Sun Apr 7, May 5, May 26. The Hostel may be available when otherwise closed - please contact Warden.

ACCOMMODATION 🛏2-4 4 🛏5-8 6 🛏9+ 1

An enlarged stone built cottage close to the centre of this popular village, overlooked by Ingleborough (2376ft) — one of the famous Three Peaks of the National Park. The Hostel sits in its own mature gardens, next to the village park. Enjoy the 4.5m circular 'Waterfalls Walk' past Ingleton's famous waterfalls or a visit to the spectacular natural White Scar Caves. The area is a centre for caving and potholing, with miles of natural underground systems. The Yorkshire Dales Cycleway passes through Ingleton.

TRAVEL INFO
🚌 Stagecoach Ribble X80, 80/1 from Lancaster (passes close BR Lancaster & Bentham) (☏ 01257 241693) 🚉 Bentham 3m; Clapham 4m.
🛈 ☏ 01468 41049

NEXT HOSTELS
Stainforth 10m, Dentdale 11m, Kendal 17m

ADDITIONAL INFO
Daytime access to all public areas.

HOW TO GET THERE
From market square take lane down hill opposite Nat West Bank.
OS 98 GR 695733

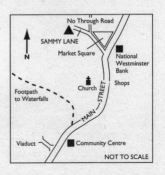

▲ ☀ 46 BEDS   Open: 17.00hrs

Keld

📞 01748 886259 Fax: 01748 886013

Youth Hostel, Keld Lodge, Upper Swaledale, Richmond, North Yorkshire DL11 6LL

Overnight Charges: Under 18 £4.60 Adult £6.75

🅿 Roadside. BABA

Jan 5 - Mar 31	Open Fr/Sat/Sun/Mon
Apr 1 - Jun 30	Open X:Mo*
Jul 1 - Aug 31	Open
Sep 1 - Oct 31	Open X:Mon/Tu
Nov 1 - Nov 30	Open Fr/Sat/Sun/Mon
Dec 27 - Jan 4 '97	Open

* Open Bank Hol Mon Apr 8 and May 27. The Hostel may be available when otherwise closed - please contact Warden.

ACCOMMODATION 🛏²⁻⁴3 🛏⁵⁻⁸5 🛏⁹⁺1

This former shooting lodge stands high in upper Swaledale, surrounded by moorland and waterfalls. The cosy lounge with log fire is welcomed by weary walkers on the Coast-to-Coast and Pennine Way routes, which cross here. The tiny grey-stone villages of Keld and neighbouring Muker appear unchanged for centuries. Tan Hill Inn (5m) at 1732ft is the highest pub in England. Below Keld the valley widens into green pastures with drystone walls, summer wildflowers and Swaledale's distinctive field barns.

TRAVEL INFO

🚌 United 30 from Richmond (infrequent) (connections from BR Darlington) (📞 01325 468771); Dales Bus (📞 01423 566061). 🚂 Kirkby Stephen (not Sun, except Apr - Oct) 11m.
ℹ 📞 01748 850252

NEXT HOSTELS

Hawes 8m, Kirkby Stephen 11m, Grinton 13m

ADDITIONAL INFO

Daytime access to porch only for shelter.

HOW TO GET THERE

Situated W of Keld village on B6270 Reeth to Kirkby Stephen Road.
OS 91 GR 891009

▲ ☀ 58 BEDS   Open: 13.00hrs

Kettlewell

📞 01756 760232 Fax: 01756 760402

Youth Hostel, Whernside House, Kettlewell, Skipton, North Yorkshire BD23 5QU

Overnight Charges: Under 18 £5.00 Adult £7.45

Family accommodation prices on p.10-13

🅿 Limited. In village. BABA

Feb 2 - Mar 31	Open X:Wed/Th
Apr 1 - Sep 30	Open
Oct 1 - Dec 21	Open X:Wed/Th

The Hostel may be available for groups when otherwise closed - please contact Warden.

ACCOMMODATION 🛏²⁻⁴4 🛏⁵⁻⁸7

This attractive stone house is in the centre of the Upper Wharfedale village of Kettlewell, which is surrounded by open fells with footpaths and bridleways in every direction. In addition to the main Hostel there is a 10 bed self contained unit, popular with families and small groups. This is superb countryside for a wide range of outdoor activities. Follow the road past the waterfalls over into Bishopdale or along the Dales Way path up Langstrothdale. Wander along inviting riverside paths or climb over the tops to reach the tiny hamlets of secret Littondale.

TRAVEL INFO

🚌 Pride of the Dales 72, Keighley & District 809 from BR Skipton, alight Grassington 6m (📞 01754 753123) 🚂 Skipton 16m.
ℹ 📞 01756 752774

NEXT HOSTELS

Linton 8m, Malham 14m, Aysgarth 13m

ADDITIONAL INFO

On the Dales Way path and the Yorkshire Dales Cycleway.

HOW TO GET THERE

OS 98 GR 970724

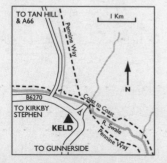

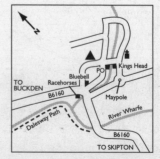

Kirkby Stephen

🌲❄ **44 BEDS**   **Open: 17.00hrs**

📞 **017683 71793 Fax: 017683 71793**

Youth Hostel, Fletcher Hill, Market Street, Kirkby Stephen, Cumbria CA17 4QQ

Overnight Charges: Under 18 £5.00 Adult £7.45

Family accommodation prices on p.10-13

🔍 ✉ 🅿 Roadside or free car park 100yds. Coach park in road behind Hostel. BABA

Feb 16 - Mar 31	Open X:Mon/Tu
Apr 1 - Jun 30	Open X:Mon
Jul 1 - Aug 31	Open
Sep 1 - Nov 2	Open X:Mon/Tu
Nov 3 - Dec 14	Open Fr/Sat

When closed advance bookings may be accepted from groups - enquiries welcome.

ACCOMMODATION 🛏³ 🛏⁵

Experience the unique character of this former chapel in the historic market town of Kirkby Stephen. Sympathetically converted to retain the traditional wooden pews, oak beams and stained glass windows — combined with all the comforts of a modern Youth Hostel. Interesting shops and places to visit make this the ideal place to linger on the Coast-to-Coast Walk or the Cumbria Cycle Way. Nearby the Settle to Carlisle Railway reaches its highest point below Wild Boar Fell at the head of the dale of Mallerstang, site of the romantic ruin of Pendragon Castle.

TRAVEL INFO
🚌 OK X74 Darlington - Carlisle (📞 01388 604581); Primrose Coaches Newcastle-Upon-Tyne - Blackpool (passes BR Kirkby Stephen) (📞 0191 413 2257). 🚉 Kirkby Stephen (not Sun, except Apr - Oct) 1½m.
ℹ 📞017683 71199

NEXT HOSTELS
Keld 11m, Dufton 10m, Hawes 15m

ADDITIONAL INFO
Daytime access to bicycle shed.

HOW TO GET THERE
Hostel in centre of town on main street A685. 12m from M6 junction 38 or 2m from A66 at Brough.
OS 91 GR 774085

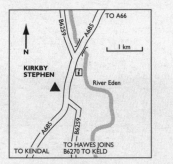

Linton (nr Grassington)

🌲❄ **38 BEDS**   **Open: 17.00hrs**

📞 **01756 752400 Fax: 01756 752400**

Youth Hostel, The Old Rectory, Linton-in-Craven, Skipton, North Yorkshire BD23 5HH

Overnight Charges: Under 18 £5.55 Adult £8.25

✉ 🅿 Cars & mini-buses only - coaches ½m. BABA

Jan 1 - Jan 7	Rent-a-Hostel
Jan 8 - Mar 2	Open Mon/Tu/Wed/Th
	Rent-a-Hostel Fr/Sat
Apr 1 - Sep 30	Open X:Sun*
Oct 1 - Oct 31	Open X:Sun/Mon
Nov 1 - Dec 19	Open Mon/Tu/Wed/Th
	Rent-a-Hostel Fr/Sat
Dec 20 - Jan 5	Rent-a-Hostel

* Open Sun Apr 7, May 5, May 26, Aug 25.

ACCOMMODATION 🛏² 🛏³ 🛏¹

A 17th century Rectory built of mellow stone in one of Wharfedale's prettiest villages. The Hostel's location and large garden make it a popular base for exploring the Yorkshire Dales. Wander around the village of Linton with its lovely old world cottages, ancient clapper bridge and packhorse bridge by the ford. Or explore the many delights of Wharfedale — Bolton Abbey (8m), Linton Falls (½m) or the shops, cafes and Folk Museum at neighbouring Grassington. Kilnsey Crag (4m).

TRAVEL INFO
🚌 Pride of the Dales 72 (📞 01756 753123) alight Linton; Keighley & District 72, 272, 809 & 76 (📞 01535 603284) alight Linton or Grassington 1m. 🚉 Skipton 8m.
ℹ 📞01756 752774

NEXT HOSTELS
Kettlewell 8m, Malham 7m (by path), Earby 15m

ADDITIONAL INFO
Daytime access to entrance hall and toilets. On the Dales Way path.

HOW TO GET THERE
Adjacent to village green (E side of Packhorse bridge over river).
OS 98 GR 998627

Malham

80 BEDS **Open: 17.00hrs**

☎ 01729 830321 Fax: 01729 830551

John Dower Memorial Hostel, Malham, Skipton, North Yorkshire BD23 4DE

Overnight Charges: Under 18 £6.15 Adult £9.10

Family accommodation prices on p.10-13

🔍 📷 ♿ ♿ 🅿 Cars and mini-buses only, coaches 200metres BABA

Jan 1 - Dec 21	Open
Dec 22 - Dec 26	Rent-a-Hostel
Dec 27 - Jan 4 '97	Open

Annexe available for Christmas Rent-a-Hostel.

ACCOMMODATION 🛏️²⁻⁴ 4 🛏️⁵⁻⁸ 12

A newly refurbished Hostel close to the centre of the popular village of Malham. With many small bedrooms, pretty furnishings and a pleasant garden, this Hostel is now a favourite with families as well as walkers (on the Pennine Way) and cyclists (Yorkshire Dales Cycleway). The huge natural amphitheatre of Malham Cove and the amazing limestone 'pavements' have created a unique landscape. Malham Tarn and its nature reserve is internationally important for nature conservation and the whole area is outstanding for cavers, geologists and birdwatchers.

TRAVEL INFO
🚌 Pennine 210 from Skipton (passes close BR Skipton) (☎ 01756 749215); West Yorkshire Dales Bus (☎ 01423 566061). 🚉 Skipton 13m, or Gargrave 8m
ℹ️ ☎ 01729 830 363

NEXT HOSTELS
Stainforth 8m, Kettlewell 10m (by path), Linton 7m (by path)

ADDITIONAL INFO
Daytime access to lounges and toilets. Travel cot and high chair available.

HOW TO GET THERE
OS 98 GR 901629

Mankinholes

40 BEDS **Open: 17.00hrs**

☎ 01706 812340 Fax: 01706 812340

Youth Hostel, Mankinholes, Todmorden, Lancashire OL14 6HR

Overnight Charges: Under 18 £4.60 Adult £6.75

🅿 Cars & minibuses only. Coaches 150yds - approach via Walsden. BABA

Feb 2 - Mar 31	Open Fr/Sat
Apr 1 - Aug 31	Open X:Sun*
Sep 1 - Oct 31	Open X:Sun/Mon
Nov 1 - Nov 30	Open Fr/Sat

* Open Bank Hol Sun Apr 7, May 5, May 26, Aug 25. The Hostel may be available for groups when otherwise closed - please contact Warden.

ACCOMMODATION 🛏️⁵⁻⁸ 4 🛏️⁹⁺ 1

A stone built house in the ancient hamlet of Mankinholes. Once the local manor house, the Hostel is now a listed building, just 1/2m from the Pennine Way. This is an area of winding lanes and packhorse routes across wild moorland, yet still close to towns such as Hedben Bridge and Halifax. The wealth of industrial heritage sites in the area are a legacy of the textile industry from the time of the Industrial Revolution. Walk the Calderdale Way or visit the magnificent Piece Hall at Halifax, the Clog Factory, Automobile Museum or Eureka children's museum.

TRAVEL INFO
🚌 Yorkshire Rider T6 from Todmorden (passes close BR Todmorden) (☎ 01422 365985). 🚉 Todmorden 2m (☎ 0113 244 8133)
✈️ Liverpool/Belfast 55m, Hull/Europe 85m - both accessible via M62 motorway
ℹ️ ☎ 01706 818181

NEXT HOSTELS
Haworth 12m (18m by Pennine Way), Earby 25m (by Pennine Way), Crowden 24m (by Pennine Way)

ADDITIONAL INFO
Paragliding school nearby. Bread and milk must be ordered in advance.

HOW TO GET THERE
Follow road to Lumbutts - Hostel ¼m E of Top Brink public house.
OS 103 GR 960235

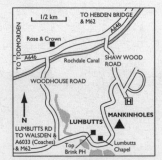

22 BEDS Open: 17.00hrs

Slaidburn

📞 01200 446656

Youth Hostel, King's House, Slaidburn, Clitheroe, Lancashire BB7 3ER

Advance Bookings 📞 015242 41567

Overnight Charges: Under 18 £3.75 Adult £5.50

🅿 Coaches & mini-buses 200yds.

Jan 1 - Apr 4	Rent-a-Hostel
Apr 5 - Apr 13	Open
Apr 14 - May 2	Open Fr/Sat*
May 3 - Sep 28	Open
Oct 1 - Oct 31	Open Fr/Sat*
Nov 1 - Dec 31	Rent-a-Hostel

Available for advance group bookings mid-week.

ACCOMMODATION 🛏️² 🛏️¹

Formerly a 17th century inn, the Hostel is in the centre of the picturesque village of Slaidburn. It offers simple self catering accommodation with open fires (but no central heating) in the heart of the Forest of Bowland — a 300 sq mile Area of Outstanding Natural Beauty. The Forest of Bowland is relatively undiscovered — despite being close to the towns of the north west and glimpsed from afar by motorists on the M6. Enjoy the hills and secret valleys on foot or by bike. From the south it is a convenient stepping stone for the Yorkshire Dales.

TRAVEL INFO
🚌 Lakeland 110/1 from Clitheroe (connections from BR Blackburn) (📞 01257 241693).
🚉 Clitheroe 8m
ℹ 📞 01200 25566

NEXT HOSTELS
Stainforth 15m, Ingleton 15m, Earby 17m

ADDITIONAL INFO
Daytime access to outside toilets. Hostel shop facilities limited. 16 bed annexe available from May to August.

HOW TO GET THERE
OS 103 GR 711523

50 BEDS Open: 17.00hrs

Stainforth

📞 01729 823577 Fax: 01729 825404

Youth Hostel, 'Taitlands' Stainforth, Settle, North Yorkshire BD24 9PA

Overnight Charges: Under 18 £5.00 Adult £7.45

🅿 Cars & mini-buses in grounds. Coaches - ask Warden.
BABA

Feb 9 - Mar 31	Open Fr/Sat
Apr 1 - Apr 30	Open X:Sun*
May 1 - Aug 31	Open
Sep 20 - Oct 31	Open X:Sun
Nov 1 - Nov 30	Open Fr/Sat

* Open Bank Hol Sun April 7.

ACCOMMODATION 🛏️² 🛏️³ 🛏️²

A handsome stone built Victorian house in its own attractive grounds. Now a listed building, the Hostel retains its original character as a large country house, with a sweeping staircase and fine plasterwork. From the graceful arch of the packhorse bridge at Stainforth, follow the River Ribble downstream to Stainforth Force. Or take the winding moorland road over to lovely Littondale, crossing the Pennine Way on its route down to Malham Tarn.

TRAVEL INFO
🚌 Ingfield Northern Rose, Settle - Horton (📞 01729 822568). Good taxi service 📞 01729 822219. 🚉 Settle (not Sun, except Apr - Oct) 2 ½m; Giggleswick 3m.
ℹ 📞 01729 823617

NEXT HOSTELS
Malham 8m, Ingleton 10m, Kettlewell 12m

HOW TO GET THERE
2m N of Settle in the Yorkshire Dales National Park. ¼m S of village on main Settle - Horton-in-Ribblesdale Road. 3 ½m S of Pennine Way at Dale Head, and 4m S of Pennine Way at Horton.
OS 98 GR 821668

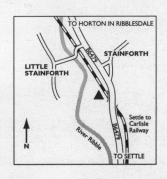

The Yorkshire Moors, Wolds and Coast

From rolling moors to spectacular coast and the magnificent city of York, the east of Yorkshire is an ideal area for a break. The North York Moors National Park contains the largest expanse of heather clad moorland in the country. It's also dotted with picturesque villages and historical attractions – from castles to prehistoric burial mounds.

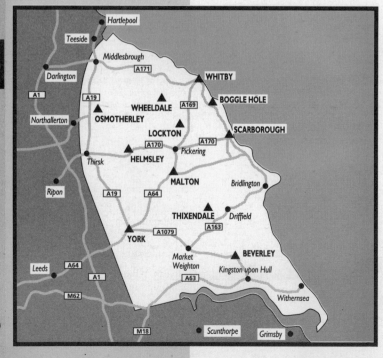

The spectacular North Yorkshire coastline combines steep cliffs and sandy beaches with quaint fishing villages and bustling resorts like Whitby and Scarborough.

Take a trip to the ancient city of York where you can explore its many Viking and Roman connections and visit the wonderful Minster and Castle.

Visit the Jorvik Centre, the National Railway Museum or take a ride on the North York Moors Railway and ask for your YHA discount – on presentation of your membership card and discount booklet.

Camping Barns

For simple, friendly accommodation try YHA Camping Barns in North Yorkshire. See pages 188-193 and tel. 01426 939215 for further details and a booking form.

Travel Information

Moors Connections is a free guide to getting around the North York Moors by bus and train. Send large s.a.e. to Tourist Information Centre, Town Hall, Market Place, Helmsley YO6 5BL. (Summer timetable available end of May).

Useful Publications

'England's North Country'
'Walking Holidays in England's North Country'
'Cleveland Way' long distance path

Helping You to Book Ahead

Coast to Coast Central Booking Service – to make it easy to organise a holiday walking the Coast to Coast, the booking office can organise your accommodation for all or part of the route.

All the above are available from the Northern Regional Office, address below (send s.a.e.)

For more information about hostelling in this area contact:

**YHA Northern England Regional Office,
PO Box 11
Matlock
Derbys DE4 2XA**

Tel: 01629 825850
Fax: 01629 824571

34 BEDS   Open: 17.00hrs

Beverley Friary

📞 01482 881751 Fax: 01482 881751

Youth Hostel, The Friary, Friar's Lane, Beverley, East Yorkshire HU17 0DF

Overnight Charges: Under 18 £4.60 Adult £6.75

🅿 Cars and mini-buses only. Coaches - contact Warden.
BABA

Apr 1 - Nov 2	Open X:Sun*

* Open Bank Hol Sun Apr 7, May 5, May 26, August 25. The Hostel may be available for groups when otherwise closed.

ACCOMMODATION 🛏1 🛏2

Stay in a mediaeval Dominican Friary, a restored listed building next to the magnificent Beverley Minster. Containing wallpaintings from the 15th century, the Friary is mentioned in 'The Canterbury Tales'. Now comfortably furnished with modern facilities, it retains much of its original character. Beverley has a wealth of historic buildings, over 400 in the town, including St. Mary's Church and the Guild Hall. An annual folk festival is held in June. It is also an excellent base for birdwatchers, with three RSPB reserves nearby — Hornsea, Bempton Cliffs and Blacktoft Sands.

TRAVEL INFO
🚌Frequent from surrounding areas (📞 01482 881213). 🚂 Beverley ¼m. 🚢 Hull/Rotterdam and Zeebrugge 12m.
ℹ 📞01482 867430

NEXT HOSTELS
Thixendale 18m, Scarborough 28m, Malton 30m

HOW TO GET THERE
¼m SE of the town centre and 100yds NE of the Minster on the left side of Friars Lane off Eastgate.
OS 107 GR 038393

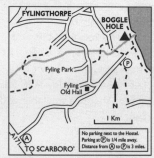

80 BEDS   Open: 13.00hrs

Boggle Hole

📞 01947 880352 Fax: 01947 880987

Youth Hostel, Boggle Hole, Mill Beck, Fylingthorpe, Whitby, North Yorkshire YO22 4UQ

Overnight Charges: Under 18 £5.55 Adult £8.25

Family accommodation prices on p.10-13

🔍 🔒 🅿 ¼m from Hostel. BABA

Dec 30 - Jan 2	Open
Mar 1 - Nov 1	Open
Nov 2 - Dec 1	Open X:Sat/Sun
Dec 2 - Dec 21	Open X:Wed/Th

Open for advance group bookings in winter closed periods.

ACCOMMODATION 🛏12 🛏2 🛏2

A Hostel almost on the beach, with the tides of Robin Hood's Bay reaching the doorstep and the North York Moors behind. Walk along the beach or cliff path (or by car from the main Whitby-Scarborough road) to reach this secluded former mill set in a wooded ravine. Busy with groups midweek during the summer term, and with families and walkers at other times. This is part of the North Yorkshire and Cleveland Heritage Coast — high cliffs, picturesque fishing villages, sheltered bays and dramatic headlands. Seabirds nest in the cliffs whilst marine life abounds on the rocky shore below. Famous for its geology, jet and ammonites can be found on the beaches.

TRAVEL INFO
🚌Tees 93A Scarborough - Whitby (pass BR Whitby & Scarborough), alight Robin Hood's Bay, 1m (📞 01947 602146). 🚂Whitby (not Sun, except Jun - Sep) 7m; Scarborough 15m. 🚢 Hull 50m
ℹ 📞01947 602674

NEXT HOSTELS
Whitby 7m, Scarborough 13m, Wheeldale 15m

ADDITIONAL INFO
Nearest access for cars ¼m. On Cleveland Way and Coast-to-Coast.

HOW TO GET THERE
OS 94 GR 954040

40 BEDS | **Open: 17.00hrs**

Helmsley

☎ 01439 770433 Fax: 01439 770433

Youth Hostel, Carlton Lane, Helmsley, York YO6 5HB

Overnight Charges: Under 18 £5.00 Adult £7.45

🔲 P Outside Hostel on road. BABA

Jan 1 - Jan 31	Rent-a-Hostel
Feb 1 - Mar 4	Open Fr/Sat
Mar 5 - Apr 8	Open X:Tu/Wed
Apr 9 - July 14	Open X:Sun
Jul 15 - Sep 1	Open
Sep 2 - Oct 31	Open X:Sun
Nov 1 - Dec 2	Open X:Tu/Wed
Dec 3 - Dec 31	Rent-a-Hostel

Open Bank Hol Mondays, May 5, May 26.

ACCOMMODATION 🛏2-4 2 🛏5-8 3 🛏9+ 1

A modern Hostel in a small North Yorkshire country town on the edge of the moors. The town's handsome buildings, are centred on an attractive market square, with the ruins of Helmsley Castle standing guard. Start the Cleveland Way from here, the Link Walk through the Tabular Hills or the Ebor Way. Nearby is Rievaulx Abbey, overlooked by Rievaulx Terrace with its classical temples. The mansion of Duncombe Park, set in extensive parkland on the edge of the town, is also open to the public. Ryedale Folk Museum is only 9m away.

TRAVEL INFO

🚌 Stevensons 5⅞, 141 from BR York (☎ 01347 838990); Scarborough & District 128 from Scarborough (passes close BR Scarborough) (☎ 01723 375463). 🚉 Thirsk 15m; Malton 16m; York 24m. ⛴ Hull/Rotterdam-Zeebrugge 60m
ℹ ☎ 01439 770173

NEXT HOSTELS

Osmotherley 15m (20m by Cleveland Way), Malton 17m, Lockton 19m

ADDITIONAL INFO

Daytime access to drying room and bike shed.

HOW TO GET THERE

¼m E of Helmsley market place at junction of Carlton Road and Carlton Lane (just off A170)
OS 100 GR 616840

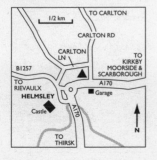

---

26 BEDS | **Open: 17.00hrs**

Lockton

☎ 01751 460376

Youth Hostel, The Old School, Lockton, Pickering, North Yorkshire YO18 7PY

Overnight Charges: Under 18 £3.75 Adult £5.50

🔲 P

Jan 1 - Mar 31	Rent-a-Hostel
Apr 1 - Sep 28	Open X:Sun
Sep 29 - Dec 31	Rent-a-Hostel

Open Bank Hol Sun Apr 7, May 5, May 26, Aug 25.

ACCOMMODATION 🛏5-8 2 🛏9+ 1

Formerly the village school, this small Hostel offers simple self catering facilities. Lockton is one of a pair of tiny villages separated by a deep and spectacular valley in the plateau of the Tabular Hills. Quiet and secluded, it is just off the main Pickering-Whitby road. Follow the scenic route out of Lockton for a few miles to Levisham Station on the North York Moors Railway. Beyond lies Cropton Forest where there are some lovely walks. There are also impressive walks along Levisham Beck to the Hole of Horcum or onto Levisham Moor, rich with tumuli and earthworks.

TRAVEL INFO

🚌 Yorkshire Coastliner 840 Whitby - Malton (passes close BR Whitby & Malton) (☎ 01653 692556). 🚉 Malton 14m; Levisham (North York Moors Rly & connecting with BR at Grosmont) 2m.
ℹ ☎ 01751 73791

NEXT HOSTELS

Wheeldale 11m (8m by path), Malton 14m, Scarborough 19m

ADDITIONAL INFO

Daytime access to toilets. The Hostel has no resident Warden or shop, and external toilets and shower.

HOW TO GET THERE

OS 94 GR 844900

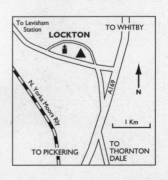

Malton

60 BEDS   Open: 17.00hrs

☎ 01653 692077 Fax: 01653 692077

Youth Hostel, Derwent Bank, 47 York Road, Malton, North Yorkshire YO17 0AX

Overnight Charges: Under 18 £4.60 Adult £6.75

| Jan 2 - Jan 16 | Open |
| Apr 1 - Aug 31 | Open X:Sun/Mon* |

* Open Bank Hol Sun Apr 7, May 5, May 26 & Aug 25. The Hostel may be available for groups when otherwise closed - please contact Warden.

ACCOMMODATION 3 / 4 / 2

A large stone built Victorian house on the banks of the River Derwent just outside Malton. Surrounded by rolling countryside, it is conveniently placed to visit the historic city of York, the North York Moors National Park and the Heritage coastline and the Yorkshire Wolds. Flamingoland Zoo and Fun Park (5m) is ideal for a family day out. Visit the fascinating Beck Isle Folk Museum at Pickering or step back in time at Eden Camp World War II Museum. Enjoy an 18-mile ride on a steam railway up to Grosmont near Whitby or admire the splendour of Castle Howard (of 'Brideshead Revisited').

TRAVEL INFO
From surrounding areas (☎ 01653 692556).
Malton ¾m.
Hull/Zeebrugge-Rotterdam-Ostend 35m
☎ 01653 600048

NEXT HOSTELS
Thixendale 10m, Lockton 14m, Helmsley 17m

HOW TO GET THERE
From traffic lights at centre of Malton follow signs for York. Hostel is last large house on left on York Road.
OS 100 GR 779711

Osmotherley

80 BEDS   Open: 17.00hrs

☎ 01609 883575 Fax: 01609 883715

Youth Hostel, Cote Ghyll, Osmotherley, Northallerton, North Yorkshire DL6 3AH

Overnight Charges: Under 18 £5.00 Adult £7.45

Family accommodation prices on p.10-13

Jan 17 - Sep 2	Open
Sep 3 - Nov 4	Open X:Sun/Mon
Dec 30 - Jan 2 '97	Open for New Year

The Hostel may be available for groups when otherwise closed - please contact Warden.

ACCOMMODATION 2 / 6 / 3

Stay in a former mill in a quiet secluded valley on the edge of the North York Moors. Modern and spacious, the Hostel has plenty of family accommodation and an area for playing outside. It is situated just outside the village of Osmotherley, with its attractive mellow stone cottages. Popular with groups midweek during the summer term and with families and walkers throughout the year. The countryside is perfect for exploring by foot, bike or car. Winding lanes across open moorland, traditional farmland and villages all combine to create a unique landscape. Visit the Moors Centre at Danby and the market town of Thirsk. On the Coast-to-Coast route, the Cleveland Way and Lyke Wake Walk.

TRAVEL INFO
Tees 90/A Middlesbrough - Northallerton (pass close BR Northallerton), alight Osmotherley ¾m (☎ 01642 210131). Northallerton 8m.
Hull 70m, Newcastle 50m
☎ 01609 776864

NEXT HOSTELS
Helmsley 15m, Ellingstring 23m, Grinton 31m

ADDITIONAL INFO
Daytime access to shelter and toilets. Local walks leaflet from Hostel.

HOW TO GET THERE
Go through village, down private drive past caravan/camping site.
OS 100 GR 461981

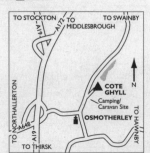

64 BEDS Open: 17.00hrs

Scarborough

☎ 01723 361176 Fax: 01723 500054

Youth Hostel, The White House, Burniston Road, Scarborough, North Yorkshire YO13 0DA

Overnight Charges: Under 18 £4.60 Adult £6.75

🅿 Cars and mini-buses. Coaches in nearby layby. BABA

Dec 31 - Jan 2	Open
Feb 1 - Mar 23	Open Fr/Sat
Mar 24 - Jul 20	Open X:Sun
Jul 21 - Sep 8	Open
Sep 9 - Dec 14	Open X:Sun/Mon

Open for advance group bookings in winter closed period - enquiries welcome.

ACCOMMODATION 5 3

A former mill in a picturesque riverside setting just outside this popular seaside resort. Situated a 10 minute walk from the sea and on the fringe of the North York Moors, this Hostel is the ideal choice to enjoy many places to visit. At the southern tip of the Heritage coastline, Scarborough is on the Cleveland Way and at the start of the 'Link Walk' through the Tabular Hills. Families can combine a traditional seaside holiday with walks in the National Park, a ride on a steam train or a visit to the Sea Life Centre.

TRAVEL INFO
🚌 Frequent from surrounding areas (☎ 01723 375463). 🚉 Scarborough 2m. ⛴ Hull 45m
🛈 ☎ 01723 373333

NEXT HOSTELS
Boggle Hole, Lockton 19m (12m by path), Thixendale 25m

ADDITIONAL INFO
Daytime access to shelter. Scarborough-Whitby cycle trail (½m away), Cleveland Way path (15 mins walk).

HOW TO GET THERE
From Scarborough follow signs to North Bay Attractions, then A165 to Whitby. Hostel is white building on river bank near bridge (2m north of town centre).
OS 101 GR 026907

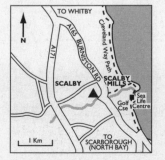

---

 18 BEDS Open: 17.00hrs

Thixendale

☎ 01377 288238

Youth Hostel, The Village Hall, Thixendale, Malton, North Yorkshire YO17 9TG

Overnight Charges: Under 18 £3.75 Adult £5.50

Apr 4 - Apr 13	Open
Apr 14 - May 23	Open Fr/Sat
May 24 - Sep 30	Open

Open Bank Hol Sun May 5.

ACCOMMODATION

Go 'back to school' at this tiny Hostel in a quiet village on the Wolds Way. The simple nature of the Hostel (a former school), cared for by the village postmistress, means that only limited facilities are available (outside toilets and no showers). The Yorkshire Wolds, a crescent of chalk hills from the Humber to the North Sea, offer gentle walking over beautiful rolling countryside. The green dales, arable farmed hilltops and chalk banks give a variety of landscape, flora and fauna — and greatly contrast with other parts of Yorkshire.

TRAVEL INFO
🚌 E Yorks 135 from Driffield (infrequent) (passes close BR Driffield), alight Fridaythorpe, 3m (☎ 01377 42133). 🚉 Malton 10m (via Birdsall).
🛈 ☎ 01653 600048

NEXT HOSTELS
Malton 10m, York 17m, Beverley 18m

ADDITIONAL INFO
Daytime access to toilets. No showers.

HOW TO GET THERE
Take the Beverley Road left out of Malton, then right on mini roundabout signposted to Birdsall and Langton. Follow road through Birdsall up the hill, left at the cross roads, signed to Thixendale, ride down the prettiest valley in Thixendale.
OS 100 GR 843610

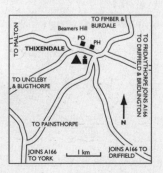

THE YORKSHIRE MOORS, WOLDS AND COAST

10

32 BEDS   Open: 17.00hrs

Wheeldale

📞 01947 896350

Youth Hostel, Wheeldale Lodge, Goathland, Whitby, North Yorkshire YO22 5AP

When the Hostel is closed, calls will automatically be diverted to another Hostel where the Warden can confirm your booking for Wheeldale.

Overnight Charges: Under 18 £3.75 Adult £5.50

Apr 1 - Jun 30	Open X:Wed/Th
Jul 1 - Aug 31	Open X:Wed
Sep 1 - Oct 1	Open X:Wed/Th

Open for groups in October if booked before Sep 30.

ACCOMMODATION

A former shooting lodge surrounded by heather-clad moorland in the heart of the National Park. This Hostel with open fire in the lounge offers basic accommodation (no heating in bedrooms, outside washrooms/toilets and no showers) in an area popular with walkers and cyclists. On the Lyke Wake Walk. Take a ride on a steam train from the 19th century railway station at nearby Goathland ('Aidensfield' in the T.V. series Heartbeat).

TRAVEL INFO
🚌Yorkshire Coastliner 840 Malton - Whitby, alight near Goathland, 2m (📞 01653 692556).
🚃 Grosmont (not Sun, except Jun - Sep) 6m; Goathland (North York Moors Rly & connecting with BR at Grosmont) 3m.
ℹ️ 📞01287 60654

NEXT HOSTELS
Lockton 8m, Boggle Hole 13m, Whitby 11m

ADDITIONAL INFO
Daytime access to toilets. No access to door by car. Please bring torch (electricity by generator).

HOW TO GET THERE
From village take Egton Bridge Road, take Hunt House road. Continue past the farm on dirt track ¼m. Cars park ¼m from Hostel in layby by turning circle above Hunt House; continue on foot. Access to Hostel for mini-buses only.
OS 94 GR 813984

---

66 BEDS   Open: 17.00hrs

Whitby

📞 01947 602878 Fax: 01947 602878

Youth Hostel, East Cliff, Whitby, North Yorkshire YO22 4JT

Overnight Charges: Under 18 £4.60 Adult £6.75

P Pay & Display adjacent to Hostel (free overnight)
BABA

Feb 2 - Mar 30	Open Fr/Sat
Mar 31 - May 19	Open X:Sun*
May 20 - Sep 7	Open
Sep 8 - Oct 31	Open X:Sun
Nov 1 - Dec 9	Open Fr/Sat
Dec 30 - Jan 2 '97	Open

* Open Bank Hol Sun Apr 7, May 5. Open for advance group bookings in winter closed period.

ACCOMMODATION

Perched on the headland above Whitby's bustling harbour, the Hostel is at the top of the famous 199 steps leading to the Abbey. Converted from a stable range, it has lots of character — with beamed sloping ceilings, a log fire and panoramic views. Cobbled streets, brightly painted boats, fishermen's cottages and a maze of old shops combine to give this ancient fishing town a lively atmosphere. Explore the Captain Cook heritage trail, take a ride on a steam train (from Grosmont 8m), enjoy a bracing clifftop walk or relax on the sandy beaches.

TRAVEL INFO
🚌Frequent from surrounding areas (📞 01947 602146). 🚃Whitby (not Sun, except Jun - Sep) ½m.
ℹ️ 📞01947 602674

NEXT HOSTELS
Boggle Hole 7m, Wheeldale 11m, Scarborough 20m

ADDITIONAL INFO
Daytime access to shelter. On the Cleveland Way. Guided walks available nearby in July/August

HOW TO GET THERE
Follow signs to abbey up Green Lane (by road) or up 199 steps (by foot)
OS 94 GR 902111

York

146 BEDS   Open: 24hrs

☎ 01904 653147 Fax: 01904 651230

International Youth Hostel, Water End, Clifton, York, North Yorkshire Y03 6LT

Overnight Charges: Under 18 £10.05 Adult £13.50

Bed & Breakfast included.

Family accommodation prices on p.10-13

 🛏 🔍 📷 ♿ **P** **BABA** **IBN**

Jan 17 - Dec 15   Open

ACCOMMODATION 🛏²⁻⁴ 7 🛏⁵⁻⁸ 7

The Peter Rowntree Memorial Hostel is an attractive Victorian house which was once the home of the Rowntree family. The Hostel offers small bedrooms including twin, family and ensuite rooms. Premium rooms have a TV and tea and coffee making facilities. The licensed 'Ebor' restaurant is open all day and offers a wide choice of great food including an extensive childrens menu. The Hostel is only 20 minutes from the city centre. Attractions include the Minster, the Jorvik Viking Centre, river cruises, guided and ghost walks, National Railway Museum and the Shambles. Contact Hostel for details of weekend package breaks or for a Conference or Group Informtion Pack. The Hostel is popular with groups during Spring and Autumn and remains a firm favourite with families and independent travellers du

TRAVEL INFO
🚌 Frequent from surrounding areas (☎ 01904 624161). 🚆 York 1m (☎ 01904 642155)
⛴ Hull-North Sea Ferries 60m
ℹ ☎ 01904 621756

NEXT HOSTELS
Thixendale 17m, Malton 19m, Helmsley 24m

ADDITIONAL INFO
Restaurant open all day until 22.00 hrs.

HOW TO GET THERE
From City Centre - Follow riverside footpath or take A19 North, turning left at Clifton Green. From outer ring road - A1237, follow map.
OS 105 GR 589528

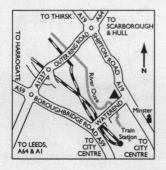

The Lake District

The Lake District is the largest National Park in the country – combining breathtaking mountains and lakes with picturesque villages and towns. The varied terrain is ideal for outdoor activities, from easy walking to rock climbing and canoeing.

If you're inspired by fine scenery and the arts make sure you visit the many local attractions illustrating the life and works of Wordsworth, Ruskin and Beatrix Potter.

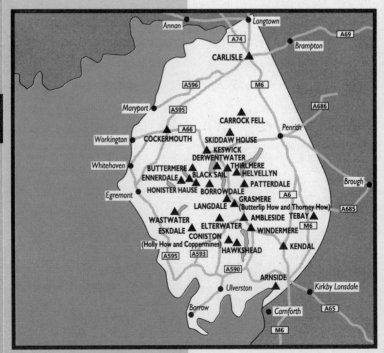

11

You'll also find exploring the area's industrial heritage interesting at the many mills, steam railways, museums and forestry centres in Lakeland.

There are Youth Hostels of all types, from a lonely shepherds hut to a grand Victorian lakeside mansion. You can explore the Lake District using the **YHA's Shuttle bus,** a Hostel door-to-door service that carries you and your backpack to many parts of the Lake District. With free pick-up from Windermere Railway Station, 'Shuttle Bus' takes care of you from the moment you arrive! For more information telephone 015394 32304.

Make the most of your YHA membership by claiming discounts at outlets and attractions such as the Windermere Iron Steamboat Co, Dove Cottage and Wordsworth Museum and the Ravenglass and Eskdale Railway.

Travel Information
This area is served by excellent public transport services. For information on travel throughout Cumbria by bus, train and boat, contact Cumbria County Council's TRAVELINK tel: 01228 812812. Cumbria-wide bus information is available from Stagecoach Cumberland, tel: 01946 63222.

Useful Publications
'Walking Holidays in England's North Country' – free

'England's North Country' – free

'Inter-Hostel Walks in the Lake District'
Send £2.00 (cheques payable to YHA), or a SAE for order form for individual routes.

Helping You to Book Ahead
The Coast to Coast Central Booking Service – to make it easy to organise a holiday walking the Coast to Coast, the booking office can organise your accommodation for all or part of the route.

All the above are available from the Northern Regional Office, address below (send s.a.e.)

For more information about hostelling in this area contact:

**YHA Northern England Regional Office,
PO Box 11
Matlock
Derbys DE4 2XA**

Tel: 01629 825850
Fax: 01629 824571

226 BEDS · Open: All Day

Ambleside

☎ 015394 32304 Fax: 015394 34408

Youth Hostel, Waterhead, Ambleside, Cumbria LA22 0EU

Overnight Charges: Under 18 £6.15 Adult £9.10

Family accommodation prices on p.10-13

🖥️ 🔍 📺 🅿️ Cars and mini-buses only. Coach park ¼m towards Ambleside. BABA IBN

Jan 1 - Jan 6	Open
Feb 9 - Jan 4 '97	Open

ACCOMMODATION 🛏️2-4 3l 🛏️5-8 2l

A large cosmopolitan Hostel, set right on the shores of Lake Windermere, England's largest lake. Gardens slope down to the Hostel's own waterfront and the Lakeside Restaurant (with daytime coffee shop) enjoys panoramic views across to the Coniston and Langdale fells. A popular starting point for exploring the Lake District for walkers, international travellers and families. Rowing boats, windsurfing, canoeing, sailing .... watersports of every kind are available on Windermere. Steamboats stop within yards of the Hostel, calling at Brockhole (National Park Visitor Centre) 2m. All around is superb country for walking, climbing and exploring.

TRAVEL INFO

🚌 Stagecoach Cumberland services from surrounding areas (many pass close BR Windermere) (☎ 01946 63222) 🚉 Windermere 3m. 🚢 Heysham/Isle of Man, Stranraer/Larne (N. Ireland), Newcastle/Bergen (Norway), Hull/Rotterdam (Holland)

🛈 ☎ 015394 32602

NEXT HOSTELS

Windermere 3m, Elterwater 3 ½m, Grasmere 5 ½m

ADDITIONAL INFO

Hostel open until 11.30pm. The Hostel has a jetty and slipway, launching facilities are available for sailing dinghies, canoes, windsurfers and rescue craft. Contact the Hostel for launching fees.

HOW TO GET THERE

1m S of Ambleside Village at Waterhead on the A591 Windermere Road, next to Steamer Pier.
OS 90 GR 377031

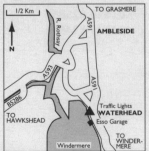

---

72 BEDS · Open: 17.00hrs

Arnside

☎ 01524 761781 Fax: 01524 762589

Youth Hostel, Oakfield Lodge, Redhills Road, Arnside, Carnforth, Lancashire LA5 0AT

Overnight Charges: Under 18 £5.55 Adult £8.25

🔍 📺 🅿️ Cars & Coaches. BABA

Feb 1 - Mar 28	Open X:Sun
Mar 29 - Oct 31	Open
Nov 1 - Nov 30	Open Fr/Sat
Dec 28 - Jan 4 '97	Open for New Year

The Hostel may be available for groups when otherwise closed - please contact the Warden.

ACCOMMODATION 🛏️2-4 8 🛏️5-8 3 🛏️9+ 3

A lovely old stone house situated on the edge of the village, high above the Kent estuary. With views across the sands to the Lakeland fells, the Hostel is a perfect base for exploring Morecambe Bay, the Yorkshire Dales and the quieter parts of South Lakeland. The area abounds in interest for the naturalist, with its limestone landscape and flowers, nature trails and the nearby RSPB reserve at Leighton Moss. It is also popular with cyclists, close to both the Lancashire and Cumbria cycleways, as well as offering cycle tours and bike hire from the Hostel. Convenient for the Cumbria Way, which starts a short rail journey away. Also for the new Lancashire and Cumbria Coastal Paths.

TRAVEL INFO

🚌 Stagecoach Cumberland 552 from Kendal (☎ 01946 63222) 🚉 Arnside 1m. 🚢 Heysham/Isle of Man 15m (rail link)
🛈 ☎ 01524 32878

NEXT HOSTELS

Kendal 12m, Ingleton 19m, Hawkshead 18m

HOW TO GET THERE

Leave M6 at Junction 35, take A6 to Milnthorpe. Take B5282 to Arnside. Turn right at T-junction, follow main road through village to YHA sign on right (Redhills Road)
OS 97 GR 452783

Black Sail

🚶 17 BEDS Open: 17.00hrs

🧭 See note below

Youth Hostel, Black Sail Hut, Ennerdale, Cleator, Cumbria CA23 3AY

There is NO TELEPHONE at this Hostel - bookings and enquiries should be made well in advance by post.

Overnight Charges: Under 18 £4.15 Adult £6.10
🔾

Mar 22 - May 24	Open X:Sun/Mon*
May 25 - Sep 3	Open X:Mon
Sep 4 - Nov 2	Open X:Sun/Mon

* Open Sun Apr 7 & May 5

ACCOMMODATION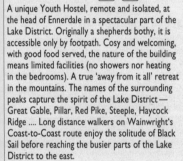

A unique Youth Hostel, remote and isolated, at the head of Ennerdale in a spectacular part of the Lake District. Originally a shepherds bothy, it is accessible only by footpath. Cosy and welcoming, with good food served, the nature of the building means limited facilities (no showers nor heating in the bedrooms). A true 'away from it all' retreat in the mountains. The names of the surrounding peaks capture the spirit of the Lake District — Great Gable, Pillar, Red Pike, Steeple, Haycock Ridge .... Long distance walkers on Wainwright's Coast-to-Coast route enjoy the solitude of Black Sail before reaching the busier parts of the Lake District to the east.

TRAVEL INFO
🚌Stagecoach Cumberland 79 Keswick-Seatoller, thence 3 ½m (🕿 01946 63222) (For BR connections see Keswick) 🚆Whitehaven 19m.

NEXT HOSTELS
Honister 3m, Buttermere 3 ½m, Ennerdale 4m

ADDITIONAL INFO
Daytime access to very basic shelter. Limited shop (no bread for sale). Groups restricted to 5 males and 5 females. No access for cars.

HOW TO GET THERE
OS 89 GR 194124

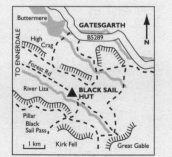

Borrowdale (Longthwaite)

🏕️ 91 BEDS Open: 13.00hrs

🕿 017687 77257 Fax: 017687 77393

Youth Hostel, Longthwaite, Borrowdale, Keswick, Cumbria CA12 5XE

Overnight Charges: Under 18 £5.00 Adult £7.45

Family accommodation prices on p.10-13

🅿 Cars & minibuses. Coaches in Seatoller 1m. BABA

| Feb 16 - Mar 31 | Open X:Mon/Tu |
| Apr 1 - Jan 4 '97 | Open |

No evening meals provided between December 19 and 27.

ACCOMMODATION 🛏️8 🛏️6 🛏️2

This Hostel with its own special character — built mainly of cedar wood to blend into its secluded riverside setting amongst oak woodlands — combines all the facilities and comfort of a large Hostel with a relaxed, informal atmosphere. Superb mountain walks direct from the Hostel, with grounds suitable for games and the river for swimming and canoeing. Borrowdale is regarded by many as the loveliest part of the Lake District. Mountains rise steeply from a green valley floor, where tiny hamlets offer an unchanging picture of Lakeland life. Keswick, the Whinlatter Forest Centre and many northern Lake District attractions are nearby.

TRAVEL INFO
🚌Stagecoach Cumberland 79 from Keswick (🕿 01946 63222) (For BR connections see Keswick) 🚆Workington 25m; Penrith 26m.
🛈🕿017687 72645

NEXT HOSTELS
Honister 2m, Derwentwater 5m, Buttermere 7m

ADDITIONAL INFO
Resident members 🕿 017687 77618

HOW TO GET THERE
Follow 'Borrowdale' signs from Keswick, turn second right after Rosthwaite village to lane end.
OS 89 GR 254142

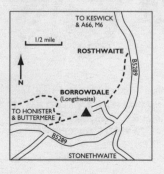

COAST TO COAST WALK

YHA booking service for independent walkers.

The easy and convenient way to plan your walk.

▲ All accommodation booked for you

▲ Meals provided or self-catering.

Also:

▲ Fully inclusive 2-week guided walking holidays with luggage transfer. Starting dates: 12 July, 26 July, 9 August, 23 August, 6 September. £495.

For details send large s.a.e. to:
YHA Northern Region PO Box 11 Matlock, Derbyshire DE4 2XA Tel: 01426 939215 (calls at local rate, 24 hrs)

---

 71 BEDS Open: 17.00hrs

Buttermere

📞 017687 70245 Fax: 017687 70231

King George VI Memorial Hostel, Buttermere, Cockermouth, Cumbria CA13 9XA

Overnight Charges: Under 18 £5.55 Adult £8.25

Family accommodation prices on p.10-13

P Limited. BABA

Jan 1 - Jan 2	Open
Jan 3 - Mar 28	Open X:Sun/Mon
Mar 29 - Aug 31	Open
Sep 1 - Nov 2	Open X:Mon
Dec 28 - Jan 9 '97	Open

Bookings from groups and parties may be accepted when otherwise closed.

ACCOMMODATION 🛏️²⁻⁴6 🛏️⁵⁻⁸9

Overlooking tranquil Buttermere and Crummock Water, the Hostel is a traditional Lakeland slate building set in its own grounds. Relax here after a day on the fells, enjoying the views from the lounge across to High Stile Ridge and the waterfalls of Sour Milk Ghyll. Low level walks along the lake shores and challenging routes over high ridges make this an ideal base for walkers of all abilites. Popular with families, rowing boats can be hired on the two lakes. There are many attractions to visit at nearby Keswick, Cockermouth and along the Cumbrian coastline.

TRAVEL INFO
🚌 From Keswick (May-Oct only) (📞 01228 812812) (For BR connections see Keswick).
🚉 Workington 18m.
🛈 📞 017687 72803

NEXT HOSTELS
Black Sail by mountain path 3 ½m, Honister 4m, Borrowdale 7m

ADDITIONAL INFO
Daytime access to drying room and toilets. Residents 📞 017687 70254

HOW TO GET THERE
¼m S of Buttermere village on road to Honister Pass and Borrowdale on B5289
OS 89 GR 178168

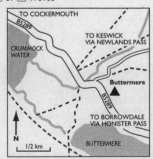

56 BEDS   Open: 17.00hrs

Carlisle

☎ 01228 23934 Fax: 01228 23934

Youth Hostel, Etterby House, Etterby, Carlisle, Cumbria CA3 9QS

Overnight Charges: Under 18 £4.15 Adult £6.10

 BABA

Feb 16 - June 30	Open X:Sun/Mon
Jul 1 - Aug 31	Open
Sep 1 - Nov 2	Open X:Sun/Mon

* Open Sunday/Monday Mar 31-Apr 1, Apr 7-8, May 26-27. Open Sunday May 5. The Hostel may be available for groups when otherwise closed. Enquiries welcome.

ACCOMMODATION

A Victorian house standing in its own grounds on the banks of the River Eden, in a quiet suburb. From the historic city of Carlisle go south into Lakeland, north up to Scotland or explore the wilds of unspoilt Northumbria. On the Cumbria Way and Cumbria Cycle Way. A good stopping point for the ferry (Ireland-Scotland). The sandstone castle, city walls and sturdy cathedral bear witness to Carlisle's turbulent past as an important Border City. Learn more about it at the Tullie House Museum, take a ride on the famous Settle-Carlisle railway or explore Hadrian's wall.

TRAVEL INFO

Stagecoach Cumberland 62 Town Hall-St Ann's Hill, thence ¼m (☎ 01946 63222) Carlisle 2m. Stranraer/Larne. ☎ 01228 512444

NEXT HOSTELS

Carrock Fell 17m, Greenhead 19m, Cockermouth 25m

ADDITIONAL INFO

Facilities are limited - no central heating and insufficient showers.

HOW TO GET THERE

Cross Eden Bridge on A7, turn left at Etterby Street which becomes Etterby Scaur, left after ¾m by Redfern Pub onto Etterby Road. Hostel ¼m on left.

OS 85 GR 386569

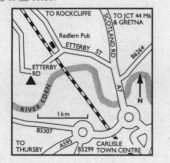

---

20 BEDS   Open: 17.00hrs

Carrock Fell

☎ 016974 78325

Youth Hostel, High Row Cottage, Haltcliffe, Hesket Newmarket, Wigton, Cumbria CA7 8JT

Overnight Charges: Under 18 £4.60 Adult £6.75

P Cars and mini-buses only.

Jan 1 - Mar 21	Rent-a-Hostel
Mar 22 - Jun 30	Open X:Mon/Tu*
Jul 1 - Aug 31	Open X:Mon
Sep 1 - Nov 2	Open X:Mon/Tu
Nov 3 - Spring '97	Rent-a-Hostel

* Open Mon Apr 8, May 27

ACCOMMODATION

This old farmhouse retains its original character with stone flagged floors, beams and an open fire. Nestling in a peaceful hamlet on the edge of the Caldbeck Fells, the Hostel offers a warm welcome in a quiet corner of the Lake District. The northern fells offer excellent walking and cycling in an area of great geological interest and Carrock Fell boasts a Bronze Age hill fort. Walk from the Hostel up onto the Cumbria Way, across to Skiddaw and down into Keswick.

TRAVEL INFO

From Penrith, Wigton (passes close by BR Penrith), to within 2 ½m (☎ 01228 812812). Penrith 15m.

NEXT HOSTELS

Skiddaw House 8m, Keswick 12m, Thirlmere 12m

HOW TO GET THERE

3m N of Mungrisdale at High Row. Turn right off Mungrisdale to Caldbeck Road. Hostel first house up track on left.

OS 90 GR 358355

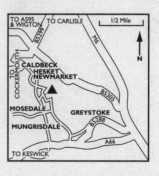

Cockermouth

28 BEDS   Open: 17.00hrs

☎ 01900 822561

Youth Hostel, Double Mills, Cockermouth, Cumbria CA13 0DS

Overnight Charges: Under 18 £4.60 Adult £6.75

🅿 P Cars and mini-buses only.

Jan 1 - Mar 21	Rent-a-Hostel
Mar 22 - Jun 30	Open X:Tu/Wed
Jul 1 - Aug 31	Open X:Wed
Sep 1 - Nov 2	Open X:Tu/Wed
Nov 3 - Spring '97	Rent-a-Hostel

Open Tu Apr 9, May 28.

ACCOMMODATION 🛏⁵⁻⁸₁ 🛏⁹⁺₂

Stay in a restored 17th century watermill, complete with waterwheels, internal workings and mill race. Set in a secluded position on the banks of the River Cocker, the Hostel is just 10 minutes walk from the town centre and on the Sea-to-Sea cycle route. Cockermouth is a charming, bustling market town close to the northern and western Lakeland fells and Cumbrian coastline. Visit William Wordsworth's birthplace, the Cumberland Toy and Model Museum, Jennings Brewery or the mining museum. Crummock Water, Loweswater and Buttermere are within easy reach.

TRAVEL INFO
🚌 Stagecoach Cumberland X5 BR
Penrith-Workington-Whithaven (passes close BR Workington) (☎ 01946 63222) 🚉 Workington 8m.
🛈 ☎ 01900 822634

NEXT HOSTELS
Buttermere 10m, Keswick 13m, Derwentwater 15m

ADDITIONAL INFO
Daytime access to shelter and toilets.

HOW TO GET THERE
From Main Street follow Station Street, left into Fern Bank, take track at end of Fern Bank. From A66 take A5086 to Cockermouth then 2nd right into Fern Bank. Approach down track off Fern Bank.
OS 89 GR 118298

28 BEDS	Open: 17.00hrs

Coniston Coppermines

☎ 015394 41261 Fax: 015394 41261

Youth Hostel, Coppermines House, Coniston, Cumbria LA21 8HP

Overnight Charges: Under 18 £4.60 Adult £6.75

🅿 Cars and mini-buses. Coaches in Coniston village 1 ½m. BABA

Mar 29 - May 31	Open X:Wed/Th
Jun 1 - Jul 6	Open X:Sun
Jul 7 - Aug 31	Open X:Wed
Sep 1 - Nov 2	Open X:Wed/Th
Nov 3 - Spring '97	Rent-a-Hostel

ACCOMMODATION

Surrounded by the Coniston fells, this little Hostel — originally home to the manager of the old coppermines — enjoys a spectacular mountain setting in the heart of classic Lake District scenery. Although it seems quite isolated, the Hostel is only 1m from the village of Coniston. Walk from the front door of the Hostel onto Wetherlam and along the ridge to Coniston Old Man and Dow Crag. Or drop down into Little Langdale, returning on a lower level route through Tilberthwaite Woods. The choice of walks is endless and views unsurpassed. Enjoy watersports, climbing and cycling.

TRAVEL INFO

🚌 Stagecoach Cumberland 505/6 from Ambleside (with connections from BR Windermere), thence 1m (☎ 01946 63222) 🚉 Ulverston 14m.
ℹ ☎ 015394 41533

NEXT HOSTELS

Coniston 1 ¼m, Hawkshead 6m, Elterwater 6m

ADDITIONAL INFO

Wet weather shelter available during daytime. The track is rough but cars can reach the Hostel.

HOW TO GET THERE

From village, take road between the Black Bull and the Co-op. The road soon becomes a track, climbing steadily then levelling, overall distance 1 ¼m.

OS 96 GR 289986

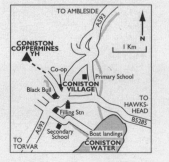

---

60 BEDS	Open: 17.00hrs

Coniston (Holly How)

☎ 015394 41323 Fax: 015394 41803

Youth Hostel, Holly How, Far End, Coniston, Cumbria LA21 8DD

Overnight Charges: Under 18 £5.00 Adult £7.45

Family accommodation prices on p.10-13

🅿 Cars and mini-buses only (coaches ¼m). BABA

Jan 19 - Mar 31	Open Fr/Sat/Sun*
Apr 1 - May 5	Open
May 6 - Jul 4	Open Fr/Sat/Sun*
Jul 5 - Sep 21	Open
Sep 22 - Nov 24	Open Fr/Sat/Sun*

* Also open for half-term holiday weeks Feb 9-25, May 24-Jun 2, Oct 18-27. May also be open Mon-Thurs after Sep 22 (please check with Warden).

ACCOMMODATION

Nestling at the foot of the fells, Coniston Holly How is a traditional Lakeland slate building in its own attractive gardens. Only a few minutes walk from the centre of Coniston village and the lake, it is surrounded by magnificent scenery — dominated by the 'Old Man of Coniston'. Cruise Coniston Water aboard the restored steam yacht Gondola, or try windsurfing or sailing. Visit Ruskin's former home at Brantwood or picnic at lovely Tarn Hows. Mountain bikes can be hired to follow the numerous forest trails, including fascinating sculpture trails through Grizedale Forest.

TRAVEL INFO

🚌 Stagecoach Cumberland 505/6 from Ambleside (with connections from BR Windermere) (☎ 01946 63222) 🚉 Windermere 13m.
ℹ ☎ 015394 41533

NEXT HOSTELS

Coniston Coppermines 1 ¼m, Hawkshead 5m, Elterwater 5m

ADDITIONAL INFO

Daytime access to ground floor (non smoking lounge, drying room, toilets, laundry etc).

HOW TO GET THERE

OS 96 GR 302980

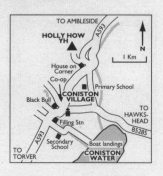

Derwentwater

95 BEDS   Open: 13.00hrs

☏ 017687 77246 Fax: 017687 77396

Youth Hostel, Barrow House, Borrowdale, Keswick, Cumbria CA12 5UR

Overnight Charges: Under 18 £6.15 Adult £9.10

🛏 🔍 P BABA

Jan 1 - Jan 5	Open
Jan 6 - Jan 31	Open X:Wed
Feb 1 - Nov 2	Open
Dec 20 - Jan 4	Open
'97	

ACCOMMODATION 🛏²⁻⁴ 1 🛏⁵⁻⁸ 7 🛏⁹⁺ 3

This magnificent 200 year old mansion overlooks Derwentwater in lovely Borrowdale. The Hostel's 15 acres of grounds, complete with 108ft waterfall, slope down to the lake shore. Nearby is a jetty landing point for the Keswick on Derwentwater Launch — a novel way to arrive at the Hostel. Skiddaw, Scafell, Catbells and other well known names bring walkers and climbers to this area. Nearby Whinlatter Forest Centre has orienteering and forest trails suitable for all ages. The Hostel offers a variety of activity and special interest breaks. It is popular with school groups midweek during the summer term.

TRAVEL INFO
🚌 Stagecoach Cumberland 79 Keswick-Seatoller (☏ 01946 63222) (For BR connections see Keswick) 🚉 Penrith 20m; Windermere 24m.
🛈 ☏017687 72645

NEXT HOSTELS
Keswick 2m, Borrowdale 5m, Thirlmere 5m

ADDITIONAL INFO
Winter walking, navigation and mountaineering courses available.

HOW TO GET THERE
2m S. of Keswick on Borrowdale Road - 100metres past turn off to Ashness Bridge/Watendlath (concealed entrance)
OS 89 GR 268200

Elterwater (Langdale)

46 BEDS   Open: 17.00hrs

☏ 015394 37245 Fax: 015394 37245

Youth Hostel, Elterwater, Ambleside, Cumbria LA22 9HX

Overnight Charges: Under 18 £5.00 Adult £7.45

P Limited. BABA

Jan 1 - Jan 2	Open
Feb 16 - Mar 28	Open Fr/Sat*
Apr 1 - Sep 30	Open
Oct 1 - Nov 2	Open X:Mon
Nov 3 - Dec 21	Open X:Sun/Mon
Dec 28 - Jan 4	Open
'97	

* Midweek bookings may be accepted from groups - enquiries welcome.

ACCOMMODATION 🛏²⁻⁴ 8 🛏⁵⁻⁸ 3 🛏⁹⁺ 1

On the edge of the tiny hamlet of Elterwater, this Hostel is at the heart of classic Lakeland scenery. Originally converted from farm buildings, its closeness to the fells at the head of Langdale makes it a favourite with walkers and climbers. The two lovely Langdale valleys — with Crinkle Crags, Bowfell and the famous Langdale Pikes towering above — offer excellent walks with fine views. Close to Ambleside and Grasmere, and within easy reach of the western lakes and coast, this is a good base for exploring the whole of the Lake District.

TRAVEL INFO
🚌 Stagecoach Cumberland 516 from Ambleside (connections from BR Windermere) (☏ 01946 63222) 🚉 Windermere 9m.
🛈 ☏015394 32602

NEXT HOSTELS
Langdale 1m, Grasmere 4m, Coniston 6m

ADDITIONAL INFO
Daytime access to shelter.

HOW TO GET THERE
OS 90 GR 327046

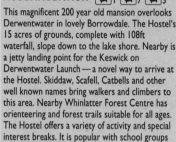

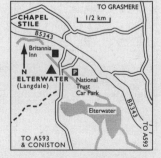

Ennerdale (Gillerthwaite)

24 BEDS | **Open: 17.00hrs**

☎ 01946 861237

Youth Hostel, Cat Crag, Ennerdale, Cleator, Cumbria CA23 3AX

Overnight Charges: Under 18 £4.60 Adult £6.75

🅿 Limited access for cars and mini-buses.

Jan 1 - Mar 21	Rent-a-Hostel
Mar 22 - Jun 30	Open X:Wed/Th
July 1 - Aug 31	Open X:Th
Sep 1 - Nov 2	Open X:Wed/Th
Nov 3 - Spring '97	Rent-a-Hostel

Open Wed Apr 10, May 29.

ACCOMMODATION 🛏2-4 3 🛏5-8 2

Converted from two former cottages in the quiet Ennerdale valley, this Hostel has no electricity but the added charm of gaslight. The cosy dining room/lounge has a log fire — a welcome sight after the first long day walk on the Coast-to-Coast route. Peaceful Ennerdale is surrounded by majestic fells and stunning ridges such as Red Pike, High Stile and Haycock. Forest trails offer more sheltered walking amongst conifers and ancient oak woodlands. On summer days enjoy a bathe in clear pools, or explore the sculpture trail on the Whitehaven cyclepath.

TRAVEL INFO

🚌 From Keswick (May-Oct only), alight Buttermere, 3m by path (☎ 01228 812812); otherwise Stagecoach Cumberland 17 from Whitehaven, alight Kirkland, 7m or Stagecoach Cumberland 79 from Keswick, alight Seatoller, 7m by path (☎ 01946 63222) (For BR connections see Keswick). 🚉 Whitehaven 15m.
🛈 ☎ 01946 695678

NEXT HOSTELS

Buttermere 3m (path), Black Sail 4m, Honister 7m

ADDITIONAL INFO

Daytime access to common room, drying room and toilets. Limited shop (no bread available).

HOW TO GET THERE

2 ½m from Bowness Knott car park along Forest Road, 5m from Ennerdale Bridge.
OS 89 GR 142141

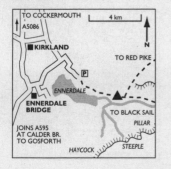

Eskdale

54 BEDS | **Open: 17.00hrs**

☎ 019467 23219 Fax: 019467 23163

Youth Hostel, Boot, Holmrook, Cumbria CA19 1TH

Overnight Charges: Under 18 £5.55 Adult £8.25

Family accommodation prices on p.10-13

🔍 🅿 Cars and minibuses only. Coaches at Woolpack Inn (400yds) BABA

Feb 16 - Mar 28	Open X:Sun/Mon
Mar 29 - Jun 30	Open X:Sun
Jul 1 - Aug 31	Open
Sep 1 - Dec 18	Open X:Sun/Mon
Dec 28 - Jan 4	Open

Open Sunday Apr 7, May 5, May 26.

ACCOMMODATION 🛏2-4 3 🛏5-8 5 🛏9+ 1

This purpose built Hostel with extensive grounds is set amidst the fells in the quiet south west corner of the Lake District. Approach by car over the spectacular Hardknott Pass, by foot descending from Scafell or Harter Fell, or even by train on the delightful Ravenglass & Eskdale Steam Railway. Peaceful riverside walks and exhilarating ridge walking make Eskdale a good base for walkers of all abilities. Close to the long coastline of Cumbria, family days out include Muncaster Castle and Gardens and Sellafield Visitor Centre. River bathing in crystal clear pools is popular.

TRAVEL INFO

🚂 Eskdale (Ravenglass & Eskdale Rly) 1 ½m; Ravenglass (not Sun) 10m; Drigg (not Sun) 10m.
🛈 ☎ 015394 32582

NEXT HOSTELS

Wastwater 7m, Coniston 10m, Elterwater 9m (all by mountain path)

ADDITIONAL INFO

Daytime access to lounge, drying room and toilets. Enquiries welcome from Groups wanting sole use of Hostel.

HOW TO GET THERE

Hardknott Pass suitable for cars and some mini-buses only. Mini-buses approach from Broughton-in-Furness. Coaches should approach from A595 Holmrook/Gosforth.
OS 89 GR 195010

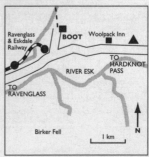

96 BEDS **Open: 13.00hrs**

Grasmere (Butterlip How)

☎ 015394 35316 Fax: 015394 35798

Youth Hostel, Butterlip How, Grasmere, Ambleside, Cumbria LA22 9QG

Overnight Charges: Under 18 £5.55 Adult £8.25

Family accommodation prices on p.10-13

🔍 📷 P For cars only - coaches in village ¼m. BABA

Jan 1 - Mar 28	Open X:Mon
Mar 29 - Sep 30	Open
Oct 1 - Nov 2	Open X:Mon
Dec 28 - Jan 4 '97	Open

ACCOMMODATION 🛏2-4 8 🛏5-8 4 🛏9+ 3

A large Victorian house built in traditional Lakeland style in lovely grounds on the edge of Grasmere village. Relax in front of a log fire in the lounge, with impressive views of the surrounding fells. Good family accommodation is available and the Hostel is popular with school groups midweek during the summer term. A picturesque old-world village and home of the Wordsworth Museum (Dove Cottage), Grasmere is deep in the heart of the Lake District. Walk up to Easedale Tarn or Helm Crag, or tackle a more strenuous route such as Helvellyn or the classic round of the Fairfield Horseshoe.

TRAVEL INFO

🚌 Stagecoach Cumberland 555 Lancaster-Keswick, W1 from Windermere; alight Grasmere, ¼m (all pass BR Windermere)(☎ 01946 63222)
🚉 Windermere 9m.
🛈 ☎015394 35245

NEXT HOSTELS

Thorney How ¾m, Langdale 2m, Ambleside 5m

ADDITIONAL INFO

Special catering service available for functions/conferences etc. Resident members ☎ 015394 35633. Rowing boats can be hired on the lake. On the Coast-to-Coast Walk.

HOW TO GET THERE

Leave the village via Easedale Road. The Hostel Drive is on your right about 400yds.
OS 90 GR 336077

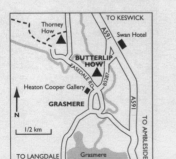

---

48 BEDS **Open: 17.00hrs**

Grasmere (Thorney How)

☎ 015394 35591 Fax: 015394 35866

Youth Hostel, Thorney How, Grasmere, Ambleside, Cumbria LA22 9QW

Overnight Charges: Under 18 £5.55 Adult £8.25

📷 P Cars & mini-buses only. Coaches in village (¾m)
BABA

Jan 1 - Jan 2	Open
Feb 16 - Mar 28	Open X:Tu/Wed
Apr 1 - Aug 30	Open
Sep 1 - Dec 20	Open X:Tu/Wed
Dec 21 - Dec 28	Open

ACCOMMODATION 🛏2-4 3 🛏5-8 3 🛏9+ 2

This old lakeland farmhouse dates from the 17th century, with a friendly atmosphere and lots of character — combined with modern facilities. Situated just outside Grasmere towards Easedale, a little further on than Butterlip How. Stop here on Wainwright's Coast-to-Coast walk, climb Helvellyn or explore the trails by mountain bike. Stroll into the village to buy some delicious gingerbread — made to a secret recipe and sold only at the tiny shop in Grasmere. Visit the Dove Cottage and the Wordsworth Museum or hire a rowing boat on Grasmere.

TRAVEL INFO

🚌 Stagecoach Cumberland 555 Lancaster-Keswick, W1 from Windermere; alight Grasmere ¾m (all pass BR Windermere) (☎ 01946 63222).
🚉 Windermere 9m.
🛈 ☎015394 35245

NEXT HOSTELS

Grasmere (Butterlip How) ¾m, Langdale (High Close) 2 ½m, Ambleside 5 ½m

ADDITIONAL INFO

Daytime access to shelter and toilets. Residents ☎ 015394 35616

HOW TO GET THERE

Take Easedale Road from village for ½m. Turn right at sign. Hostel on left after ¼m
OS 90 GR 332084

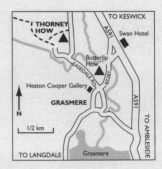

Hawkshead

015394 36293 Fax: 015394 36720

Youth Hostel, Esthwaite Lodge, Hawkshead, Ambleside, Cumbria LA22 0QD

Overnight Charges: Under 18 £6.15 Adult £9.10

Family accommodation prices on p.10-13

Feb 16 - Mar 28	Open X:Sun/Mon
Mar 29 - Nov 2	Open
Nov 3 - Dec 21	Open X:Sun/Mon
Dec 28 - Jan 4	Open
'97	

ACCOMMODATION

This handsome Regency mansion — set in lovely wooded grounds overlooking Esthwaite Water — retains many of the elegant features that characterised it as the home of novelist Francis Brett Young. The courtyard contains excellent family accommodation, and the main Hostel is popular with groups mid-week in summer term time. Hawkshead, with its squares, courtyards and cobbled alleys, is an attractive old-world village. Nearby Sawrey is the 'birthplace' of Beatrix Potter's much loved characters. Visit Grizedale Forest with its sculpture park, theatre and orienteering and cycle trails. Trout fishing permits available.

TRAVEL INFO

Stagecoach Cumberland 505/6 from Ambleside (connections from BR Windermere) alight Hawkshead 1m (01946 63222) Windermere 7m (by vehicle ferry).
015394 36525

NEXT HOSTELS

Coniston 5 ½m, Ambleside 6m, Windermere 9m (via ferry)

ADDITIONAL INFO

Residents 015394 36588

HOW TO GET THERE

OS 96 GR 354966

THE HERRIOT WAY

A 55-mile circular walk in the Yorkshire Dales. Discover the wild fells and green valleys of Swaledale and Wensleydale.

The YHA offers:

▲ **Information pack for independent walkers (send £1.00).**

▲ **Booking Bureau – the easy and convenient way to book your accommodation.**

▲ **Fully inclusive 1-week guided walking holidays with luggage transfer. Starting dates: 25 May, 20 July, 17 August. £215.**

For details send large s.a.e. to:
YHA Northern Region
PO Box 11 Matlock,
Derbyshire DE4 2XA
Tel: 01426 939215
(calls at local rate, 24 hrs)

THE LAKE DISTRICT

11

TO AMBLESIDE & CONISTON
HAWKSHEAD
1/2 km
N
B5285
NEWBY BRIDGE ROAD
Esthwaite Water
TO WINDERMERE FERRY
TO GRIZEDALE
ESTHWAITE LODGE
B5285

64 BEDS Open: 17.00hrs

Helvellyn

☎ 017684 82269 Fax: 017684 82269

Youth Hostel, Greenside, Glenridding, Penrith, Cumbria CA11 0QR

Overnight Charges: Under 18 £5.00 Adult £7.45

🅿 Cars & mini-buses only. Coaches in Glenridding 1 ½m.
BABA

Jan 1 - Jan 6	Open
Jan 7 - Mar 28	Open Fr/Sat
Mar 29 - Jun 30	Open X:Sun
Jul 1 - Aug 31	Open
Sep 1 - Nov 2	Open X:Mon/Tu
Dec 28 - Jan 4 '97	Open

Open Sun Apr 7, May 5, May 26. Bookings from groups may be accepted when Hostel would otherwise be closed.

ACCOMMODATION 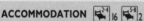 16 2

Dramatically set at 900ft above sea level, this Hostel is isolated and peaceful, yet only 1 ½ miles from the village of Glenridding. Nestling beneath the towering mass of the Helvellyn range, it is an ideal centre for walking and climbing the high level ridges. For less strenuous walks try Place Fell or Glenridding Dodd. Or take a steamer ride on Ullswater and stroll back along the lake shore path. Boats and mountain bikes are available for hire, with pony trekking nearby.

TRAVEL INFO
🚍 From Penrith, Windermere, alight Glenridding, 1 ½m (☎ 01228 812812). 🚆 Penrith 14m, Windermere 15m.
🛈 ☎ 017684 82414

NEXT HOSTELS
Patterdale 2 ½m, Thirlmere 4m, Grasmere 8m (all by mountain path)

ADDITIONAL INFO
Daytime access to drying room and toilet. Resident ☎ 017684 82488.

HOW TO GET THERE
Hostel is due W of Glenridding Village on sign posted route. The lane up to the Hostel is untarmaced for the last ¾m.
OS 90 GR 366173

---

30 BEDS Open: 17.00hrs

Honister Hause

☎ 017687 77267

Youth Hostel, Honister Hause, Seatoller, Keswick, Cumbria CA12 5XN

Overnight Charges: Under 18 £4.60 Adult £6.75

🅿 Cars & mini-buses adjacent to Hostel.

Mar 22 - Jun 30	Open X:Wed/Th
July 1 - Aug 31	Open
Sep 1 - Nov 9	Open X:Wed/Th

Open Wed Apr 10, May 29.

ACCOMMODATION 4 1

This Hostel sits at the summit of Honister Pass, a high level route (1200ft) connecting lovely Borrowdale with tranquil Buttermere to the west. A true mountain Hostel in a spectacular location, it is naturally popular with walkers and climbers seeking ease of access to the highest peaks. Nearby are the most famous names of central Lakeland — Scafell, Great Gable, Pillar, Red Pike, Steeple …. and many more. Dramatic descents into the neighbouring valley are rewarded by breathtaking views. All around is a skyline of fells and ridges.

TRAVEL INFO
🚍 Stagecoach Cumberland 79 Keswick-Seatoller, thence 1 ½m (☎ 01946 632220) (For BR connections see Keswick) 🚆 Workington 23m. 🚢 Haysham/Isle of Man, Ireland 70m
🛈 ☎ 017687 77294

NEXT HOSTELS
Borrowdale 2m, Buttermere 4m, Black Sail 3m by mountain path.

ADDITIONAL INFO
Daytime access to porch only.

HOW TO GET THERE
OS 89 GR 224135

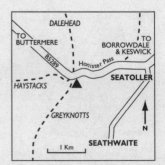

50 BEDS Open: 17.00hrs

Kendal

☎ 01539 724066 Fax: 01539 724906

Youth Hostel, 118 Highgate, Kendal, Cumbria LA9 4HE

Overnight Charges: Under 18 £5.55 Adult £8.25

P Turn left just before Hostel for car park. Pay and display (free overnight). BABA

Jan 1 - Jan 2	Open
Feb 16 - Mar 28	Open X:Sun/Mon
Mar 29 - Aug 30	Open
Sep 1 - Dec 20	Open X:Sun/Mon
Dec 21 - Dec 28	Open

ACCOMMODATION 🛏2-4 7 🛏5-8 4 🛏9+ 1

Occupying a prime position in the centre of Kendal, the Hostel is a pleasantly furnished Georgian town house. At hand are all the amenities of a busy market town, on the fringe of England's largest National Park. Easy to reach from the M6 motorway, Kendal lies between the Lake District and the Yorkshire Dales. Walkers explore the secluded valleys of Kentmere and Longsleddale, or stop here on the 'Dales Way' long distance path. Adjacent to the Hostel is the Brewery Arts Centre — a popular venue for theatre, music and art.

TRAVEL INFO

🚌 Frequent from surrounding areas (☎ 01228 812812). 🚉 Kendal ¾m; Oxenholme 1 ¾m. 🚻 ☎ 01539 725758

NEXT HOSTELS

Windermere 12m, Arnside 12m, Tebay 11m

ADDITIONAL INFO

For details of events at Brewery Arts Centre, send sae to Warden.

HOW TO GET THERE

OS 97 GR 515924

---

 91 BEDS Open: 13.00hrs

Keswick

☎ 017687 72484 Fax: 017687 74129

Youth Hostel, Station Road, Keswick, Cumbria CA12 5LH

Overnight Charges: Under 18 £6.15 Adult £9.10

🔍 🖥 P Cars & coaches in town. BABA

Feb 16 - Mar 28	Open X:Wed
Mar 29 - Oct 31	Open
Nov 1 - Dec 17	Open X:Wed
Dec 28 - Jan 4 '97	Open

Advance bookings may be accepted on Hostel closed nights - enquiries welcome.

ACCOMMODATION 🛏2-4 7 🛏5-8 1 🛏9+ 2

Standing above the River Greta, the verandah at Keswick Youth Hostel is a fine place to relax on a summer's evening. Close to the centre of this popular Lakeland town, the Hostel looks out across the park to Skiddaw and the North Western fells. Keswick is the northern hub of the Lake District — close to Derwentwater, Bassenthwaite and Thirlmere. Browse around interesting shops, visit museums or relax at the indoor leisure pool. Spectacular scenery, walks in every direction, cycle hire and watersports - you will be spoilt for choice!

TRAVEL INFO

🚌 Stagecoach Cumberland X5, Wrights 888 from BR Penrith; 555 from Lancaster (pass BR Windermere) (☎ 01228 812812) 🚉 Windermere 22m; Penrith 17m. 🚢 Stranraer/Larne 140m 🚻 ☎ 017687 72645

NEXT HOSTELS

Derwentwater 2m, Skiddaw House 6m, Thirlmere 5m

ADDITIONAL INFO

Resident ☎ 017687 72485. Park opposite for games. Climbing wall in town. Whinlatter Forest Centre with orienteering.

HOW TO GET THERE

Follow Leisure Pool signs to Station Road. Turn left onto walkway by river.
OS 89 GR 267235

96 BEDS — Open: 17.00hrs

Langdale (High Close)

☎ 015394 37313 Fax: 015394 37101

Youth Hostel, High Close, Loughrigg, Ambleside, Cumbria LA22 9HJ

Overnight Charges: Under 18 £5.55 Adult £8.25

🔍 **P** Cars and minibuses only. Coaches ¾m. BABA

Jan 1	Open
Jan 12 - Feb 15	Open Fr/Sat*
Feb 16 - Mar 28	Open X:Sun
Mar 29 - Aug 30	Open
Sep 1 - Nov 2	Open X:Sun
Dec 24 - Dec 28	Open

* Midweek bookings may be accepted.

ACCOMMODATION 🛏2-4 2 🛏5-8 3 🛏9+ 6

An impressive rambling Victorian mansion set in lovely gardens and woodland, owned by the National Trust. The Hostel is situated high on Red Bank between Elterwater and Grasmere, with panoramic views of Windermere and the Langdale Valley. Popular with groups midweek during the summer term and families and walkers at weekends and holiday times. This is an excellent walking base, close to the high Langdale Pikes and lower level lakeshore paths. From here stroll down into Grasmere, admire tiny Rydal Water from Loughrigg Terrace or tackle one of the classic Lakeland ridge walks.

TRAVEL INFO

🚌 Stagecoach Cumberland 516 from Ambleside, alight ¾m before Elterwater, then walk ¾m. Or any bus to Grasmere, then walk 1 ½m. ☎ 01946 63222. 🚉 Windermere 10m.
ℹ️ ☎ 015394 32729

NEXT HOSTELS

Elterwater 1m, Grasmere (BH) 2m, Ambleside 4m

ADDITIONAL INFO

Daytime access to shelter and toilets. Resident members ☎ 015394 37212

HOW TO GET THERE

From Ambleside take the A593 (Coniston and Langdale). After 2 ½km turn right and follow minor road uphill for 2.8km. At summit of Red Bank turn left and High Close is 0.4km on the left.
OS 90 GR 338052

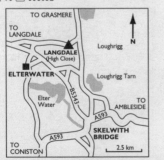

82 BEDS — Open: All Day

Patterdale

☎ 017684 82394 Fax: 017684 82034

Youth Hostel, Goldrill House, Patterdale, Penrith, Cumbria CA11 0NW

Overnight Charges: Under 18 £6.15 Adult £9.10

🖥 **P** Cars & minibuses only. Coaches ¼m. BABA

Feb 16 - Mar 31	Open X:Wed/Th
Apr 1 - Aug 31	Open
Sep 1 - Nov 2	Open X:Th
Nov 3 - Dec 19	Open X:Wed/Th
Dec 20 - Dec 28	Open

Advance bookings may be accepted during winter closed period. Enquiries welcome.

ACCOMMODATION 🛏2-4 3 🛏5-8 8 🛏9+ 2

A unique Scandinavian style building designed to blend with the fine scenery just south of Ullswater, set in large grounds with river access for canoeing down to the lake. Inside a warm welcome awaits, an atmosphere enhanced by the pine woodwork and spacious modern accommodation. Take in the splendour of Ullswater on a steamer trip, sail, swim or fish in its deep, clear waters. Classic walks — such as the ascent of Helvellyn via Striding Edge — are on the doorstep, complemented by gentler low level routes along the lake shores.

TRAVEL INFO

🚌 CMS no 108 from Penrith to Patterdale, not Sundays (tel: 01228 812812) 🚉 Penrith 15m.
ℹ️ ☎ 017684 82414

NEXT HOSTELS

Helvellyn 2 ½m, Grasmere 9m (by path), Ambleside 10m

ADDITIONAL INFO

Resident ☎ 017684 82441

HOW TO GET THERE

¼m S of Patterdale Village, just off A592 leading to Kirkstone Pass.
OS 90 GR 399156

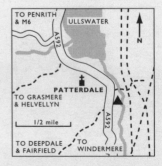

| 🚶🚴 | **15 BEDS** | Open: 17.00hrs |

Skiddaw House

Youth Hostel, Bassenthwaite, Keswick, Cumbria CA12 4QX

Postal bookings direct to Hostel. For information and telephone enquiries, contact: Carrock Fell Youth Hostel ☎ 016974 78325

Overnight Charges: Under 18 £3.75 Adult £5.50

🔍 **P** Cars can be left at end of Blease Road via Threlkeld at Fell car park, or at Lattrigg behind Keswick.

Mar 22 - Nov 2   Open

ACCOMMODATION 🛏️2-4 1 🛏️5-8 3

At 1550ft this is one of the highest, most remote and isolated buildings in the U.K., with no sign of civilization in any direction. A former shooting lodge beneath the summit of Skiddaw with panoramic views all around. Self catering accommodation is available for walkers and cyclists. The simple nature of the Hostel means no showers, very basic foodstore and no heating in the bedrooms. NO ACCESS BY CAR. Surrounded by high fells and right on the Cumbria Way, Skiddaw House is approached by a choice of footpaths from Keswick, Carrock Fell, Bassenthwaite or Threlkeld.

TRAVEL INFO
🚌 Stagecoach Cumberland X5, Wright 888 from BR Penrith, alight Threlkeld thence 4 ½m
(☎ 01228 812812)
ℹ️ ☎ 017687 72645

NEXT HOSTELS
Keswick 6m, Carrock Fell 8m, Thirlmere 9m

ADDITIONAL INFO
Daytime access to shelter. Hot water on tap. 24 volt lighting only. No access by car - nearest tarmac road 3 ½m. Poor postal service - book well in advance. Due to remote location, no-one will be turned away. Credit cards are not accepted.

HOW TO GET THERE
From Keswick via Lattrigg and Lonscale Fell. From Carrock via Caldew Valley. From Threlkeld via Glenderaterra Valley. Bassenthwaite via Dash Beck path.
OS 89 GR 288291

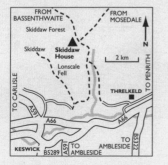

| 🚶🚴 | **46 BEDS** | Open: 17.00hrs |

Tebay

📞 015396 24286 Fax: 015396 24286

Youth Hostel, The Old School, Tebay, Penrith, Cumbria CA10 3TP

Overnight Charges: Under 18 £5.00 Adult £7.45

🔍 💷 🖼️ **P**

Feb 9 - Nov 30   Open X:Th

ACCOMMODATION 🛏️2-4 3 🛏️5-8 2 🛏️9+ 2

A converted stone built school in the village of Tebay, close to junction 38 of the M6 motorway. This is a privately owned Hostel adopted by the YHA. There are no self catering facilities; home cooked meals are available if booked in advance. Tebay is in the Lune Valley on the edge of the Howgill Fells. Sandwiched between the Lake District and the Pennines, it is surrounded by walking and cycling country to suite all abilities. The many attractions of the lovely Eden Valley are nearby.

TRAVEL INFO
🚌 From Kendal, Penrith, Kirkby Stephen (pass close BR Kendal & Penrith) (☎ 01228 812812). 🚉 Kendal 11m; Kirkby Stephen (not Sun, except Apr - Oct) 11m; Oxenholme 13m.

NEXT HOSTELS
Kirkby Stephen 10m, Kendal 11m, Dufton 14m

ADDITIONAL INFO
Daytime access to toilets and drying room. No credit cards accepted. No self-catering kitchen, but kettle and evening drinks available. This is a privately owned Hostel operated under an agreement with YHA.

HOW TO GET THERE
Opposite recreation ground.
OS 91 GR 618045

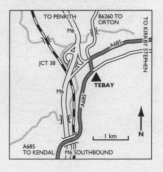

Thirlmere

🕿 017687 73224

Youth Hostel, The Old School, Stanah Cross, Keswick, Cumbria CA12 4TQ

Overnight Charges: Under 18 £3.75 Adult £5.50

🅿 Very limited (check with Warden for alternatives).

Mar 22 - Jun 13	Open X:Mon/Tu
Jun 14 - Sep 14	Open X:Mon
Sep 15 - Nov 9	Open X:Mon/Tu

Open Mon Apr 8, May 27

ACCOMMODATION 🛏2-4 1 🛏9+ 2

A cosy little building with a friendly atmosphere, complete with wood burning stove and welcoming pot of tea. The simple nature of the Hostel means limited facilities (no fitted carpets or T.V.), but lots of character. Formerly the village school in the tiny hamlet of Legburthwaite. The best ascent of Helvellyn's west flank starts within yards of the door and classic Lakeland crags of Castle Rock and Raven Crag are within a few minutes walk. Easy to reach from Keswick and Windermere (the bus stops here) Thirlmere offers a true 'away from it all' break.

TRAVEL INFO

🚌 All services to the Grasmere Hostels, alight Stanah, 100yds. National Express coaches will stop at Hostel if requested in advance. 🚉 Penrith 18m, Windermere 18m.
🅸 🕿017687 74101

NEXT HOSTELS

Keswick 5m, Grasmere 6m, Helvellyn 4m

ADDITIONAL INFO

Daytime access to shelter. All meals MUST be booked in advance. Limited meals service with vegetarian/wholefood a speciality. Continental breakfast only. Teddy Bear convention every October. Limited shower facilities. Nearest shops Keswick (5m).

HOW TO GET THERE

On B5322 100yds from A591 junction.
OS 90 GR 318190

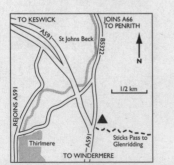

Wastwater

🕿 019467 26222 Fax: 019467 26056

Youth Hostel, Wasdale Hall, Wasdale, Seascale, Cumbria CA20 1ET

Overnight Charges: Under 18 £5.55 Adult £8.25

Family accommodation prices on p.10-13

🔍 🅿 BABA

Jan 1 - Jan 2	Open
Jan 3 - Mar 31	Open X:Tu/Wed
Apr 1 - Aug 31	Open
Sep 1 - Nov 2	Open X:Tu/Wed
Dec 20 - Dec 28	Open

ACCOMMODATION 🛏2-4 2 🛏5-8 2 🛏9+ 2

This lovely half timbered house, dating from 1829, has been carefully refurbished in period style and retains many original features. Standing in its own grounds sloping down to the shores of Wastwater, it offers a high standard of accommodation in a breathtaking location. Wasdale is famous for the deepest lake, highest mountain and smallest church in England. Vast scree slopes descend into the deep dark waters, ringed by a skyline of challenging mountains. Visit the many family attractions of the Cumbria coastline, including the castle and owls at Muncaster.

TRAVEL INFO

🚌 Stagecoach Cumberland 12 Whitehaven - Seascale (passes close BR Seascale), alight Gosforth, 5m (🕿 01946 63222). 🚉 Seascale (not Sun) 9m; Irton Road (Ravenglass & Eskdale Rly) 5 ½m.
🅸 🕿01946 695678

NEXT HOSTELS

Black Sail 7m by mountain path, Eskdale 10m by road, Borrowdale 9m by mountain path.

ADDITIONAL INFO

Daytime access to self catering kitchen and dining area. Ideal for sole usage groups and conferences.

HOW TO GET THERE

From the south, come via A590, Greenodd, A595 Broughton-in-Furness, Ulpha, Eskdale Green, Santon Bridge to Nether Wasdale. From the north: A5086 to Egremont, Gosforth and Nether Wasdale.
OS 89 GR 145045

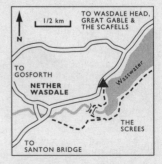

Windermere

☎ 015394 43543 Fax: 015394 47165

**Youth Hostel, High Cross, Bridge Lane,
Troutbeck, Windermere, Cumbria LA23 1LA**

Overnight Charges: Under 18 £5.00 Adult £7.45

Family accommodation prices on p.10-13

🅿 ♿ 🅿 BABA

Jan 6 - Nov 16	Open
Dec 28 - Jan 4	Open
'97	

ACCOMMODATION

A large house enjoying an elevated position with panoramic views of Windermere Lake and the mountains of South Lakeland. Situated in extensive wooded grounds 2 miles outside the busy town, the Hostel now has many small rooms ideal for families. There is plenty to do in the area, with numerous high and low level walks. The National Park Visitor Centre at Brockhole is nearby, an indoor swimming pool (1m), cruises and watersports on Windermere, the Windermere Steamboat Museum (2m) and the Beatrix Potter Exhibition (3m).

TRAVEL INFO
🚌 Frequent from surrounding areas (☎ 01946 63222). 🚉 Windermere 2m.
🚲 ☎ 015394 46490

NEXT HOSTELS
Ambleside 3m, Hawkshead 9m by ferry, Patterdale 11m

ADDITIONAL INFO
Resident members ☎ 015394 46147

HOW TO GET THERE
From Windermere follow the A591 N for 1m to Troutbeck Bridge. Take first turning right after filling station - Hostel is well sign-posted off the main road and is ¾m up lane, on left, just after Broad Oaks.
OS 90 GR 405013

Northumberland and the North Pennines

Northumbria has some of the last wilderness countryside in England – from the North Pennines in the south to the Scottish Borders in the north.

In the Northumberland National Park, you'll find the Cheviot Hills and undiscovered valleys, while Hadrian's Wall which crosses the region offers a wealth of Roman remains and museums to explore. Deserted sweeping sandy beaches, spectacular castles and abbeys are all part of the impressive Northumbrian coastline.

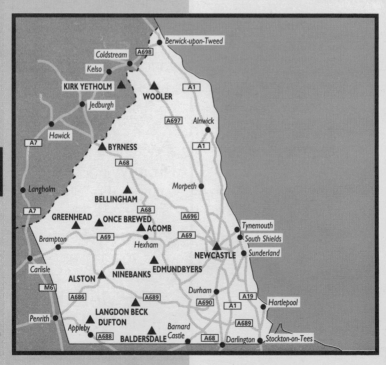

Further south, the North Pennines are home to many rare plants and wildlife. Outdoor activities and industrial heritage abound and if that's not enough, spend a day at the Metro Centre.

The area's main city is Newcastle, with its fine historic buildings, shops and museums. Out in the country are the bustling market towns of Hexham, Alston and Barnard Castle.

And to ensure you always get value for money, present your YHA membership card to claim your discounts at attractions as varied as Alnwick Castle and boat trips to the Farne Islands.

Camping Barns
For simple friendly accommodation try YHA Camping Barns in the North Pennines. See pages 188-193 and tel: 01426 939215 for further details and a booking form.

Useful Publications
'Steel Bonnets Bike Ride'
'England's North Country'
'Northumberland and Hadrian's Wall Inter Hostel Cycling Route' – send a SAE to the YHA Regional Office listed below.

Sea to Sea Cycle Route (C2C) Tel Sustrans on 01207 281259

Helping You to Book Ahead
Pennine Way Central Booking Service – to make it easy to organise a holiday walking the Pennine Way, the booking office can organise your accommodation for all or part of the route – send a large SAE to the Regional Office listed below, for more details.

For more information about hostelling in this area contact:

YHA Northern England Regional Office, PO Box 11 Matlock Derbys DE4 2XA

Tel: 01629 825850
Fax: 01629 824571

40 BEDS   Open: 17.00hrs

Acomb

☎ 01434 602864

Youth Hostel, Main Street, Acomb, Hexham, Northumberland NE46 4PL

Overnight Charges: Under 18 £3.75 Adult £5.50

P On street

Jan 1 - Feb 29	Open Fr/Sat
Mar 1 - Jul 21	Open X:Mon*
Jul 22 - Sep 1	Open
Sep 2 - Oct 31	Open X:Mon
Nov 1 - Dec 21	Open Fr/Sat
Dec 27 - Dec 31	Open

* Open April 8 and May 27. May be available to groups on closed days - enquiries welcome.

ACCOMMODATION

A simple Hostel in a small village in the valley of the River Tyne. Converted from stable buildings, it offers basic self catering facilities in an ideal location for visiting Hadrian's Wall and the Roman heritage sites. Nearby is the bustling market town of Hexham, dominated by its fine church (Hexham Abbey). A network of winding lanes and pretty villages are ideal for exploring by bike or foot. Enjoy low level river walks, forest trails and the solitude of the high moorlands.

TRAVEL INFO

🚌 Tyne Valley 880-2 from Hexham (pass BR Hexham); otherwise Northumbria 685, X85 Carlisle - Newcastle upon Tyne, alight Hexham, 2½miles (☎ 01670 533128). 🚉 Hexham 2m.
⛴ Newcastle/Bergen-Gothenberg-Oslo-Esbjerg-Hamburg 25m.
🛈 ☎ 01434 605225

NEXT HOSTELS

Once Brewed 15m, Bellingham 15m, Edmundbyers 16m

ADDITIONAL INFO

Daytime access to shelter and outside toilets and shower.

HOW TO GET THERE

A69 to 1m past Bridge End roundabout, turn right on A6079, then 1st right at Acomb Village sign and follow Main Street uphill to Hostel.

OS 87 GR 934666

---

30 BEDS   Open: 17.00hrs

Alston

☎ 01434 381509 Fax: 01434 381509

Youth Hostel, The Firs, Alston, Cumbria CA9 3RW

Overnight Charges: Under 18 £5.00 Adult £7.45

P Cars & minibuses only. Coaches 300yds behind Hendersons Garage. BABA

Jan 1 - Mar 21	Rent-a-Hostel or other group bookings
Mar 22 - Apr 30	Open X:Sun/Mon
May 1 - June 28	Open X:Sun
Jun 29 - Aug 31	Open
Sep 1 - Nov 2	Open X:Sun/Mon
Nov 3 - Spring '97	Rent-a-Hostel or other group bookings

Open Sun/Mon Apr 7-8. Open Sun May 5 and 26. Bookings from groups may be accepted when Hostel would otherwise be closed.

ACCOMMODATION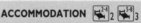

Set on the edge of the highest market town in England, Alston Hostel overlooks the South Tyne River in an Area of Outstanding Natural Beauty. Here 'on top of the world' the steep cobbled streets and stone houses of the town are surrounded by wild, solitary moorland. Walking and pony trekking are favourite activities, on old drovers roads or the Pennine Way. Walk to the top of Cross Fell, the highest point of the Pennines (2930ft) or take a ride on the South Tynedale Railway, England's highest narrow gauge line. Stop here on the Sea-to-Sea (C2C) cycle route.

TRAVEL INFO

🚌 Wright Bros. 681 from BR Haltwhistle, 888 from BR Penrith (☎ 01434 381200).
🚉 Haltwhistle 15m; Penrith 19m.
🛈 ☎ 01434 381696

NEXT HOSTELS

Ninebanks 8m, Langdon Beck 15m, Greenhead 15m (17m by Pennine Way)

ADDITIONAL INFO

Daytime access to drying room and toilets.

HOW TO GET THERE

OS 86 GR 717461

Baldersdale

46 BEDS   Open: 17.00hrs

☎ 01833 650629 Fax: 01833 650629

Blackton, Baldersdale, Barnard Castle, County Durham DL12 9UP

Overnight Charges: Under 18 £4.60 Adult £6.75

Cars only - coaches 200 metres. BABA

Mar 29 - May 10	Open X:Wed/Th
May 11 - Aug 31	Open X:Sun
Sep 1 - Nov 2	Open X:Wed/Th
Nov 3 - Spring '97	Rent-a-Hostel

ACCOMMODATION 2 5 1

Baldersdale is a peaceful tributary valley of Teesdale, which leads up to the highest part of the Pennines. The half-way point on the Pennine Way, the Hostel is a stone built farmhouse surrounded by open countryside, with views of Balderhead Reservoir. Meals must be booked in advance. This wild landscape offers solitude and tranquility, but with many places to visit nearby. Not far from the old market town of Barnard Castle is the magnificent Bowes Museum, built in the style of a French chateau and home to a European art collection.

TRAVEL INFO

United 75/A from BR Darlington, alight Cotherstone, 6m (☎ 01325 468771).
Darlington 27m.
☎ 01833 690000

NEXT HOSTELS

Langdon Beck 15m, Keld 15m, Kirkby Stephen 18m

ADDITIONAL INFO

Daytime access to drying room and toilets. Fishing at five reservoirs nearby.

HOW TO GET THERE

Use road from Romaldkirk (not Cotherstone) - no access by road via Clove Lodge.
OS 91 GR 931179

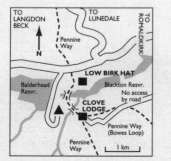

Bellingham

34 BEDS   Open: 17.00hrs

☎ 01434 220313

Youth Hostel, Woodburn Road, Bellingham, Hexham, Northumberland NE48 2ED

Overnight Charges: Under 18 £4.15 Adult £6.10

Jan 1 - Feb 29	Rent-a-Hostel
Mar 1 - Jul 14	Open X:Sun*
July 15 - Aug 31	Open
Sept 1 - Oct 31	Open X:Sun
Nov 1 - Feb 28	Rent-a-Hostel

* Open Bank Hol Sun Apr 7 & May 26.

ACCOMMODATION 1 2

A comfortable Hostel built of red cedarwood, situated on the Pennine Way high above the picturesque border town of Bellingham. Well equipped self catering facilities are provided here in a cosy, homely atmosphere enhanced by the cast-iron stove in the lounge. Bellingham is the nearest town to Kielder Water, with its 27 miles of shoreline surrounded by the Northumberland hills and great Border Forest, as well as facilities for watersports including sailing and windsurfing. Hadrian's Wall is within easy reach and the quiet lanes offer excellent cycling routes.

TRAVEL INFO

Tyne Valley 880 from Hexham (passes BR Hexham) (☎ 01434 602217). Hexham 16m.
Newcastle
☎ 01434 220616

NEXT HOSTELS

Acomb 15m, Byrness 15m (walking via Pennine Way), Once Brewed 18m

ADDITIONAL INFO

Daytime access to drying room. Credit cards are not accepted.

HOW TO GET THERE

OS 80 GR 843834

28 BEDS **Open: 17.00hrs**

Byrness

☎ 01830 520425

Youth Hostel, 7 Otterburn Green, Byrness, Newcastle upon Tyne, NE19 1TS

Overnight Charges: Under 18 £4.15 Adult £6.10

🅿

Apr 3 - Jul 16	Open X:Tu*
Jul 17 - Aug 31	Open
Sep 1 - Sep 30	Open X:Tu

* Open April 18 & May 30 following Bank Hols.

ACCOMMODATION 🛏️2-4 3 🛏️5-8 3

This simple self catering Hostel, comprising two adjoining houses in the peaceful village of Byrness, is situated just 5m from the Scottish border in the foothills of the Cheviot Hills. An ideal stopping off point to and from Scotland and the Borders. Well located for exploring picturesque Jedburgh and the Cheviots, Byrness is at the heart of the Northumberland National Park. Explore the great Border Forest on the Forest Drive from Redesdale to Kielder Castle at the tip of Kielder Water. Roe deer and red squirrels are among the species of wildlife.

TRAVEL INFO

🚌 National Express Edinburgh - Newcastle-upon-Tyne (pass close BR Newcastle & Edinburgh) (☎ 0191 261 6077). 🚉 Morpeth 34m, Newcastle 40m. ✈ Newcastle 40m

NEXT HOSTELS

Bellingham 15m, Kirk Yetholm 27m, Wooler 28m - all by Pennine Way

ADDITIONAL INFO

Hostel keys available to families to give all day access.

HOW TO GET THERE

OS 80 GR 764027

---

 40 BEDS **Open: 17.00hrs**

Dufton

☎ 017683 51236 Fax: 017683 51236

Youth Hostel, 'Redstones', Dufton, Appleby, Cumbria CA16 6DB

Overnight Charges: Under 18 £5.00 Adult £7.45

🅿 BABA

Jan 1 - Jan 18	Rent-a-Hostel
Jan 19 - Mar 31	Open X:Tu/Wed
Apr 1 - Aug 31	Open X:Tu
Sep 1 - Nov 2	Open X:Tu/Wed
Nov 3 - Spring '97	Rent-a-Hostel

ACCOMMODATION 🛏️2-4 2 🛏️5-8 4

A large stone built house (with a welcoming log fire) on the green of a quiet, pretty village. Extensive gardens are available for croquet, badminton, games and campfires. The Hostel is popular with cyclists and walkers; both the Pennine Way and the Cumbria Cycle Way pass through the village. Unspoilt and untamed, the wild moorland of the North Pennines rises above Dufton to Cross Fell (its highest point) and the famous High Cup Nick. The green valley of the River Eden can be explored — on foot, bike or from the Settle to Carlisle railway. Historic Appleby is 3 ½m away.

TRAVEL INFO

🚌 No service. Local taxi service to Appleby. 🚉 Appleby (no Sun service Nov - Mar) 3 ½m; Penrith 13m. 🎫 ☎ 017683 51177

NEXT HOSTELS

Langdon Beck 12m by Pennine Way, Kirkby Stephen 15m, Alston 22m by Pennine Way

ADDITIONAL INFO

Daytime access to porch. CROSS COUNTRY SKIING courses for beginners in Feb. Ski hire also available.

HOW TO GET THERE

Leave A66 at Appleby, follow signs for Long Marton and Dufton 3 ½m.
OS 91 GR 688251

NORTHUMBERLAND AND THE NORTH PENNINES

12

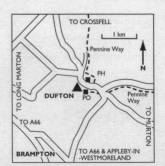

Durham

Youth Hostel,

ACCOMMODATION
We regret that this Youth Hostel is now closed.
The nearest Youth Hostels are Newcastle upon
Tyne (13m with good public transport links) and
Edmundbyers (21m).

👣 🚲 **36 BEDS**   **Open: 17.00hrs**

Edmundbyers

📞 **01207 255651 Fax: 01207 255345**

**Youth Hostel, Low House, Edmundbyers,
Consett, County Durham DH8 9NL**

Overnight Charges: Under 18 £4.15 Adult £6.10

🅿 Roadside. BABA

Jan 1 - Mar 31	Rent-a-Hostel
Apr 1 - Oct 31	Open X:Sun
Nov 1 - Dec 31	Rent-a-Hostel

Open Bank Hol Sun Apr 7, May 5, May 26 and
Aug 25

ACCOMMODATION 🛏²⁻⁴|1 🛏⁵⁻⁸|3 🛏⁹⁺|1

This former inn dating from 1600 — situated in
an attractive village surrounded by heather
moorland — offers simple self catering facilities,
ideal for walkers and cyclists exploring the quiet
lanes and countryside of this Area of Outstanding
Natural Beauty. Only 1/2m away is Derwent
Reservoir, popular with anglers and yachtsmen
and a pleasant spot for a picnic or to explore
Pow Hill Country park. Nearby is the pretty
village of Blanchland, named after the white habits
worn by the monks of the 12th century abbey.
Durham is 20m and Beamish Museum 16m.

TRAVEL INFO
🚌 Northumbria 773 Consett-Townfield, with
connections on Go-Ahead Northern 719, 765
Durham Consett (pass close BR Durham) or X12,
745, 770/2 Newcastle-upon-Tyne - Consett (pass
BR Newcastle); otherwise alight Consett 5m
(📞 0191 383 3337) 🚃 Hexham 13m.
🚉 Newcastle 25m
ℹ 📞 01207 591043

NEXT HOSTELS
Acomb 16m, Newcastle 20m

ADDITIONAL INFO
No Hostel shop but local store open until 6.30pm
(ex. Mon and Thurs). On the Sea-to-Sea (C2C)
cycle route.

HOW TO GET THERE
At the junction of trackways from the Tyne to
Weardale and Allendale, 6m W of Shotley Bridge,
1/2m from Derwent Reservoir.
OS 87 GR 017500

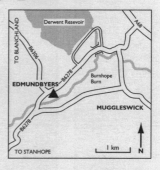

Greenhead

40 BEDS   **Open: 17.00hrs**

☎ 016977 47401 Fax: 016977 47770

Youth Hostel, Greenhead, Carlisle, Cumbria CA6 7HG

Overnight Charges: Under 18 £4.60 Adult £6.75

🅿 Limited. BABA

Dec 30 - Jan 2	Open
Jan 3 - Jan 27	Open Fr/Sat
Mar 1 - Apr 4	Open X:Wed/Th
Apr 5 - Jun 30	Open X:Sun
Jul 1 - Aug 31	Open
Sep 1 - Dec 17	Open X:Wed/Th
Dec 31 - Jan 2 '97	Open

Open Bank Hol Sun Apr 7, May 5, May 26.

ACCOMMODATION 🛏5-8 6

Stay in a former methodist chapel in the hamlet of Greenhead on Hadrian's Wall. Complete with high beamed roof, arched windows and thick stone walls, this Hostel has a spacious yet cosy feel to it. Situated on the Pennine Way, it is popular with walkers. On the edge of the Northumberland National Park and the North Pennines Area of Outstanding Natural Beauty, Greenhead offers many opportunities for walking in wild, unspoilt countryside. A network of quiet lanes, tracks and forest trails are superb for cyclists. Royal Army Museum (1m).

TRAVEL INFO

🚌 Northumbria 685 Carlisle - Newcastle upon Tyne, (passes BR Haltwhistle) (☎ 01434 602061). 🚉 Haltwhistle 3m.
🔼 ☎ 01498 20351

NEXT HOSTELS

Once Brewed 7m, Alston 17m (by Pennine Way), Ninebanks 16m

ADDITIONAL INFO

Daytime access to common room and toilet after 1.00pm. On the 'Steel Bonnets' Cycle Route (sae for details).

HOW TO GET THERE

OS 86 GR 659655

Langdon Beck

34 BEDS   **Open: 17.00hrs**

☎ 01833 622228 Fax: 01833 622228

Langdon Beck, Forest-in-Teesdale, Barnard Castle, County Durham DL12 0XN

Overnight Charges: Under 18 £5.55 Adult £8.25

📷 🔲 🅿 On roadside. BABA

Jan 1 - Jan 31	Rent-a-Hostel
Feb 1 - Mar 28	Open Fr/Sat only
Mar 29 - Apr 30	Open X:Sun/Mon*
May 1 - Aug 31	Open X:Sun*
Sep 1 - Oct 31	Open X:Sun/Mon*
Nov 1 - Nov 30	Open Fr/Sat only
Dec 1 - Jan 4 '97	Rent-a-Hostel

* Open Bank Hol Sundays and Sundays in August. During Feb, Mar and Nov Hostel may be available on a self-catering basis - please contact Warden.

ACCOMMODATION 🛏2-4 2 🛏5-8 4

Set high amid the wild moorland of Upper Teesdale, just off the road from Middleton to Alston, this is a stone built Hostel with all modern comforts. On the Pennine Way, it is popular with walkers seeking the solitude of the remote northern fells. This is an area rich in plants and wildlife, of special interest to botanists, geologists and industrial archaeologists.

TRAVEL INFO

🚌 United 75/A from BR Darlington alight High Force (☎ 01325 468711). 🚉 Darlington 33m.
🔼 ☎ 01833 690909

NEXT HOSTELS

Dufton 35m (12 by pathway), Baldersdale 16m, Alston 15m

ADDITIONAL INFO

Daytime access to shelter. Out of season the Hostel may be available for individuals on a self-catering basis - please contact the Warden in advance.

HOW TO GET THERE

Sited on B6277 7m N of Middleton-in-Teesdale.
OS 91 GR 860304

Newcastle upon Tyne

60 BEDS **Open: 17.00hrs**

☎ 0191 281 2570 Fax: 0191 281 8779

Youth Hostel, 107 Jesmond Road, Newcastle upon Tyne NE2 1NJ

Overnight Charges: Under 18 £4.60 Adult £6.75

Seasonal Prices April 1 - Oct 31: Under 18 £5.00 Adult £7.45

🔍 P BABA IBN

Feb 1 - Feb 29	Open X:Mon/Tu
Mar 1 - Oct 31	Open
Nov 1 - Nov 24	Open X:Mon/Tu

ACCOMMODATION 🛏²⁻⁴7 🛏⁵⁻⁶6

A large town house conveniently located for the centre of this vibrant city, the regional capital of the north east. Best viewed from one of the six bridges crossing the river Tyne, the city is a blend of ancient and modern — at the heart of which is the historic Quayside. Explore the city's Roman heritage, maritime history, first class museums, galleries and shops. Visit Europe's largest shopping centre (the Metro Centre) at nearby Gateshead, or the Theatre Royal. The wild countryside of the Northumberland National Park and superb stretches of coastline are nearby.

TRAVEL INFO

🚌 Frequent from surrounding areas (☎ 0191 232 5325). 🚇 Jesmond (Tyne & Wear Metro) ¼ mile; Newcastle 1 ½m. 🚢 Services (7m) to Hamburg-Esbjerg-Gothenburg (seasonal), Bergen-Stavanger (all year), Amsterdam (seasonal).
ℹ ☎ 0191 261 0691

NEXT HOSTELS

Acomb 20m, Edmundbyers 20m, Wooler 50m

ADDITIONAL INFO

Hostel has partial heating and limited meal service. On 'Steel Bonnets' cycle route (send sae for details). 'Wet 'n' Wild' water fun park.

HOW TO GET THERE

Excellent transport links by road, rail, air and ferry. To Jesmond Metro from city rail and bus stations and airport.
OS 88 GR 257656

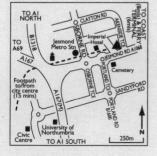

Ninebanks

26 BEDS **Open: 17.00hrs**

☎ 01434 345288 Fax: 01434 345288

Youth Hostel, Orchard House, Mohope, Ninebanks, Hexham, Northumberland NE47 8DQ

Overnight Charges: Under 18 £3.75 Adult £5.50

P BABA

| Jan 2 - Dec 23 | Open |
| Dec 24 - Jan 1 '97 | Open for groups booked in advance |

ACCOMMODATION 🛏²⁻⁴1 🛏⁵⁻⁸1 🛏⁹⁺2

A stone built lead-miners cottage in the valley of the Mohope burn in the North Pennines Area of Outstanding Natural Beauty. Situated above the village of Ninebanks at Mohope, this Hostel offers simple self catering accommodation for individuals and groups who will appreciate a welcoming fire and coffee pot. Visit Kilhope Lead Mining Centre to discover the history of lead mining in the area. Or explore the secluded valleys and wild moorland of this undiscovered area — rich in wildlife, industrial archaeology, flora and fauna. Allen Banks (NT) and suspension bridges are 8m.

TRAVEL INFO

🚌 Wright Bros 888 Newcastle - Hexham - Alston - Penrith - Keswick alight Ouston 1m (☎ 01434 381200). Wright Bros 688 Hexham - Allenheads. Alight Allendale. 🚉 Haydon Bridge 11m. Hexham 15m.
ℹ ☎ 01434 605225

NEXT HOSTELS

Alston 8m, Greenhead 16m, Once Brewed 16m (12m by path)

ADDITIONAL INFO

Cross country skiers welcome. On the Sea-to-Sea (C2C) cycle route. Shops/pubs 6m. Credit cards are not accepted. This is a privately owned Hostel operated under an agreement with YHA.

HOW TO GET THERE

Signposted from A686 2 ½m S of Whitfield. Hostel at Mohope signposted from Ninebanks hamlet.
OS 86 GR 771514

SEASONAL ASSISTANT WARDEN VACANCIES

March to October 1996

Ever thought about working in a Youth Hostel?

During the busy season, we need to recruit Assistant Wardens to carry out any part of the Warden's responsibilities. Assistants will be 18+, have experience in dealing with the general public, an appreciation of good customer service and a pleasant personality. Their proven ability to cook for large numbers or perform clerical work would also be considered desirable.

Accommodation and food will be provided with a monthly salary of £320+. Opportunities to take up a permanent career with training in NVQ occupational qualifications could also be available for the hard-working enthusiast.

For an application form and further details, send an A4 SAE to the:
Personnel Dept (SES3)
YHA
Trevelyan House
8 St Stephen's Hill
St Albans
AL1 2DY

---

87 BEDS   Open: 13.00hrs

Once Brewed

☎ 01434 344360 Fax: 01434 344045

Youth Hostel, Military Road, Bardon Mill, Hexham, Northumberland NE47 7AN

Overnight Charges: Under 18 £5.55 Adult £8.25

Family accommodation prices on p.10-13

🔍 💻 ♿ 🅿 BABA

Feb 1 - Mar 31	Open X:Sun
Apr 1 - Oct 31	Open
Nov 1 - Nov 30	Open X:Sun

ACCOMMODATION 🛏️2-4 16 🛏️5-8 5

A modern, comfortable Hostel just 1/2 mile from Hadrian's Wall and adjacent to the Visitor Centre. With plenty of accommodation for families, and surrounded by a wealth of places to visit, an excellent base for exploring the beauty of the Northumberland National Park and the North Pennines. Popular with groups midweek during the summer term. Close to some of the best preserved Roman Heritage sites in the country including Roman forts and museums at Vindolanda, Housesteads, Carvoran, Chesters and Birdoswald. Further afield are lead mines, deer farms, forests, Kielder Water and the North of England Open Air Museum (Beamish).

TRAVEL INFO

🚌 From Hexham, Haltwhistle (passes BR Hexham & Haltwhistle), peak summer only; otherwise Northumbria 685 Carlisle - Newcastle upon Tyne, alight Henshaw, 2m (☎ 01670 533128). 🚉 Bardon Mill 2 ½m. ⛴ Newcastle/Scandinavia-Holland 40m
ℹ ☎ 01434 344396

NEXT HOSTELS

Greenhead 7m, Bellingham 15m, Acomb 15m

ADDITIONAL INFO

Courses and special events can be arranged - call for details. Limited wheelchair access. Lunches and morning/afternoon teas are available for groups and coach parties if booked in advance.

HOW TO GET THERE

On B6318 above Bardon Mill. On corner of crossroads next to the National Park Visitor Centre.
OS 86 GR 752668

Wooler (Cheviot)

52 BEDS   Open: 17.00hrs

☎ 01668 281365 Fax: 01668 282368

Youth Hostel, 30 Cheviot Street, Wooler, Northumberland NE71 6LW

Overnight Charges: Under 18 £5.00 Adult £7.45

🅿 Cars and mini-buses (coaches in village ⅓m)
BABA

Jan 1 - Feb 18	Rent-a-Hostel
Feb 19 - Feb 24	Open
Feb 25 - Mar 30	Open Fr/Sat
Mar 31 - Jul 6	Open X:Sun
Jul 7 - Aug 31	Open
Sep 1 - Nov 2	Open X:Sun
Nov 3 - Nov 30	Open Fr/Sat
Dec 1 - Spring '97	Rent-a-Hostel

Open Bank Hol Sun Apr 7, May 5 and 26.

ACCOMMODATION 🛏²⁻⁴ 10 🛏⁵⁻⁸ 3

The most northerly of English Youth Hostels lying in the foothills of the Cheviot Hills. On the edge of the Northumberland National Park and close to the Scottish border, the Hostel is on the outskirts of the market town of Wooler. The area is steeped in history — with ancient hill forts, Roman remains and splendid Border castles. Explore the magnificent Northumbrian coastline, including Holy Island, fairytale Lindisfarne Castle, as well as castles at Alnwick and Warkworth.

TRAVEL INFO
🚌 Northumbria 464, 470/3, Peter Park/Gold Leaf 267 from Berwick-upon-Tweed & Alnwick, with connections from Newcastle (pass close BR Newcastle) (☎ 01670 533128).
🚉 Berwick-upon-Tweed 16m.
🛈 ☎ 01668 81602

NEXT HOSTELS
Kirk Yetholm 14m, Byrness 28m by path, Newcastle 50m

ADDITIONAL INFO
Daytime access to toilets. Facilities for disabled visitors.

HOW TO GET THERE
OS 75 GR 991278

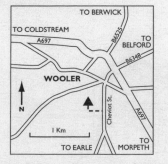

Kirk Yetholm

36 BEDS   Open: 17.00hrs

☎ 01573 420631

Youth Hostel, Kelso, Roxburghshire TD5 8PG

Mar 15 - Sep 30   Open

ACCOMMODATION 🛏²⁻³ 3 🛏⁹⁺ 2

This small modernised Hostel — ideally situated at the end of the Pennine Way — is owned and operated by the Scottish Youth Hostel Association (7 Glebe Crescent, Stirling FK8 2JA. Tel: 01786 451181). Families are welcome. This is an excellent centre for hill walking in the Cheviots. Kirk Yetholm was the home for gypsies and 'Gypsy Palace' cottage of the Faa Family can be seen from the road leading to the Halter Burn Valley. In Kelso (8m) there is an abbey, Rennies Bridge over the Tweed and Floors Castle.

TRAVEL INFO
🚌 Lowland Scottish 81 from Kelso (☎ 01573 24141) (Kelso is linked with BR Berwick-upon-Tweed by Swan/Northumbria 23 - ☎ 01835 23301). 🚉 Berwick-upon-Tweed 24m.

NEXT HOSTELS
Wooler 14m, Melrose 24m, Byrness 27m

HOW TO GET THERE
The Hostel is 50yds down the lane at the west corner of the village green.
OS 74 GR 082802

NORTHUMBERLAND AND THE NORTH PENNINES

12

Page 187

Camping Barns

The YHA has four networks of Camping Barns – in the Forest of Bowland; North Yorkshire; North Pennines; and Exmoor, Dartmoor and Tarka country.

They make excellent bases for exploring the countryside with good access to spectacular walking and cycling routes.

Sometimes known as stone tents, camping barns are farm buildings owned and operated by farmers which provide basic communal accommodation – with wooden sleeping platforms, tables and benches for preparing and eating food, a supply of cold water and a flush toilet. Barns are not usually heated so it's essential that you bring a good sleeping bag and warm clothing with you. Prices start from £2.75 per person per night.

Brompton-On-Swale

Sleeps: 12 🗺 🅿

ACCOMMODATION

A former byre in a farmyard in the attractive village of Brompton-On-Swale. Sleeping accommodation is on the first floor, along with the toilet and shower. Drying facilities available. Electric light, a heater, a cooker and crockery are available.

It makes an excellent stopping off point for the Coast to Coast Walk which is ½m away.

OS 99 GR 216997
📞 01748 850252

Farndale

Sleeps: 12 🗺

ACCOMMODATION

Within the North York Moors National Park, the barn is in High Farndale. Sleeping accommodation is in the barn loft with electic light, a heater and a cooker available. There is a small farm shop at the Farm.

Activities include the Coast to Coast Walk ½m, Cleveland Way 3m, Lyke Wake Walk 2m and Rosedale Circuit 2 ½m.

OS 94 GR 659986
📞 01904 621756

Kildale

Sleeps: 12 🗺

ACCOMMODATION

Superbly located in the North York Moors National Park, the building was formerly a barn and wheelhouse. Sleeping accommodation is in the first floor loft. Electric light, heat and cooking facilites are available on a meter. Toilet in adjacent building.

Attractions include the Esk Valley Railway. There are many good local walks including the Cleveland Way.

OS 94 GR 602085

Leyburn

Sleeps: 12 🗺

ACCOMMODATION

A field byre with magnificent views of Wensleydale. The building contains bunk beds, a gas cooker, two toilets and washbasins. Metered electricity powers the light, heater, fridge and shower.

Visit nearby Wensleydale or try one of the several local walks including the riverside footpath along the River Ure.

OS 99 GR 121895
📞 01969 22773

Lovesome Hill

Sleeps: 15 🗺

ACCOMMODATION

Ideally placed for exploring both the Yorkshire Dales and North York Moors National Park. There is electric light and a heater, plus a cooker and shower on meter. Sleeping accommodation is on the first floor and there are two toilets on the ground floor.

On Coast to Coast walk 16m E of Richmond. Popular cycling area. Working farm with plenty to see. 8m from Cleveland Way. Many waterways for fishing.

OS 99 GR 361998
📞 01609 776864

Low Row

Sleeps: 15 🗺

ACCOMMODATION

Well located in Swaledale in the Yorkshire Dales National Park. Sleeping accommodation is on the first floor, with toilets and a shower on the ground floor. There is electric light and a calor gas heater and cooker available.

As well as the Coast to Coast Walk (1m), there are many local walks including the Corpse Road between Keld and Reeth.

OS 92 GR 003983

Richmond

Sleeps: 12 🗺

ACCOMMODATION

Consisting of three former byres, this camping barn is located on the edge of the Yorkshire Dales National Park and has sweeping views across Swaledale. Sleeping accommodation is in two rooms. There is electricity and a flush toilet. Heat and cooking facilities available on meter.

There are several pleasant local walks as well as the Coast to Coast Walk.

OS 99 GR 133016
📞 0174882 2943

Free leaflet and booking details from: Camping Barn Booking Service, YHA Northern Region, PO Box 11, Matlock, Derbyshire DE4 2XA Tel: 01629 825850

NORTH YORKSHIRE - CAMPING BARNS

Sinnington

Sleeps: 12

ACCOMMODATION

Converted granary on family farm, with selection of animals to see. Situated on edge of North York Moors. Sleeps nine on first floor, three on ground floor. Electric light, heat, cooking facilities available. Toilets, shower, washing facilities are in an adjacent building.

Attractions include the Pickering to North Yorks Steam Railway, Crofton Forest and Flamingo Land. Many local walks including Sinnington-Cropton, Sinnington-Rosedale, Newtondale Trial (3m) and the Link (2m).

OS 100 **GR** 752849
i ☎ 01751 73791

Westerdale Bunk House

Sleeps: 12

ACCOMMODATION

Set in the North York Moors National Park, the building has lovely views over Westerdale Moor and Castleton Rigg. Formerly a byre, it is now equipped with electric lights, heaters, showers and a calor gas cooker.

There are many local walks including the Coast to Coast Walk (3m), Lyke Wake Walk (3m) and the Rosedale Circuit.

OS 94 **GR** 671049

Free leaflet and booking details from: Camping Barn Booking Service, YHA Northern Region, PO Box 11, Matlock, Derbyshire DE4 2XA   Tel: 01629 825850

NORTH PENNINES - CAMPING BARNS

Holwick

Sleeps: 20

ACCOMMODATION

A field bunkhouse barn near the River Tees. Sleeping accommodation is in beds on the first floor. The ground floor has a cooking area, worktops, and hot and cold water supply. There are two flush toilets, a shower and a sitting area. There is gas heating and lighting upstairs and downstairs. A separate self contained 8-bedded bunkhouse barn is also available to a similar standard with all accommodation on ground floor. Close to High Force and the Pennine Way with lots of good walks nearby.

OS 92 **GR** 914270

Lartington

Sleeps: 15

ACCOMMODATION

Set in a farmyard, this former corn store is a listed building. The sleeping accommodation is on the first floor along with a toilet. On the ground floor there are two more flush toilets, two showers and an area for cooking and sitting. There is also electric light, drying facilities and heating.

An excellent base for exploring Teesdale, with Barnard Castle nearby.

OS 92 **GR** 029177

Wearhead

Sleeps: 12

ACCOMMODATION

A listed building, formerly a farmhouse, this barn is next to a stream. On the ground floor there is an area for cooking food, sitting and eating where there is also a coal fire. The sleeping accommodation and flush toilet are on the first floor. Weardale Way ½m.

OS 91 **GR** 851397

Witton

Sleeps: 15 **P** Plenty.

ACCOMMODATION

A former byre and dairy, this barn is on the Witton Castle Estate which offers a range of facilities including an outdoor swimming pool, public bars, games and TV rooms, a shop and cafeteria. The barn itself is a single story building with sleeping platform, a cooking/eating area and two flush toilets. There is electric light, a wood burning stove and a cooker. As well as Weardale Way only ½m away, Escombe Saxon Church and Hamsterly Forest are also well worth a visit.

OS 92 **GR** 155298
i ☎ 01833 690000

Free leaflet and booking details from: Camping Barn Booking Service, YHA Northern Region, PO Box 11, Matlock, Derbyshire DE4 2XA   Tel: 01629 825850

Chipping

Sleeps: 15 🅿

ACCOMMODATION

A former stable, this barn has superb views of Wolf Fell and Parlick Pike, just ½m away. Sleeping accommodation is on the upper floor, with shower, hand basin and toilet with two further toilets in a converted pig sty. Electic on a meter. Two hot plate cookers and woodburner available.

🆗 102 **GR** 616435
ℹ ☎01200 25566

Downham

Sleeps: 12 ☒ 🅿 In former quarry opposite.

ACCOMMODATION

A field barn in an attractive setting near the foot of Pendle Hill. Downham Camping Barn is ideally situated for walkers and is just 4m from Clitheroe. Sleeping accommodation is provided on the first floor of the barn. Flush toilet on the ground floor. There is gas lighting, cooking rings and a wall mounted heater available on a meter.
As well as attractions like Downham, Pendle Hill and Clitheroe, the Lancashire Cycle Way, Ribble Way and Pendle Way are all close by.

🆗 103 **GR** 795445
ℹ ☎01200 25566

Giggleswick

Sleeps: 12 ☒ 🅿 Rear of the barn.

ACCOMMODATION

This camping barn, built in 1761, is situated in the farmyard opposite Grain House only 6m from Ingleborough. Sleeping accommodation is on the first floor. Electric light, cookings rings and shower are provided on a meter. There is also a wood burning stove and drying area.
Local attractions include the town of Settle, the Settle to Carlisle Railway and the Three Peaks. Walkers will find the Ribble Way 1 ½m and North Bowland Traverse 2 ½m.

🆗 98 **GR** 795632
ℹ ☎01468 62252

Hurst Green

Sleeps: 12 ☒ 🅿 In the farmyard.

ACCOMMODATION

Henry VII is reputed to have stayed in the former hunting lodge adjacent to this converted byre. The barn is only a mile from Longridge Fell. Sleeping accommodation is on the upper floor and the toilet is in another building close by. Barbeque available. Electic light, cooking rings and a drying room are provided on a meter. There is a wood burning stove and hot water boiler. Attractions include Stoneyhurst College, Ribchester and Clitheroe. Ribble Way 2m.

🆗 103 **GR** 674389
ℹ ☎01200 25566

Quernmore

Sleeps: 15 ☒ 🅿 In the farm yard.

ACCOMMODATION

This field barn enjoys a superb remote location on an elevated hill top with magnificent open views over Morecambe Bay and the Lake District Fells. Sleeping accommodation is in two areas on the ground foor. There are two wood burning stoves. There is no electicity so bring a torch. Snacks available 1m, farm cafe.
There are two flush toilets. Cars can be parked in the farmyard 10-15 mins walk from the barns. There is no access for vehicles to the barns. Attractions include the Clougha Access Area and North Bowland Travers (Tambrook Fell).

🆗 97 **GR** 528588
ℹ ☎01200 25566

Beech Hill

Sleeps: 12 Ⓐ Ⓟ

ACCOMMODATION

Ideally located for walking or cycling in rural countryside on the Two Moors Way. A converted coach house, this bunkhouse style barn has good facilities including shower, electric lights, cooking facilities and fridge. Meals area available on request, you will also find a local pub, post office and shop 1 ½ miles away.

[OS] 191 [GR] 781086

Chenson

Sleeps: 16 Ⓧ Ⓐ Ⓟ

ACCOMMODATION

A mere ½m from the Tarka Trail for walking or cycling, Chenson is a former cob and timber barn formerly used for cider pressing with 2 separate sleeping areas. Cooking facilities, hot shower (small charge) and electric lighting. Local amenities are just 2m away.

[OS] 191 [GR] 705099
[i] ☎ 01363 772006 (seasonal)

Fox & Hounds

Sleeps: 12

ACCOMMODATION

Ideally situated on the western edge of Dartmoor for direct access to the moor. This barn provides bunk bedded accommodation with electric lighting. The nearby pub (100m) provides breakfast and meals but please note the barn does not provide a catering area.

[OS] 191 [GR] 525866

Great Houndtor

Sleeps: 14 Ⓟ

ACCOMMODATION

A restored house sleeping 14 in two separate areas on the first floor. Ground floor has toilets, a shower and washroom and large cooking and recreation area. Open fire, wood available. Electric light, 50p electric meter. Nearest pub 1 ½m. On the eastern edge of Dartmoor near Manaton, underneath the famous Houndtor. Bridleways to the open moor.

[OS] 191 [GR] 749795

Great Potheridge

Sleeps: 24

ACCOMMODATION

Well equipped bunk bedded barn with fridge, cooking facilities, hot shower and drying room. The area offers on-site outdoor activities such as canoeing and archery. The barn is situated on well established cycle and walking routes, along the Tarka Trail.

[OS] 180 [GR] 513146

Higher Cadham

Sleeps: 12 Ⓧ Ⓟ

ACCOMMODATION

A converted barn in peaceful farmyard setting. Accommodation all on one floor with toilets, shower, small cooking area, recreation area and sleeping for 12-15. Meals and small shop on farm. Electric light. Heater and drying facilities. Nearest Post Office and Pub 1 ½m.
On Tarka Trail and West Devon Cycle Route in heart of Tarka Country with nearby walks.

[OS] 191 [GR] 585025

Northcombe

Sleeps: 15

ACCOMMODATION

A network of footpaths and bridleways link Northcombe to Exmoor and the river valley of Barle. This beautifully converted watermill now provides camping barn accommodation in 2 sleeping areas, its own cooking facilities, fridge, shower, and electric lighting. Food supplies are also available at the barn. Local amenities of Post Office, pub and shop and all within 1m.

[OS] 181 [GR] 916292

Runnage

Sleeps: 15 Ⓧ Ⓐ Ⓟ

ACCOMMODATION

Upstairs sleeping area. Showers and toilets. The cooking and sitting area on the ground floor. Big breakfast available! Electric light. Woodburner. Nearest pub, shop and P.O. ½m.
In the middle of Dartmoor with many walking opportunities and close to Bellever Forest and the River Dart.

[OS] 191 [GR] 668792

13

Free leaflet & booking details from: North Devon Holiday Homes, 19 Cross St, Barnstaple, Devon, EX31 1BD. Tel: 01271 24420 Fax: 01271 46544
More Barns will open during the year - please call for an update.

Sticklepath Halt

Sleeps: 16 ⌧ P

ACCOMMODATION

The 'Old Bakery' now provides dormitory sleeping, large catering and separate recreation areas with good washing/shower facilities. Electric light, electricity on meter. Post office and pub adjacent. Beneath the imposing Cosdon Beacon in the village of Sticklepath, the Halt offers direct access to spectacular walking routes over North Dartmoor and beyond. Also on the 180m Tarka Trail.

OS 191 GR 643941

Watercombe Farm

Sleeps: 12 ⌧ P

ACCOMMODATION

Large barn with five separate sleeping areas including one family/disabled room. Separate ladies and gents toilets and showers and large kitchen and recreation areas. Electric light. Nearest pub and post office 2m.
On the southern tip of Dartmoor with direct access to open moorland, and close to the Two Moors Way.

OS 202 GR 625613

Woodadvent

Sleeps: 12 ⌧ P

ACCOMMODATION

Former cider barn in farmyard with sleeping for 12 upstairs and cooking/sitting area downstairs. Toilet within building. Electric light. Nearest post office and pub 1m.
In a quiet and unspoilt corner of Exmoor National Park, close to the picturesque village of Rondwater and with an excellent footpath network.

OS 181 GR 037374

Holne

Sleeps: 14 ⌧ A P

ACCOMMODATION

A converted barn, ideal base for groups with parking, and backing on to small camping field. Good facilities including showers and toilets, cooker, fridge and drying. Woodburning stove and wood available. Electric light. Post Office and pub ¼m.
On southern slope of Dartmoor in attractive village of Holne. Only 4m from A38, on 'Two Moors Way' and close to River Dart.

OS 202 GR 706696

> **For further details and booking for Holne please ring: 01364 643920**

The YHA Democracy

YHA is a registered charity and is not funded by the Government. We welcome you to join us in conservation work, Youth Hostel maintenance, voluntary Wardening, fund-raising and publicity work. YHA member-volunteers and YHA Local Groups often organise working parties and other activities which are both sociable and fun.

YHA is a membership organisation with 250,000 members. It wholly owns and controls the limited company, YHA (England and Wales) Limited (which is also a registered charity) which employs a team of full-time professional managers to run its operations.

The policies they follow are decided by YHA members through the democratic structure shown below:

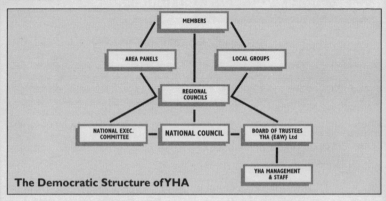

The Democratic Structure of YHA

Area Panels co-ordinate the activities of groups of volunteers. Your Area Panel is elected at an open Area AGM announced in **YHA News.** This meeting is a good place to find out what is happening in your area. Activities are organised on a 'Voluntary Area' basis (you are welcome to join us in any area) and YHA Voluntary Areas are shown on the opposite page.

Regional Councils are involved in developing policy, encouraging members to participate in YHA activities and monitoring the service provided to members.

There are four Regional Councils — Northern England, Central, Wales and South England. These are elected at an open Regional AGM and are drawn from members nominated at the meeting, together with representatives of Area Panels and Local Groups.

YHA NEWS is a newspaper for those who want to keep in close touch with the policies and activities of the YHA. Voluntary subscriptions are invited. Apply to YHA (address on p.1) if you would like to be put on the mailing list.

YOUR VOTE COUNTS! You are welcome to come along to your Regional AGM and ask questions, express opinions, propose motions (with appropriate notice), stand for elections and vote. For details, contact Sarah Burbridge on 01727 855215 ext.201 or see **YHA News.**

NATIONAL COUNCIL, which consists mainly of Regional representatives, meets annually and establishes the principles of YHA. It elects a National Executive Committee which determines policies within these principles and a Board of Trustees of the Company which has legal responsibility for managing all Youth Hostels. These policies are then implemented by the management and volunteers as appropriate.

YHA voluntary activities are organised on an area basis and the Voluntary Areas are indicated by the dotted lines on the map below. You can choose to participate in any area that suits you.

1	BORDER AND DALES	9	SOUTH ENGLAND 2
2	YORKSHIRE	10	SOUTH ENGLAND 1
3	EAST ENGLAND	11	MIDLAND
4	SOUTH ENGLAND 7	12	SOUTH WALES
5	SOUTH ENGLAND 6	13	NORTH WALES
6	SOUTH ENGLAND 5	14	PEAK
7	SOUTH ENGLAND 4	15	LAKELAND
8	SOUTH ENGLAND 3		

YHA
AUSTRALIA OFFERS

 Complete travel packages which include accommodation, 12 month valid coach travel, entrance tickets to Australia's favourite tourist places and more.

 Packages are from as little as AUD$25 a day – e.g. Aussie Explorer "Best of East" bus pass with Australian Coachlines with 60 nights accommodation for AUD$1,380.

 Stay in over 130 Australian YHA Hostels. There are also over 5,500 Hostels in over 65 countries, all with friendly, helpful hostel staff.

 No age limits in any Australian YHA Hostels with 24 hour access.

 A centralised booking system where YHA Hostels can be booked for your next destination throughout Australia.

 Sydney, Brisbane, Melbourne, Cairns, Adelaide and Perth can all be booked on the IBN Computer Reservation System.

 Access to over 800 discounts throughout Australia – a saving of thousands of dollars to YHA members only. Ask for the free YHA Discount Book.

 YHA Hostels that feature clean and comfortable accommodation at all of Australia's favourite tourist destinations.

 Self catering facilities to help you save money.

 Travel Agencies in every State capital city as well as Alice Springs, Cairns, Airlie Beach and Canberra. Each Travel Office offers special discounts to YHA members on a wide range of travel products from international airline tickets, coach passes, travel insurance and local tours.

- ✂

Please send further information on the excellent travel packages available from YHA Australia

Name: ....

Address: ....

.... **Postcode:** ....

Country: ....

Send to: Australia YHA, Level 3, 10 Mallett Street, Camperdown NSW 2050 Australia. EW95/96

YHA Adventure Shops understand what **YOU** as a YHA member want from an outdoor clothing and equipment retailer.

That's why, as the UK's most dynamic specialists in their field, more YHA members use YHA Adventure Shops knowledge, information and quality products than any other outdoor retailer.

YHA Adventure Shops' buyers have travelled the world to assemble one of the most comprehensive ranges of clothing, equipment and travel accessories available. Each one of their 12,000 individual products offers quality and value for money. And each has a price promise that guarantees the lowest prices, plus a 10% discount for YHA members.

Amongst the international names you will find at YHA Adventure Shops are Berghaus, Karrimor, Line 7, Zamberlan, Coleman and Reef. They are also supporting the newly emerging economies of Czechoslovakia, Poland, Vietnam, Indonesia and Afghanistan.

The resulting range – including their exclusive own label Mountaincraft – offers an incredible diversity of products suitable for beginners and professionals alike.

In addition you will find a range of services unlike any other retailer in the outdoor world; an in-house travel agency, YHA membership information and enrolment, a pre and post customer sales service, a mail order department, a privileged client facility, a specialist cycling outlet – even a windsurfing and watersports retailer (in Brighton only).

All the services **YOU** have requested.

And with services like this on offer, you would expect that the product range just can't be beaten. Here are just some of the products you'll find:

- Rucsacs, Travel sacs, Daypacks and Accessories
- Adult and Childrens Footwear
- Mens, Womens and Childrens Clothing
- Tents and Tent Accessories
- Sleeping Bags, Sheet Bags and Accessories
- YHA Approved Items
- First Aid Kits and Survival Equipment
- Travel Accessories
- Cooking and Lighting Equipment
- Ski Clothing and Equipment
- Guide and Travel Books
- Foreign and Domestic Maps
- Climbing Equipment *(Covent Garden only)*
- Cycles, Cycle Clothing and Accessories *(larger stores only)*
- Windsurfing and Watersports *(Brighton Store)*
- Gift Vouchers
- 10% Discount for YHA members

But the best way to see just what YHA Adventure shops have to offer is by visiting one of their branches – **YOU** won't be disappointed.

Branches at: London – Covent Garden 0171 836 8541 • Victoria 0171 823 4739 • Kensington 0171 938 2948 • Manchester 0161 834 7119 • Birmingham 0121 236 7799 • Brighton 01273 821554 • Bristol 0117 929 7141 • Cambridge 01223 353956 • Cardiff 01222 399178 • Leeds 0113 246 5339 • Liverpool 0151 709 8063 • Nottingham 0115 947 5710 • Oxford 01865 247948 • Reading 01734 587722 • Salisbury 01722 422122 • Sheffield 0114 276 5935 • Southampton 01703 235847 • Staines 01784 452987.

For full details of future store openings and any other facilities call 01784 458625 (24 hours).

All retailers get letters

> **❝** My Mountaincraft equipment was excellent – much admired by others in the group in Peru and Bolivia. ....I thoroughly recommend it. **❞**
>
> **J. Newman**, London.
> Independant Traveller

> **❝** I love my waterproof outfit. I can scrunch it all up and pack it in my rucsac **❞**
>
> **James Johnson**
> (Age 8)

> **❝** One of my favourite haunts is YHA Adventure Shops in Southampton Street, Covent Garden, London. Your can buy gear there at knock down prices & the staff are always very helpful, though on this occasion they were non-plussed to hear about my objective (to climb Mount Everest) all the time smiling & shaking their heads at my requests... **❞**
>
> **Brian Blessed** (actor & adventurer)
> from his book The Turquoise Mountain

> **❝** Hiring is a brilliant idea for camping... We were able to kit out our family for the weekend.
>
> Now we know what we've been missing for all these years **❞**
>
> **J. Baker**
> Hampshire

> **❝** Whether in the Kalahari desert, or the shores of Lake Malawi, I knew I could rely on my Mountaincraft gear. The only problem I experienced was that other people liked too...My daysac was stolen in Tanzania!
>
> **David LLo..**
> Adventure and expedition lead..

> **❝** We would like to thank YHA Adventure Shops whose products and assistance are of great help to us **❞**
>
> **THE BRITISH MOUNT KONGAR EXPEDITION TO CHINA**

Over 12,000 products – Guaranteed lowest price..

ADULT & CHILDRENS FOOTWEAR • RUCSACS • DAYSACS • TRAVEL SACS & ACCESSORIES
TENTS & TENT ACCESSORIES • SLEEPING BAGS • SHEET BAGS & ACCESSORIES
WATERPROOFS • FLEECES • MENSWEAR • LADIES WEAR • CHILDRENS WEAR
TRAVEL ACCESSORIES • FIRST AID KITS & SURVIVAL EQUIPMENT • COOKING & LIGHTING
EQUIPMENT • GUIDE & TRAVEL BOOKS • FOREIGN & DOMESTIC MAPS • SKI CLOTHING
& EQUIPMENT (most stores in winter season) • CYCLES, CYCLE CLOTHING AND
ACCESSORIES (larger stores only) • CLIMBING EQUIPMENT (larger stores only) • WINDSURFING AND
WATERSPORTS (Brighton store only) • FITNESS CLOTHING & EQUIPMENT (Brighton store only)

THE YHA DISCOUNT BOOKLET ?

What's so great about that?

Record Shops

Exhibitions

Holiday
Insurance

Outdoor Gear

Museums

Cruises

Zoos

Tours

Castles

Well, if you're Hostelling and you plan to visit any of the 300+ attractions, historic sites and retail outlets listed in our 1996 Discount Booklet, you'll find the savings great for a start!

▲ The London Dungeons are just minutes from
  the Rotherhithe or City of London Hostels
  £2 off for Adults & £1.50 off Student rate

▲ The Museum of Science & Industry is just around
  the corner from the new Manchester Hostel
  Save up to £4 on admission

▲ Cut-rate Travel Insurance from Europ Assistance
  Up to 25% discount on some schemes

▲ Buy CDs, Videos and Games at any UK HMV shop
  £1 off listed items costing over £12.99

▲ The Jorvik viking Centre is just minutes walk
  from York Hostel   *10% off admission*

G

YHA ENROLMENT FORM

To YHA, TREVELYAN HOUSE, ST ALBANS, HERTS, AL1 2DY

Please enrol me as a member of the YHA.

I have been resident in England or Wales for at least 12 months.

PLEASE COMPLETE IN BLOCK CAPITALS

Title	Surname	First names	Date of Birth	Membership No. (if already a member)

We now offer our members the opportunity to receive mailings and offers from a few carefully selected companies, whose products and services are particularly appropriate to the interests of YHA members.

Address [   ] Post Code [   ]

If you do not wish to receive such mailings, please indicate by placing a tick in the box provided. □

Telephone No. _____ Signature _____

I enclose £ _____ (Under 18: £3.20/Adult: £9.30). PLEASE MAKE CHEQUES PAYABLE TO YHA.

Do you intend to stay in Youth Hostels in England & Wales □ Abroad □

Please note that membership prices are valid from 1 Jan 96. **For applicants under 16 a signature from a parent or guardian is required.**

Date _____

NOTICE OF CANCELLATION

In all cases, if you have to cancel your visit please let the Hostel staff know — even at the last minute — as someone else can then use your bed.

In mountain and remote areas, it is vital that you contact the Youth Hostel if you decide not to take up your reservation. Otherwise the police or rescue teams may be called out to look for you.

REFUNDS

Individuals and families

Individuals and family members of the YHA (England and Wales) and other Associations within the International Youth Hostel Federation network are covered by YHA's free Cancellation Refund Package.

Every claim will be subject to an administration fee of £5.

Under this scheme, YHA will refund members in respect of loss of charges paid to the Association for their accommodation and/or meals not taken up (up to £100 per individual) where the member is forced to cancel or curtail his or her journey provided three days notice of cancellation has been given to the Hostel concerned.

Activity Holidays

Activity Holidays run by the YHA are subject to separate insurance policies. Details are contained on the booking form and policies are sent to participants before the holiday.

Groups

A cancellation refund package is available to those making group bookings. This is strongly recommended and available for a nominal charge. See the reverse of the YHA Group Booking Form for full details, or contact our Customer Services Department on 01727 845047.

How to Apply

To apply for a refund, just complete an application form (available from Hostels or any YHA office) and send it, together with all supporting documentation — including appropriate copy booking forms, invoice and receipts, as well as any medical certificates — to YHA National Accounts Office (address on the form). Applications are normally processed within 28 days of receipt.

1996 YHA ACCOMMODATION GUIDE

ISBN 0-904530-23-X

Public Transport information by Barry Doe of Travadvice (see page 85).
Produced by Elanders.
Published November 1995 by the Youth Hostels Association (England and Wales).

If you would like more information on YHA please write to :
YHA
FREEPOST
St Albans AL1 2BR
or telephone the Customer Services section on 01727 855215.